New Crops, New Uses, New Markets

Industrial and Commercial Products
From U.S. Agriculture

1992 Yearbook of Agriculture

Office of Publishing and Visual Communication • U.S. Department of Agriculture

Trade and company names are mentioned herein solely to provide specific information. Inclusion of a trade or company name constitutes neither a warranty nor an endorsement by the U.S. Department of Agriculture to the exclusion of other products or organizations not mentioned.

Pesticides used improperly can be injurious to humans, animals, and plants. Follow the directions and heed all precautions on the labels. Registrations of pesticides are under constant review by the Environmental Protection Agency. Use only those pesticides that bear the EPA registration number and carry appropriate directions. Remember: When in doubt, consult your local county Extension office to determine if changes in pesticide registration have occurred.

For sale by the Superintendent of Documents, U.S. Government Printing Office, Washington, DC 20402

Foreword

America is a global leader today. We must ensure that our position as a competitive world force remains strong tomorrow. To accomplish this, we must be realistic about the challenges ahead. That is why it is important for America to lead in the research and development of alternative uses for agricultural products.

Now is the time to intensify our efforts in this area. Finding new ways to tap the abundance of our natural resources will benefit not only agriculture but consumers and society as a whole. Developing industrial possibilities for agricultural commodities could open up new domestic markets for American farm products, generate new jobs, and ensure greater prosperity in rural communities.

Creating new domestic markets for our farm products—markets that offer stability and permanence—is a realistic goal. Last year, the United States imported billions of dollars worth of goods, many of which could have been produced here at home. Substituting domestic crops or products for those we now import could add $15 billion to $20 billion to U.S. farm income. For example:

- The United States imports nearly half of its petroleum. Starch and vegetable oils replace the need for petroleum in manufactured products such as plastics, paints, fuels, lubricants, and inks.
- All of the natural rubber used nationwide is imported at an annual cost of nearly $1 billion. Guayule, a plant native to the desert Southwest, produces natural rubber.
- And the United States imports two-thirds of its newsprint at an annual cost of about $4.5 billion. Kenaf, an annual fiber crop grown in areas such as Texas and Louisiana, is used to make newsprint and other products.

In addition, biofuels such as ethanol can reduce dependence on foreign oil. The ethanol industry has shown tremendous potential in this area. In 1979, for example, 20 million gallons of ethanol were produced in the United States. Last year, production increased by 5,000 percent to a billion gallons.

Expanding domestic markets for agricultural commodities also will help ensure economic vitality in rural America. In fact, developing new uses could boost farm income by $30 billion a year and employment by 750,000.

New uses increase production, processing, transportation, and selling of innovative high-value products. And most of this activity occurs in rural areas close to the source of raw materials. In turn, this broadens the tax base and strengthens schools and other services in rural communities.

Investing in research and development will benefit consumers. Resulting value-added products offer greater choice, better quality, and healthier alternatives—all at lower cost. Economists estimate that the typical family gets back $3 (mostly in lower food bills) for every dollar invested in agricultural research.

Many of the environmental challenges we face today are really opportunities in disguise. Using technology to expand agriculture helps to protect the environment. For example: New products can provide renewable alternatives to finite resources such as oil. Biofuels burn cleaner than petroleum-based fuels, thereby reducing air pollution. And products such as packing pellets and disposable diapers made from vegetable starches are biodegradable.

I am encouraged by the progress of American entrepreneurs and companies who are pioneers in this new field. But we need to do more. That is why I have committed USDA resources to help move products from the field, through the labs, and to the marketplace rapidly.

An investment in the research and development of alternative uses is an investment in America. Working together, government and industry can generate new markets for farmers, jobs for rural America, greater choice for consumers, and a healthier environment for future generations.

Edward Madigan
Secretary
U.S. Department of Agriculture

Introduction:
Historical Models for Change

by Douglas E. Bowers,
Head, Agricultural and Rural History, ERS
USDA, Washington, DC

New Crops and New Uses: Historical Trends
The search for new crops and new ways to use old crops has interested Americans inside and outside the agricultural sector since America's colonial days.

Over the past century that interest has intensified. The major recent theme in this quest has been how to better utilize—in industrial as well as agricultural ways—the surpluses produced by American farmers.

A second theme has also been important at many times, including today: the need to find substitutes for commodities currently in use, whether to cut our dependence on foreign imports, replace critical materials in short supply during wartime, or exchange products that harm the environment for environmentally sound ones.

Historically, these themes have tended to alternate, with times of crisis also being times when research in these areas has received the most support. In the past quarter century the two strains (to use agricultural surpluses and to find substitute commodities) have come together to reinforce each other. There have been many achievements in both areas, and conditions today promise even more success in the future.

Early American Adaptations
From the beginning, American farmers were responsive to market signals and looked for new crops and markets that would increase their incomes. Many of the crops new to the colonists had long been grown by North American Indians—corn, potatoes, squash, and tobacco, for example. Some of these crops were taken back to Europe by the first Spanish explorers, where their adoption depended on how well they fit the needs and expectations of European farmers and consumers.

Before Columbus' discovery of the New World, Europe's major food crops offered only meager yields and left Europeans vulnerable to famine. Corn succeeded in Europe because it offered a high-producing alternative to other grains and required relatively little work. Potatoes had such great yields that they became a staple in the diets of the poor, from Ireland to Germany. On the other hand, tomatoes, suspected of being poisonous and not offering a ready substitute for anything, required several centuries to become an important food crop outside of a few areas. Corn itself was restricted mainly to animal food because Europeans found it too coarse to eat.

European adoption of American crops revealed a pattern that would repeat itself in this country: Farmers replaced low-yielding or high-labor crops that they had grown for centuries with ones that were cheaper to produce—and which consumers would buy.

Early American farmers soon faced a surplus problem that threatened to hold back the development of commercial agriculture. In a country where over 90 percent of the people were farmers, most markets had to come from overseas. But to simply duplicate the crops of Europe would have made it difficult for them to compete with European farmers. Many farmers, therefore, turned to newer crops that they could export to their advantage—tobacco, rice, and indigo, for example. In the 19th century, farm exports (especially cotton) provided the income that our young country needed to industrialize.

Pioneer farmers also found an industrial use for something otherwise considered a nuisance. As they cleared the fields of trees, they were able to sell tree ashes as potash for use in making lye. This became a profitable source of income even before crops were planted.

American farmers had a continuing interest in trying out new varieties and new species and this interest was one of the main reasons for establishing the U.S. Department of Agriculture. The first specifically agricultural activity of the Federal Government was to encourage United States embassies to collect seeds from different parts of the world for distribution to farmers in the United States. By the 1840's this activity was centered in the Patent Office, where the results of research by private farmers began to be published as an annual report that Congressmen distributed to constituents. (In fact, this volume was the forerunner of the Yearbook of Agriculture.) When the Department was founded in 1862, seed distribution and research were an integral part of its efforts. The Hatch Act of 1887 greatly expanded research by setting up experiment stations at each of the land-grant colleges.

The Rise of Utilization Research

Initial agricultural research focused on improving productivity by using better agricultural practices and varieties. Ironically, the very success of that research created the potential for production to exceed demand, thus depressing prices below the level of profitability. By the turn of the century it was becoming clear that new uses for farm products would have to be found if surpluses were to be avoided and byproducts efficiently used.

Within USDA, utilization research, as it was called, became increasingly important. In 1920—at a time when farm prices were collapsing because of a contraction in exports—an Office of Development Work was set up in the Bureau of Chemistry to find ways to chemically break down farm products into substances that industry could use. World War I also provided an incentive for research into industrial uses for agricultural products. When imports of medicinal plants were cut off, USDA's Bureau of Plant Industry helped establish such plants in Florida. Similarly, the disruption of dye imports from Germany prompted USDA to begin research on dye materials; this led to the establishment of the vat dye industry in the United States.

One of the most successful utilization researchers early in this century was George Washington Carver at Tuskegee Institute in Alabama. Carver saw that the South was suffering from the overproduction of cotton, almost to the exclusion of other crops. Not only were cotton prices low, but the boll weevil was also beginning to devastate cotton farms that stood in its path.

Carver believed farmers would turn to other crops if enough new uses could be found for them to create a sufficient market. He concentrated on peanuts and sweet potatoes, two crops southerners already knew how to grow but that were not widely planted for commercial purposes. Over the years, Carver developed hundreds of new products from peanuts and sweet potatoes; the best known to consumers is probably peanut oil. USDA's Extension Service helped disseminate information throughout the South about converting from cotton to other crops. Largely thanks to Carver's research, peanut acreage quadrupled between 1910 and 1940. Carver also found new uses for cotton and soybeans; in fact, soybeans can be seen as the most successful "new" crop in the United States this century.

Surplus production became an even greater problem during the Depression of the 1930's, when domestic markets fell and exports nearly dried up. Congress took a major step toward the expansion of utilization research when it passed the Agricultural Adjustment Act (AAA) of 1938; this act created four regional research laboratories as part of what is now the Agricultural Research Service. Each laboratory specialized in the crops grown in its region—for example, cotton in the South; wheat, fruits, vegetables, and alfalfa in the West; animal products, milk, and tobacco in the East; and grain crops, soybeans, and other oilseeds in the North.

With the AAA of 1938, the basic institutional structure of today's national, regional, and State experiment station laboratories was established. The present-day advisory committee system, by which representatives of farmers and land-grant universities are given a voice in setting research priorities, was also foreshadowed by a committee on utilization research appointed just after the 1938 act was passed. Advisory committees and research on utilization and marketing were strengthened by the Research and Marketing Act of 1946, which sought to redress the imbalance between production and postproduction research. That act also set up the mechanism for contracting with private research facilities, permitting the Government to draw on the expertise of private sector scientists as well as its own. This institutional framework—combining the perspectives of Federal and State Governments, as well as university, Government, and private researchers—was well geared to support research into the problems of particular areas and to supply quick answers to questions of national importance.

World War II showed how rapidly the research establishment could respond to a national crisis. The war redirected the regional laboratories toward finding substitutes for critical materials and other war needs.

Some notable successes came out of this effort, including synthetic rubber, replacements for chemical cellulose, dehydrated foods, and the extraction of wheat starch, which was used to supplement corn in feeding livestock. Most important, in 1943 USDA scientists discovered a way to mass-produce penicillin, making this miracle drug widely available for the first time.

Postwar Research

After the war, attention again focused on crops in surplus. In 1957, with farm productivity soaring from the greatly increased use of chemicals and machinery, Congress created a Commission on Increased Industrial Use of Agricultural Products to recommend new research in this area. The Commission noted that the greatest advances came "when utilization research in agriculture has had the benefits of adequate expenditures and large teams of workers"—as it had had during the war. It urged a broadly expanded program of research, including more basic research. Funds were increased but not to the level that the Commission had hoped for.

Nevertheless, the first two decades following the war saw some striking accomplishments from the regional laboratories, whose efforts were directed toward particular agricultural problems. The development of frozen food technology in the 1940's and 1950's enabled consumers to enjoy fresher tasting foods all year round and helped even out seasonal swings in vegetable and fruit prices. Development of frozen orange juice concentrate was a particular achievement. Concentrate produced from Florida oranges climbed from 226,000 gallons in 1945 to more than 84 million gallons in 1960. Frozen foods paralleled and accelerated a consumer trend toward convenience foods.

That same trend helped ensure the success of another USDA product, instant potato flakes. Potato flakes were developed at a time when potato consumption was falling. Their introduction gave potatoes a new market. By 1969, dehydrated potatoes represented over 9 percent of the total potato crop, and per capita consumption had turned upward.

Another crop in trouble by the 1950's was cotton. During and after World War II, cotton faced increasing competition from synthetic fibers, which required less ironing than cotton fabrics. Research on cross-links between cotton fibers led to chemical finishes that imparted to cotton and cotton blend fabrics the wrinkle resistance they needed to satisfy consumers. These new fabrics helped stem the tide toward polyester and nylon.

New Sources of Demand

Since the 1960's, rising productivity has kept interest high in using surplus crops. In addition, the past several decades have also been a time of renewed interest in finding agricultural substitutes for industrial materials. New demands for research have likewise appeared. One such incentive came from the dramatic oil price hikes by the Organization of Petroleum Exporting Countries in 1973 and 1979. Not only did energy costs soar, but Americans became painfully aware of their dependence on foreign oil, which kindled interest in organic substitutes for petroleum. Research to replace part of the petrochemicals used to manufacture plastics with biodegradable corn starch derivatives promises to increase the demand for corn. Soy ink, made from soybeans, is beginning to supplant petroleum-based ink products for some uses. New research to replace gasoline with ethanol or other fuels from renewable resources could sharply cut our reliance on oil imports and provide a large market for corn.

Another attraction of organic fuels is that they likely will generate less pollution than petroleum products. Interest in the environment has brought a call to substitute biological pesticides for chemical ones and to find biodegradable and recyclable materials to conserve natural resources and reduce waste disposal problems.

Another source of demand for utilization research has been the expanded interest in nutrition by increasingly articulate and discriminating consumers. (The widespread desire to reduce consumption of fat, for example, has led animal scientists to breed leaner beef and pork.) As people increase their intake of grain products, higher protein wheat and oats have been developed. Research has also been done on brans, such as rice bran, which can add fiber and possibly reduce cholesterol. Similarly, concerns about chemical additives in meat have brought about ways to reduce nitrosamines in bacon and other cooked meats.

In the 1970's, strong exports of grain, soybeans, and other crops made the United States even more a part of the global market than it had been in the past. Trade deficits in the 1980's underscored both the vulnerability of farmers to shifts in world markets and the urgent need to find alternatives to traditional products that had to be imported. This, coupled with the desire to replace nonrenewable substances with renewable ones, has revived the effort to find new plants. Plant explorers from the Agricultural Research Service each year bring back thousands of new plants from abroad for testing.

Historically, introducing new plants has been harder than finding new uses for old ones because new crops must be able to be grown here and must be accepted by farmers and the marketplace. Nevertheless, a number of potentially useful plants have been experimented with in the past two decades, including guayule (for rubber), kenaf (as a substitute for wood pulp in making paper), and crambe (for industrial oil). Using biotechnology, plant breeders should be able to develop new and better varieties faster than in the past and better predict their chemical properties.

A Promising Future

Today opportunity and necessity combine to create a more favorable climate for the introduction of new crops and new uses than at any other period short of wartime. The utilization research establishment has been solidly in place for over 50 years, and it has the facilities and experience to undertake a major expansion if it is called on to do so. Plant and animal scientists looking for new varieties or species to introduce have an even longer history to draw on, plus the advantage of using biotechnology, a tool that opens a vast new horizon.

At the same time, the demand for research has rarely been greater and has never come from so many different directions. New crops and new uses for old ones hold out promise to restore the balance of trade, reduce our dependence on imports such as oil, and make us more competitive in agricultural exports. They may also make it possible for us to replace our depletable resources with renewable ones and in many cases benefit the environment as well.

Another potential advantage would be reduced spending on farm programs because of stronger demand for program commodities or lower supply of surplus crops caused by a shift to new crops. The Food, Agriculture, Conservation, and Trade Act of 1990 provides farmers with the sort of flexibility they need to experiment with new crops.

Finally, utilization research could benefit some rural economies by bringing new rural factories to process raw materials. Research could lead to greater farm sales from land that in the past has been diverted by Government programs to reduce production.

Seldom, if ever, has the time been more favorable for new initiatives in research.

Contents

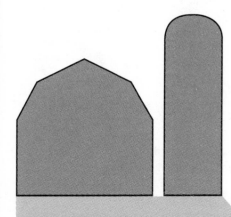

Part I.
Markets

Agriculture Provides U.S. Industry With Diverse Raw Materials

by Sam Brownback, Kansas Secretary of Agriculture, Kansas State Board of Agriculture, and Lewrene Glaser, Agricultural Economist, ERS, USDA, Washington, DC

U.S. agriculture is expanding its mission. It is rapidly transforming itself into a more diverse business of food, fuels, medicines, and materials.

Farmers and agribusiness have long desired to recover markets lost to the petrochemical industry during the last 50 years. The original nylon was made from corn cobs and now it is all petroleum based. Latex paints have replaced oil-based paints that were made with vegetable oils such as linseed and tung. Synthetic fibers have gained major inroads in textile markets, especially carpeting.

In recent decades, most of this interest in expanding markets for agricultural materials has been prompted by surpluses of traditional commodities, rather than by demands from the marketplace. That situation has radically changed today. Consumers are demanding more environmentally sensitive products. One way individuals want to help the Earth is by decreasing their own consumption of nonrenewable commodities.

Businesses are responding to consumers' concerns. They are also looking at their production systems in an environmental light. It is expensive to dispose of trash and toxic wastes. Increasingly, businesses are trying to minimize the creation of waste products during manufacturing and then to dispose of them in an ecologically sound manner.

Another factor that has changed the equation is agriculture's increasing ability to provide industry with raw materials at competitive prices. For example, the real (adjusted for inflation) price of corn has declined since World War II, while the real price of crude oil, a nonrenewable resource, has increased significantly (see fig.1). This bodes well for the position of agricultural materials compared with petroleum products.

Technological advances have also expanded the ability to competitively derive new, innovative products from agricultural raw materials. Corn and potato starches are being made into ethanol and polymers. Vegetable oils are ingredients in lubricants and inks. Plants and animals are providing doctors and patients with drugs and other complex biochemicals.

Ethanol

Technological improvements, such as energy-efficient cogeneration of steam and electricity or inexpensive processes that separate ethanol and water, have lowered operating costs for modern ethanol plants. Ethanol is now a net producer of energy, according to a recent study by the U.S. Department of Energy. When it was originally produced in large quantities 15 years ago, it was a net energy consumer.

More than 95 percent of the Nation's ethanol is made from corn. But many small plants are using locally available materials—such as whey, molasses, and potato and brewery wastes—that would otherwise be disposed of in lower value uses or as waste products. Current U.S. production capacity for fuel ethanol is about 1.1 billion gallons per year, with facilities that will provide another 300 million gallons of capacity under construction.

The Clean Air Act creates new market opportunities for fuel ethanol as a component in oxygenated gasolines. The act's 1990 amendments designate 39 urban areas in the United States to sell oxygenated gasoline for at least 4 months a year in an attempt to reduce carbon monoxide levels.

Polymers

Not only is corn a raw material for ethanol, it is also used in the manufacture of moldable polymers. When starch-additive plastics first emerged less than 5 years ago, they contained 2-3 percent starch and 97-98 percent petroleum-based polymers. Today's technologies, however, use starch as the principal ingredient.

National Starch and Chemical Company has developed a biodegradable replacement for expanded polystyrene loose fill (packing peanuts) called Eco-Foam. Resembling a noodle-shaped snack, Eco-Foam is

Figure 1

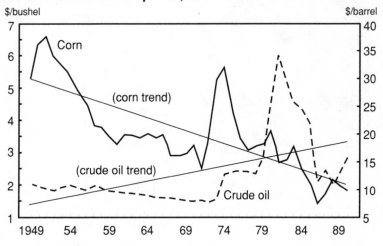

Real corn and crude oil prices, 1982=100

100 percent corn starch. Output in 1991, the first year of production, was 2.5 million pounds. Currently, Eco-Foam is manufactured in nine U.S. locations. The market is large—50 million pounds of expanded polystyrene loose fill is used annually in the United States. Although Eco-Foam now costs about twice as much per pound as conventional polystyrene loose fill, its cost will probably come down.

Warner-Lambert's Novon Products Division is marketing a line of starch-based polymers derived from corn or potatoes. Production began in early 1992 at Warner-Lambert's facilities in Rockford, IL. The factory has an annual production capacity of 100 million pounds. Currently, NOVON polymers are used to make packing

Not only is corn a raw material for ethanol, but cornstarch is the principal ingredient in the manufacture of moldable polymers.
USDA SD-885

peanuts, candle cups for churches, and golf tees. Potential uses for NOVON include fast-food packaging such as cups, drink lids, straws, and cutlery.

Both Eco-Foam and NOVON will decompose in sewage treatment plants or in soil composts. One issue in the future will be the need to create compost centers that will take these totally degradable starch-based polymers and truly recycle them.

In addition, corn is now a common raw material for the manufacture of citric and lactic acids. These acids are widely used in diverse chemicals and polymers.

A company named Grand Metropolitan, in conjunction with the Michigan Biotechnology Institute, is developing corn-based protein polymer coatings as replacements for polyethylene and wax coatings on fast-food wrapping paper and paperboard containers. The new coatings are also good barriers to moisture and grease.

And what about edible plates made from wheat? Several foreign firms are in that business, and perhaps American companies soon will be producing edible tableware too. Future restaurant diners not only might order their meals, they might also specify the flavor of their plates!

Vegetable Oils Have Many Industrial Uses

Fats and oils have long been used in the manufacture of soaps, fatty acids, paints and varnishes, resins, lubricants, and other industrial products. But their uses are expanding—replacing petrochemicals as raw materials in a number of new product areas. Specialty lubricants, newspaper inks, paints and coatings, and diesel fuel are just a few such examples.

Lubricants. A Seattle-based manufacturer of industrial lubricants, International Lubricants, Inc. (ILI), uses the unique attributes of various seed oils and their derivatives in its current line of automotive and industrial lubricants and lubricant additives. These products contain derivatives of industrial rapeseed, crambe, jojoba, or meadowfoam oils.

In addition to being partially derived from renewable agricultural commodities, these products have superior properties and are environment-friendly. For instance, ILI's Lubegard cutting oil has given the metalworking industry an excellent alternative to traditional chlorinated cutting oils. According to the company, Lubegard cutting oil's advantages include the following:

• Lower oil concentrations are needed in the coolant (a mixture of the cutting oil and water), which cools and lubricates metal parts while they are being cut.

• Workers' skin irritations and rashes caused by the harsh chlorinated oils are avoided.

• Cutting machines last longer and the parts being cut have smoother finishes.

• Once the coolant has reached the end of its useful life, the used oil and water are easily separated for disposal.

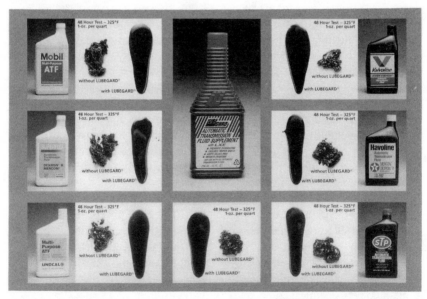

International Lubricants, Inc., a Seattle, WA, based industrial lubricants manufacturer, uses the unique properties of various seed oils and their derivatives. The company markets a line of automotive industrial lubricants and lubricant additives with the proprietary name Lubegard. These products contain derivatives of industrial rapeseed, crambe, and jojoba.
USDA 92BW0780

- The used oil is not classified as a hazardous waste, as are traditional cutting oils that contain chlorine, so disposal costs are decreased significantly.

ILI's ultimate goal is to develop products made entirely from seed oils that can be directly disposed of through water treatment facilities.

Soybean Oil Inks. First marketed in 1987, soybean-oil-based printing inks have experienced a phenomenal surge in usage. Over one-third of the Nation's daily and weekly newspapers are using either color or black soy ink. Color soy inks have been widely adopted because of their superior performance, despite their slightly higher price. Black soy inks are more expensive than their petroleum-based counterparts, thus limiting their use.

However, two environmental factors could encourage more newspapers and other lithographic printers to use soy inks: lower worker exposure to harsh petrochemicals and decreased emissions of volatile organic chemicals (VOC's). With soy inks, VOC levels are 2-4 percent, compared with 25-40 percent for petroleum-based inks.

Researchers at the USDA ARS National Center for Agricultural Utilization Research in Peoria, IL, are already working on a second generation of lithographic soy inks. They contain no petrochemical compounds (except for pigments), provide a wide range of viscosities, and are expected to be more cost competitive with petroleum-based inks.

Paints and Coatings. VOC's are one of the principal components in chemical reactions in the air that form ozone, which in the lower atmosphere is a pollutant that can cause respiratory problems. According to Environmental Protection Agency air pollution estimates for the United States, 18.7 million metric tons of VOC's were released into the atmosphere last year, down from a high of 25 million metric tons in 1970. As total emissions have declined in the last few years, so have emissions from transportation sources, primarily gasoline-powered vehicles. Industrial processes are now the largest source of VOC emissions.

Surface coatings are the largest single source of industrial VOC emissions. However, because paints and coatings are used in so many widely differing circumstances, they do not lend themselves to solvent recovery (where the solvent could be reused or recycled). Therefore, producers are looking for alternative raw materials to use in paints and coatings to meet EPA-required reductions in VOC's.

Scientists are examining vegetable oils, particularly vernonia oil and epoxidized soybean oil, as replacements for solvents in paints and coatings. The modified coatings have lower VOC's and superior properties, and they are cheaper than traditional paint formulations. About 50 million pounds of vegetable oils could be used in these applications annually.

Fuels. Biodiesels are receiving attention as a replacement for petroleum diesel fuel. Tractors and other farm equipment, commercial truck fleets,

6

railroad engines, barges, and military vehicles and ships all run on diesel fuel. Production agriculture alone uses 3 to 3.5 million gallons annually. Besides being a renewable resource, biodiesel fuel can also help reduce air pollution. It is low in sulfur and gives off fewer particulates during combustion. Research is being conducted to develop diesel fuel from soybean oil, rapeseed oil, and tallow.

Drugs and Health Products

Plants and animals are increasingly being used to provide modern medicine with high-value drugs and biochemicals.

Taxol has recently emerged as a potent cancer-fighting drug. In clinical trials, it has shown significant activity against refractory ovarian cancer and good activity against advanced breast cancer. Further trials are in progress. Bark from the Pacific yew tree, *Taxus brevifolia Nutt*, is the current source of taxol. However, the long-term demand for taxol may outstrip this supply. Therefore, various projects are under way to find alternatives—from both domestic and wild sources.

For example, *Taxus* species are widely grown by the nursery industry as ornamental shrubs. Michigan-based Zelenka Nursery and researchers from the University of Mississippi and Ohio State University are demonstrating the feasibility of supplying dried needle and twig clippings from these plants

Ralph Shugert, staff horticulturalist at the Zelenka Nursery in Grand Haven, MI, samples a few of the millions of ornamental yew cuttings propagated by the nursery. Through a cooperative agreement with USDA and the National Cancer Institute, Zelenka Nursery will harvest, scientifically sample, dry, and ship enough yew needles and twigs to produce 2.5 kilograms of taxol. That would be enough to treat about 1,250 ovarian and breast cancer patients.
Bob Nichols/USDA 92BW0735-10

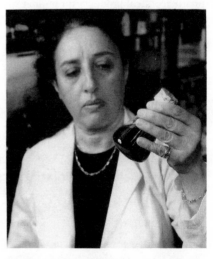

Professor Hala ElSohly, of the Research Institute of Pharmaceutical Sciences, University of Mississippi, Oxford, MS, examines a simple extraction of ornamental yew clippings before weighing and partitioning the solution to extract the taxol. The Zelenka Nursery provides the research material used at the university.
Bob Nichols/USDA 92BW0595-19

for taxol extraction. In tests at the National Cancer Institute, the clippings have had about twice the taxol content as does Pacific yew bark. Bristol-Myers Squibb will purify the drug and is pursuing commercialization of taxol from this source. In the future, perhaps the nursery industry will grow various plants for pharmaceutical uses.

Numerous companies are racing to produce human blood substitutes due to AIDS and other infectious diseases affecting the U.S. blood supply. A significant portion of the research is examining methods to extract the hemoglobin from cattle and pig blood for use in human blood substitutes. Research is also being conducted to develop animals that would produce pharmaceutical products for human consumption. For instance, Pharmaceutical Proteins, Ltd., a firm in Edinburgh, Scotland, has genetically engineered a sheep that produces a

protein named alpha-1-antitrypsin (AAT) in its milk. The 1 in 2,000 people who are deficient in this protein can suffer pulmonary emphysema and irreversible lung tissue damage.

A Promising Future

Although U.S. agriculture has made great strides in expanding its mission, the best is yet to come. The use of agricultural commodities as industrial raw materials will rise as nonrenewable resources become increasingly scarce and expensive, as businesses modify their manufacturing systems to use renewable materials and minimize waste generation, and as consumers use their purchasing power to indicate their concerns for a better environment.

Biotechnology promises enormous payoffs for agriculture. The ability to take a gene from one animal or plant and insert it into another will create

Frank Perez, a nurseryman at Zelenka Nursery in Grand Haven, MI, prunes 2-year-old ornamental yews with a combine. The combine was designed by Dr. Robert Holmes at the Agriculture Research and Development Center, Ohio State University. *Bob Nichols/USDA 92BW0736-25A*

market opportunities for a whole new class of commodities. For instance, tobacco plants are relatively easy to genetically modify and could be a future source of pharmaceuticals or other products requiring complex molecules. Microbial and enzymatic processes will be used to make the commodities and specialty chemicals that are the raw ingredients in nylons, polyurethanes, polyesters, and other polymers.

Continued technological improvements and effective partnerships between industry and Government will be paramount in achieving quick delivery of new products to the marketplace. Competition from abroad will be fierce as the agricultural industries in other countries look to these same fields.

Yet, if the United States takes advantage of its productive agricultural complex, along with its technological know-how, it should be able to provide a broad array of high-value products to consumers both here and abroad. U.S. agriculture will keep at its core the provision of food and fiber, but will continue to increase production of fuel, medicines, and industrial materials.

The transition to agriculture's new, expanded mission and marketplace will occur in this decade. It is an exciting time, with numerous opportunities for growth, expansion, and profit. Agriculture must seize the moment and bolster its capacity to produce what consumers desire—renewable bioproducts, made with the Earth in mind. ❏

How New Products Find Their Place in the Marketing System

2

by Julie A. Caswell, Associate Professor of Resource Economics, University of Massachusetts at Amherst, Amherst, MA, and Warren P. Preston, Assistant Professor of Agricultural Economics, Virginia Polytechnic Institute and State University, Blacksburg, VA

New product introduction is a risky business. Successful new products can make a company and keep it competitive in its industry, while providing steady outlets for its input suppliers, such as farmers. However, failure rates are high, so it is very important for suppliers, manufacturers, and distributors to understand the forces that affect new product success.

A new product's path from development to market acceptance depends on the type of buyer targeted. There are two basic buyer types: intermediate users, such as processors and manufacturers, and final consumers. Marketing channels and the prerequisites of success vary depending on which is targeted.

Manufacturers use new crops and new products from existing crops, both industrial (such as fuels) and foodstuffs, as intermediate inputs in producing final goods. This market is made up of professional buyers who base purchasing decisions on strict price/quality specifications and who are highly knowledgeable about the availability of substitute inputs. Selling them on a new product requires being responsive to their price, quality, quantity, and delivery needs.

Where the targeted buyer is the final consumer, the selling environment differs. While consumers make the same type of price/quality comparisons as professional buyers do, they usually have less complete information, and factors such as brand name, advertising, packaging, coupons, convenience, and image play a bigger role. These elements make communication a crucial factor in successful new product introduction.

The consumer market also differs because the producers are not in direct selling contact with the buyers, as they are in the intermediate goods market. The retail distribution chain links the two so that the producer is faced with a double selling job—to convince the retailer to carry the product and the consumer to buy it. For foodstuffs, this can become a triple selling job: for example, encouraging the cookie manufacturer to use a new oil, the retail chain to carry the cookie line, and the consumer to demand cookies made with the oil.

To further describe the path to new product acceptance, we focus first on the market for intermediate or industrial goods used in production processes. Then we turn to the market for new consumer products.

Intermediate and Industrial Goods

Three key elements that largely shape the environment in which new intermediate or industrial goods compete are characteristics of 1) the product itself, 2) the product's buyers, and 3) the marketing system through which the product is distributed.

Product Characteristics. Intermediate agricultural goods are sold as inputs for further processing and distribution. Hence, buyers need reliable information on the product's technical and functional characteristics. The producer must be able to demonstrate how the new product performs in its intended application. Buying decisions hinge on whether the new product contributes to the buyer's bottom line. Price is clearly an important consideration.

If the new product does not offer a price advantage relative to alternative inputs, then it must offer some performance edge in the manufacturing process.

Selling an intermediate good may also require the ability to customize the product to the buyer's specifications. Adapting to a particular buyer's needs may entail physical changes in the product, packaging changes, or changes in delivery methods. High levels of postsale service may be needed in the industrial market. The seller needs to build a field staff not only to service customers' accounts but also to help troubleshoot any problems the customer may encounter in using the product.

Buyer Characteristics. Industrial buyers differ substantially from household buyers. Buyers of intermediate goods are well informed about prices and product characteristics. While consumers of final goods may be willing to buy a new product on "impulse," an industrial buyer purchasing a vital input needs to know much more about a product before committing to a new supplier.

Compared to most household consumers, industrial buyers face higher switching costs and risks in trying new products. Switching costs are one-time costs of changing to a new supplier. Such costs and risks for a consumer trying a new food or fiber product generally are small—an improperly cooked meal or an unenjoyable dining experience may be the only result of an unsuccessful experiment. For an industrial buyer, switching costs and risks may be large. For example, a new or substitute ingredient may fail to perform as expected, resulting in unsatisfactory and even unsalable products. Other risks include uncertainties about the new supplier's reliability and lack of experience in using a new product.

In many cases, the seller of a new intermediate good needs to work with buyers to develop new product formulas. High fructose corn syrup, for instance, has replaced cane and beet sugar in many applications such as baked goods. To accommodate this change, however, product formulas and even the products themselves had to be altered. To provide assurance to buyers, the supplier may have to assume some of the financial risk that accompanies the switch to a new product.

Prices in producer goods markets adjust frequently to changing market conditions. Sellers of a new product must be prepared to negotiate prices with the buyer, rather than simply offering a "take-it-or-leave-it" price.

Marketing System Characteristics. Distribution networks play an important role in determining a new product's success. For agricultural goods, shipping costs frequently are high relative to the product's value.

Yu Cha McGibney selects a package of rice sticks from the ethnic food section of a supermarket. Winning acceptance for new products is the key to food manufacturers' marketing strategies.
Ken Hammond / USDA 92 BWO796-13A

That is, many agricultural products are bulky and costly to move long distances. Markets are likely to be local or regional in scope, presenting opportunities for entry by smaller scale operations.

In addition to geographic market concentration, both buyer and seller concentration are important strategic considerations for the developer of a new product. For example, three firms control most of the ready-to-eat breakfast cereal market. Potential buyers for a new input for use in cereal manufacturing are few. Conversely, there are many plants, both large and small, that manufacture cheese. A new ingredient for use in cheese manufacturing would have many potential buyers.

Seller concentration helps determine the potential response by competitors to a new product's introduction. If concentration is high, with just a few large sellers, then existing sellers may compete vigorously to minimize sales lost to a new entrant. If the selling industry is competitively structured with many smaller producers, then a new product may be able to enter the market with little response from existing firms.

Consumer Goods Sold Through Retail Stores

Winning acceptance for new products is of key importance to food manufacturers because introducing such products is a centerpiece of their marketing strategies. Over 12,000 new food products were introduced in 1991 alone, a 100-percent increase over the number introduced in 1986. Failure rates are believed to be stunningly high as well—as much as 80 percent. How do new products find their place on retailers' shelves and in consumers' shopping carts? The process has two stages: creating consumer demand (product pull) and encouraging distributors to give the product shelf space (product push).

Creating Product Pull. The ultimate success of a new product, of course, depends on generating strong consumer demand. Manufacturers of branded products seek to develop offerings with the price, quality, and convenience characteristics consumers will want, using advertising and coupons to make consumers aware of them. Advertising is a particularly important strategy for gaining new product acceptance because it plays a dual role. It builds consumer demand and signals to retailers and other manufacturers that the company is committed to spending the resources necessary to support the product in the early going. Large advertising expenditures are routinely involved in introducing new branded products. For example, it is estimated that as much as $20 million was recently spent on initial advertising of two new lines of "healthy" soups. This type of support builds the demand pull necessary to establish a new grocery store product.

Providing Product Push. Successful introductions in the retail channel also require the manufacturer to provide push for the new product. Push refers to incentives offered to wholesalers and retailers to carry the product. Some are offered across the board, such as special introductory prices and free goods, while others are negotiated individually. Wholesalers and retailers frequently use buyers and buying committees to evaluate whether a new product is "unique enough" and/or has sufficient manufacturer support to merit shelf space. Recent research indicates that most products do not make it past this stage. This is not surprising, given that about 90 percent of new products are extensions (for example, new flavors) of existing lines.

> The ultimate success of a new product, of course, depends on generating strong consumer demand.

Push is necessary because retailers face restrictions in accommodating new products. Although average store size has increased, product numbers far outpace available shelf space, giving retailers a strategic advantage in choosing products to carry. In addition, new product introductions generate costs such as establishing warehouse slots, resetting retail shelves, and changing store computer files. Product failures also generate costs. Given these strategic and cost factors, wholesalers and retailers have increasingly demanded more trade support (push) dollars for new products. One form this takes is charging slotting (and sometimes failure) fees to manufacturers. These and other related fees and services are a significant cost factor in budgets for new product introductions.

Other Considerations. A further factor complicating manufacturers' introduction strategies is the strong growth of alternative retail formats such as club warehouses and other deep discounters. These formats often stress selling branded goods at very low prices, placing a premium on the manufacturers' abilities to service these accounts cheaply. The skills required for successful introductions in alternative formats differ, making a wider array of skills necessary in selling new products to the retail sector. Overall, the length of the path to and costs of successful branded product introduction suggest that while profit potential is a key consideration, an ability to invest over time in order to reach that potential is also critical.

The new product introduction process for private label (store brands) and unbranded products (such as produce) bears a closer resemblance to that of intermediate goods than of branded consumer goods. Here the manufacturer concentrates on selling to wholesale or retail buyers who are professionals choosing products based on strict price/quality criteria. The emphasis is on cost-effective production of knockoff products, and the successful company does not need to be skillful in directly communicating with consumers. In contrast, the most salient point about the new product introduction process for branded goods is its multistage nature: creating demand pull from consumers and providing incentives that push the product through the distribution channel and onto the supermarket shelf.

Finding a Place in the Market

Research and development are just one step in the process of introducing new products to the marketplace. An equally important step is developing an appropriate marketing strategy that moves a new product from the laboratory toward commercial success. At the outset, the range of potential strategies is nearly boundless. The task for the developer is to choose a path for commercial introduction that balances risks and potential rewards.

A fundamental question that must be answered is, "What is the new product's target market?" If it cannot be answered in very specific terms, then the chances for a new product's success are limited. Important considerations are:

- Who is the intended buyer—processors, food service firms, or consumers?
- When will the product be produced and consumed—and how will seasonal differences in supply and demand be accommodated?
- Where is the market located—in a region, across the Nation, or on the other side of the world?
- How will the new product be distributed—through existing marketing channels or a new one?

- What is the competitive environment in the intended market—in terms of demand, number and size of competitors and buyers, and degree of product differentiation?

These questions about marketing strategy must be considered from the earliest stages of product development—and they must be answered as the product comes close to commercialization. A new product, whether it uses nontra-ditional materials or uses traditional materials in a new way, must have a solid marketing plan if it is to have any chance of success. Those involved in developing new crops and new uses must develop not only the technical and economic aspects, but also a marketing plan that considers the issues raised in this chapter.

Several other chapters in this book (including, Chapter 14 on kenaf, Chapter 16 on rapeseed and crambe, Chapter 18 on milkweed, Chapter 19 on jojoba and other new oilseed crops, Chapter 39 on Lactaid, and others) give specific examples of marketing plans that are integral and necessary aspects of developing these new products. ❏

Changing Food Marketing Systems

3

by John M. Connor, Professor, Department of Agricultural Economics, Purdue University, West Lafayette, IN, and Alan D. Barkema, Senior Economist, Federal Reserve Bank of Kansas City, Kansas City, MO

Over half of all new packaged consumer products introduced each year are foods and beverages. Almost daily, new product introductions bombard consumers and retailers with the need to evaluate product claims. New product marketing has become a major strategic concern of food processors and is profoundly affecting farmers' decisions about what to produce and how to sell their output.

Nearly all new foods are designed initially by food manufacturers that sell branded products. After a few months of market testing with small consumer "focus groups" or in a city or two, the manufacturer tries to entice food distributors to stock the new products in their warehouses and grocery stores. Because there are always more new products trying to gain acceptance than there is room for them on the grocers' shelves, only a tiny share of new products offered actually "make it"—that is, gain a respectable share of the market within about a year of introduction. This "battle of the brands"—the jockeying and jostling for shelf space by competing brands—is one of the great spectator sports of the modern food system. Additional rivalrous thrusts and parries

may occur some years later when manufacturers of private-label products learn how to imitate at low cost some successful new category of food or beverages.

How Many New Products?

This question is harder to answer than it appears at first blush.

Consider milk. In the late 19th century, milk was available in only one form: raw, full-cream, in glass quart bottles. Today, fluid milk is almost always pasteurized and homogenized. Moreover, it is now sold branded and unbranded, in many sizes, with many butterfat levels, and in lighter, less breakable containers. Goat's milk and soy milk are available for the lactose-intolerant. Ultra-high-temperature treatments permit milk to stay fresh-tasting for 1 year or more. Flavored, carbonated canned beverages may well be the next new form of milk to hit the market.

The number of new products introduced each year into the Nation's grocery stores has been estimated at from just a handful to above 20,000 depending on who is counting. A conservative count of just new brands shows that more than 3,000 are launched

Table 1. New grocery brands introduced March 1989-March 1990

Product groups	Number of brands	Product groups	Number of brands
Shelf-stable foods:	**1,665**	**Refrigerated and frozen foods:**	**907**
Candy	197	Frankfurters, sausages, lunchmeats	74
Tomato and other sauces	170	Cheeses	55
Canned fruits and vegetables	125	Ethnic foods, including pizza	79
Chips, salty snacks	101	Meat and fish dishes	61
Mayonnaise and salad dressings	71	Frozen vegetables	42
Canned juices	58	Juices	34
Spices	52	Fruit-flavored drinks	28
Crackers, crumbs, croutons, etc.	76	Frozen yogurt	32
Ready-to-eat cereals	50	Pies, pastries, sweet baked goods	25
Diet meals, dressings, desserts	38	Other frozen and refrigerated foods	477
Canned seafood	34		
Other breakfast cereals	33	**Health and beauty aids**	**394**
Pickles, pickled vegetables	30	**Nonfood grocery products**	**308**
Dog and cat food	37	**Total**	**3,274**
Other dry foods	664		

Source: SAMI (1990). Note: Of all the brands introduced during this 12-month period, only 191 or 5.8 percent were successful in reaching $1 million in U.S. sales by March 1990.

each year, but that only 100 to 200 will still be around a year after they are introduced.

New brand activity is most prominent in such categories as candy, sauces, snacks, juices, breakfast cereals, salad dressings, and highly processed frozen and refrigerated foods (table 1). These categories generally have higher growth rates and heavy consumer advertising support. On the other hand, there were a number of new brands introduced in such slow-growing categories as canned fruits and vegetables, butter, and bacon.

High failure rates among newly introduced products have not discour-aged food firms from bringing yet more new items to the U.S. market (fig. 1). In the late 1960's, only 1,900 grocery products were being launched each year. In the last 20 years, the number of new grocery products introduced has increased by an average of 11 percent each year. The number has doubled since 1986 alone. Even the 1991 recession failed to stem the tide of new products.

The Role of Food Manufacturers

Food manufacturers are primarily responsible for the decisions that launch new products, with brand firms taking the lead and private-label makers following their lead a few years later. Manufacturers continually monitor consumer trends as well as the product introductions of rival manufacturers; they listen to the needs expressed by grocery retailers, wholesalers, and foodservice firms.

The marketing and product-development divisions interact to design the formulas, cooking characteristics, and packaging they think their customers want. Most new items are test-marketed for a few months along with a coordinated advertising and promotion campaign designed by the firm's advertising agency. If early indications are promising, production may occur in secret for a couple of months to

Figure 1

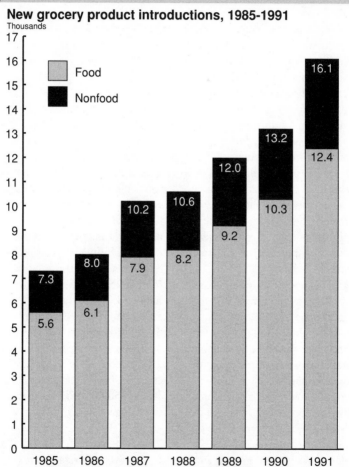

New grocery product introductions, 1985-1991

Note: The source is *New Product News,* which since 1964 has been counting all branded, packaged grocery items except wine, spirits, clothing, and hardware items introduced into grocery, health-food, and gourmet food stores. New flavors, colors, and varieties are counted, but not reformulations ("new, improved"), and new sizes of old packages are not counted.

build up inventory for a regional or national rollout, thereby taking rivals by surprise.

Why do food processors feel such an intense need to constantly introduce new food products, most of which are minor variants of existing products? The simple answer is to enhance company growth and maintain targeted profitability. The fact is, the U.S. food industry is growing quite slowly. In the 1960's, industry volume grew at only about 2.5 percent per year; after the year 2000 it is expected to slow to less than 1 percent per year. At the same time, demand by U.S. households is becoming ever more fragmented into smaller and smaller segments. Food products are increasingly aimed at just men, women, children, teens, or mature buyers; at smaller families; at families with dual-career heads of household; at health-conscious or environmentally concerned individuals; at up-scale young professionals; at certain ethnic groups; or at numerous other distinct categories.

Beginning about 20 years ago, sufficiently disaggregated food purchasing data became available so that processors could exploit these narrow demand segments, a process that has accelerated with the introduction of electronic scanner data.

While some leading grocery brands are enjoying their second century of successful sales, these brands are the exception to the rule. Most brands go through a cycle of rapid growth and slow decline. Leading brand manufacturers attempt to develop a portfolio that includes new, fast-growing brands as well as older, well-established, slow-growing brands. New items usually are priced such that when large-scale production is achieved, the margins earned by manufacturers are higher than the margins on the older, comparable brands which the manufacturers hope the new products will replace.

Newer products are nearly always introduced with claims for superior quality: convenience, microwaveability, taste, nutrition or health benefits, or the like. In other words, although it is often difficult to substantiate, new products claim to have higher value added. And indeed, value added, as conventionally measured by economists, has crept up slightly faster than sales in the food industry.

Leading processing firms account for a significant share of new products. In 1989, the top 20 food manufacturers launched about 15 percent of new foods and beverages brought to market. Philip Morris alone introduced 332 items. The most rapid rate of new food product introductions occurs in industries where the four leading firms account for 60 to 70 percent of industry sales, where advertising intensity is high, and where manufacturers spend a lot on packaging. Food manufacturers now spend more for packaging (about $50 billion) than they do for wages and salaries.

The Role of Food Retailers

In general, food retailers resist the introduction of new grocery products, for the simple reason that their shelves are already crowded with thousands of items. Confronted with thousands of new items each year, retailers must either drop some slower moving items from their shelves (perhaps thereby incurring the wrath of loyal customers who are used to the dropped item) or expand their store size. Thus, grocery retailers have experimented with new store designs (called superstores, combination stores, or hypermarkets) that allow more items to be stocked than the conventional supermarket, which itself has grown bigger in recent decades. The huge floor space and time commitment required for shopping in such big stores have generated some consumer resistance, prompting the return of some shoppers to specialized food stores and smaller grocery stores.

The professional buyers for grocery retailers use several guidelines to accept or reject new product offerings. In general, new products are more likely to be accepted if buyers rate them high on "uniqueness" (quality or newness), if the expected growth of their category is high, if other retailers have already accepted the product, if the product is from a large manufacturer that will advertise heavily, and if the retailer's unit profit is high. Research shows that professional buyers do a pretty good job of predicting which products will remain on the shelves for a few years, though there is some tendency on their part to be overly optimistic about high-priced, highly novel products in slow-growth industries.

Changing Vertical Market Organization

The food market is the elaborate communication and trading system linking consumers to food producers and processors. A smoothly functioning food market enables production from the Nation's farms, ranches, and food plants to reach the Nation's kitchens in the form and quantity that consumers appear to want. Aiming myriad new food products at a growing array of smaller consumer niches requires more precise quality attributes than the food market's traditional structure can offer.

Under the traditional marketing system for farm products, marketing commitments are left open until the production process is complete. When products are ready for market, the producer accepts the prevailing market price and the processor accepts whatever quantity and quality the producer brings to market. An effective agricultural grading system provides modest price incentives to encourage farmers and ranchers to produce products within a narrow quality range. Otherwise, food processors have traditionally had very little control over the quality of farm products entering the market.

This traditional system works reasonably well for generic products that are sorted into a few very broadly defined categories. But as product specifications become more detailed, market signals can be inaccurate or misinterpreted. Thus, a new market structure is evolving to shorten and clarify the market signals that link food producers, food processors, and distributors. The new system emphasizes customized farm and food products—rather than generic commodities—up and down the food system from farm to grocery. In brief, the food industry is moving away from the traditional open markets to nonmarket coordinating mechanisms that are leading to more closely integrated subsectors. New marketing arrangements, including various forms of contractual agreements, joint ventures, and mergers, are blurring the distinctions between previously independent segments of the food system. New computerized inventory control systems that are being adopted by food retailers and wholesalers are also

What's New in Foods?

Estimates of the number of new food and beverage products introduced annually vary considerably. To some extent, newness is in the eye of the beholder.

Every difference in form and brand of food requires a unique Universal Product Code (UPC) number so that grocers can stock the items. Whenever the most minor change in product description occurs, a new UPC code number must be assigned. There are more than 300,000 packaged grocery items in distribution somewhere in the United States—many found in only one or two States—and the typical supermarket stocks about 30,000 such items. Counting new items at this most extreme level of detail would yield more than 20,000 new products per year. If one eliminates changes in package sizes or designs and minor ingredient reformulations, then the number of new grocery products is more like 15,000 per year today.

A more stringent definition of "newness" would count only new *brands* of grocery products. In many cases these brands are being test-marketed in only one city; while some may eventually be sold nationwide, most will achieve only regional distribution. During the year ending March 1990, one source counted 3,274 new brands of packaged grocery products. Of these, 2,572 were edible products—foods and beverages.

Editors of trade magazines and other experts have applied an even more selective concept of newness in counting new food products. Editors of food industry magazines give awards or recognition to at most 5 or 10 new food products per year. A classic study of new foods identified only 22 "distinctly new" food products introduced during 1945-65. These were products such as frozen concentrated citrus juices that required novel production technologies and that essentially created an entirely new category of products. Another indicator of newness is market acceptance of new products. Most business-management studies of new products conclude that a maximum 5 to 10 percent of newly launched consumer brands achieve planned levels of sales, market share, or profitability. Of the 3,274 new grocery brands listed in table 1, a mere 191, or 5.8 percent, were able to reach $1 million in sales during the first year, and many of these were withdrawn later.

speeding up and tightening manufacturer-distributor linkages.

Integration shifts risks among food system participants. Previously, the greatest risks faced by both producers and processors were the big shifts in the supply of farm products and the corresponding swings in market prices. Although these risks remain large, risks associated with quality variability are becoming increasingly important today. While new processing technologies enable more precise targeting of specialized products, they also increasingly demand uniformity of products coming from our Nation's farms and ranches. Thus, food processors are using the new marketing arrangements to encourage farmers to adopt the latest technologies to reduce variability in input quality.

The integration process is virtually complete in the U.S. broiler industry. The wave of integration that swept the broiler industry some 40 years ago is advancing rapidly in other segments of U.S. agriculture. More than one-fifth of cattle and about one-seventh of hogs are now fed under some form of contractual or ownership arrangement with major packers and processors, up markedly from just a decade ago. Contractual production of the major crops also appears to be advancing, but at a less rapid pace than in livestock production.

Changing Horizontal Market Organization

In addition to changes in vertical relationships, the 1980's saw vast changes in ownership in the Nation's food manufacturing and distribution industries. Beginning in about 1987, hundreds of leading food firms merged, were acquired, or spun off. Several firms that had been publicly traded were taken private by management groups using leveraged buyouts. Billions of dollars in debt were created in the process, often in the form of high-yield and high-risk ("junk") bonds. Large cash flows were needed to service the interest on this debt, putting great pressures on firms to raise their profit margins. Most of the targeted firms either managed portfolios of well-established brands generating large cash flows or were adept at developing successful new products.

Chief among the acquiring firms were multinational food firms, most of them headquartered in Europe. Some evidence suggests that North American and Western European food expenditure patterns have been becoming more similar in recent years. Part of this convergence of food tastes may be attributed to travel, immigration, and other forms of personal contact. Moreover, U.S. imports and exports of processed foods have grown rapidly, reaching nearly $40 billion today, the greatest part of it from trade with Western Europe. Finally, of increasing importance is direct investment by U.S. food firms in Europe (with 1990 sales of about $45 billion, more than 10 percent of the EC market) and the reverse flow of investment into the United States ($25 billion in U.S. sales, about 6 percent of the U.S. market). These trade and investment relationships appear to be stimulating similar new product programs in both geographic regions. ❏

Overcoming Obstacles to Change

4

by Paul O'Connell, Director, Alternative Agricultural Research and Commercialization Center (AARC), USDA, Washington, DC, and Gregory R. Gajewski, Agricultural Economist, Economic Research Service, USDA, Washington, DC

The U.S. farm sector has an excellent record of moving the results of conventional production research and development into commercial use, and doing so quickly. However, efforts to commercialize *nonfood* uses beyond the farm gate have been less spectacular. More work and improved structure are needed.

There is a growing awareness that industrial uses of both existing and new agricultural products offer one of the most promising areas for expansion of markets for U.S. agriculture. USDA and others have done a great deal of research and development on industrial uses, but all too often progress stops where actual commercial application begins. Overcoming this barrier is what "commercialization" is about.

Before private firms will invest in commercial-scale plants to process raw industrial materials from agriculture, they must have technical information from industry laboratories—and those findings must be validated in prototype facilities. Some specific examples of commercialization activities are:
- Identifying viable market needs,
- Designing equipment,

- Testing products for performance and consumer acceptance,
- Obtaining regulatory clearance,
- Scaling up prototype equipment to a commercial level,
- Conducting precommercial runs,
- Verifying that the technology performs on a commercial scale, and
- Developing technical, cost, price, and other economic data for financial institutions.

In Japan and the European Community (EC), the overall rate of investment in these developmental activities for new industrial uses of agricultural materials is higher than in the United States, in part because their governments give more up-front support to commercialization.

Why Not More Commercialization?

Many private firms cannot afford to wait the 5 to 10 years required to obtain adequate returns on their investment in promising technologies. Often, their limit is 2 years or less. In addition, private companies hesitate to commercialize new products or technologies because "being first" can put them at a competitive disadvantage later. For example, a firm building the first commercial-scale plant will go through a "learning by doing" period that, unless kept secret, will benefit competitors by enabling them to build a second-generation plant that produces at a lower cost.

There are two "gaps" in the U.S. commercialization process: the first is a gap in funding and the second is a gap in institutional structure. In this country, the Federal Government provides the majority of funds for basic research. Public expenditures are justified because the timing and size of the payoffs are often too far off and too uncertain for private firms to undertake. At the other extreme, the private sector provides most of the funds for manufacturing and marketing activities. In between is the funding gap (see fig. 1).

In the EC and Japan, the public sector is aware of the problems private firms face in bringing new products to the marketplace and has programs to promote commercialization. For example, in agriculture, the EC awarded $83.9 million to 35 private/public partnerships in 1989 to fund research and development of new industrial uses from agricultural materials. The EC also has a Research, Technology Development, and Demonstration (RTD&D) program that is funded through 1994. The program includes $58 million for commercialization of nonfood industrial uses. In general, the EC's RTD&D commercialization projects require private firms to put up 70 percent of the funding.

Japan has a similar, but better funded, program to find naturally

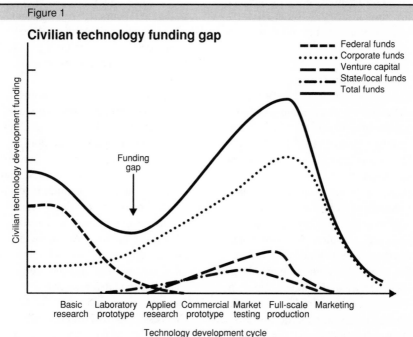

Figure 1

Civilian technology funding gap

Legend:
- Federal funds
- Corporate funds
- Venture capital
- State/local funds
- Total funds

Y-axis: Civilian technology development funding

Funding gap

X-axis (Technology development cycle):
Basic research, Laboratory prototype, Applied research, Commercial prototype, Market testing, Full-scale production, Marketing

occurring agrichemicals and pharmaceuticals from plants and animals. In addition, Japan has a different institutional structure. In the United States, the economy is organized along functional lines—by disciplines. Research and commercialization tend to be done by totally separate entities. But Japan's economy is organized along project lines, with a great deal of interdisciplinary interaction. Researchers are assigned to commercial production facilities.

As a result of these structural differences, other countries have all too frequently learned of U.S. research findings, commercialized them, and then exported the new products to the United States. Some experts maintain that while the functional structure found in the United States is well suited for basic research, the project structure, more common in Japan, seems better suited for commercializing technologies.

Who Benefits?

The task at hand is to benefit farmers and consumers by finding and commercializing new industrial uses for agricultural materials. The United States now has excess productive capacity to produce agricultural materials and new industrial products. In 1991, about 60 million acres of cropland were idled under Government programs, and direct Government payments to farmers totaled $9 billion. While progress at the Uruguay Round of the GATT trade talks would help open new markets for U.S. farmers, export markets are not the sole answer to growth in real farm income. New

markets are needed, and commercialization of farm products for industry is a key to unlocking new prospects.

Benefits will also go to the communities in farm States where the industrial crops are grown. Jobs and income will be generated as the crops are taken from the farm gate through the processors to the wholesalers and retailers. The post-farm-gate activity will provide jobs in the transportation, manufacturing, distribution, and support sectors.

Accelerating the use of agricultural materials in industrial products holds promise for employing idled farm and rural resources. As more agricultural materials are used in industrial products, more farm inputs and outputs will be used in farm States. In addition, many of these agricultural materials have low bulk density, and at least initial processing will occur relatively near where they are produced.

The question is sometimes asked, "Why should taxpayers invest in these activities?"

- Studies have shown that finding new uses for farm commodity program crops will lessen farmers' reliance on Government support programs and will generate benefits to consumers of new products. And with the increased planting flexibility authorized by the Food, Agriculture, Conservation, and Trade Act (farm bill) of 1990, these effects are likely to follow finding new uses for new crops as well.
- The Federal Government has a time-honored tradition of funding successful agricultural research. Most of it has focused on raising

yields and reducing the costs of producing traditional crops. This research infrastructure can equally well be directed to research and commercialization of new industrial uses that will increase the *demand* for agricultural materials.

- In general, farm-grown raw materials may impose fewer environmental costs than synthetic sources — especially materials derived from petroleum. Also, renewable resources will be used instead of nonrenewable resources. Examples include degradable plastics, lubricants, alcohol fuels, cosmetics, and a host of other products.
- Compared to the early 1980's, the United States is importing a higher percentage of total agricultural materials purchased. Including food, fiber, fish, and forest products, these imports amounted to $45 billion in 1991 (see fig. 2). Yet the United States has excess productive capacity to produce agricultural materials. Commercializing new industrial uses likely will cut the trade deficit, especially imports of petroleum.

To date, however, there have been no cost-benefit studies or studies of the rate of return on USDA commercialization projects. Most of the industrial products are new, and marketing is still in the experimental stage.

The Government's Role

Through its research and commercialization efforts, government at all levels can provide more access to information, increase competition, reduce barriers for firm startups, bear risk, and allow for long-term horizons for investments. But not all government support of these activities has paid off—the intervention must be carefully crafted.

Research done in the early 1980's on the role of government in promoting research and development (R&D) and technical change in seven major U.S. industries gives some pointers on how to most effectively boost commercialization of agricultural materials. The research found that government succeeded in promoting technical change in defense, space, and natural resource management areas— because government itself was the user of the technology.

Government also succeeds in promoting the so-called "generic technologies" that are a step or two removed from commercial applications. Much of this knowledge cannot be patented and involves broad design concepts, properties of materials, biological processes, inventories, and testing concepts. Such generic activity falls in between the work that an academic would pursue and the kinds of results-oriented research that would interest most corporate R&D laboratories.

When government moves closer to applied research, its role becomes more complex. Private firms want to maintain technical advantages over their competitors and consider it a threat when the advances are made freely available to all. However, in agriculture, government support for more applied research has resulted in a mutual benefit to producers and consumers. The Federal-State system of agricultural research and education evolved to take advantage of agriculture's market structure, marshaling the support of farmers and giving them an important position in the evaluation and selection of projects. Research has shown this type of "clientele-directed applied R&D" to be highly successful.

However, government has generally not succeeded when it has tried to "pick winners." Examples include synfuel projects, specific housing designs, and the supersonic transport (SST) program. For these, Federal

Figure 2

Agricultural, fish, and forestry products
(Changing trade balance for U.S.)

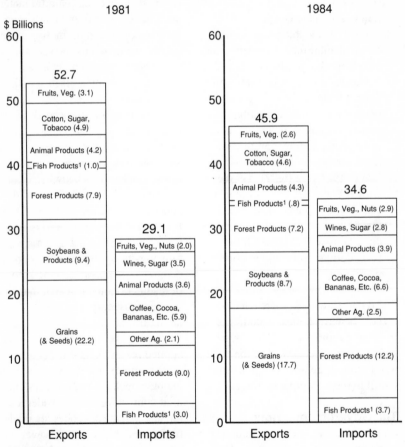

[1] (Edible)
[2] 1990 figures
Source - Departments of Agriculture and Commerce

agencies tried to insert themselves directly into the business of developing technologies for a commercial market in which they had little or no procurement interest and without the full participation of the relevant business interests.

Overall, the record shows that government support of research and development works best when both the users and the scientists are involved in directing the specifics of the work.

How the Research-Extension System Works

The relationship between research, extension, and farmers has led to a very productive agriculture in the United States. This successful marriage of government and producers didn't just happen. People with vision, such as John Gregory and Eugene Hilgard, established the State Agricultural Experiment Stations. Others led the way for the formation of the nationwide Cooperative Extension System and the Agricultural Research Service (ARS).

Scientists and engineers came up with plants and animals that grew faster, resisted disease, and were more nutritious; soil management practices that enhanced production; laborsaving equipment; and farm management techniques that allowed the producer to become a better business manager. The county extension agent transferred this knowledge to the farmer using easy-to-read technical publications, demonstration projects, and one-on-one interaction.

This model works well because there is a continual flow of information among the scientists, the extension agents, and the farmers. When a new seed variety, piece of equipment, or soil conservation practice becomes available, it is tested on farms managed by progressive operators. If there are any flaws in the idea, the problems go back to the researcher for further study and correction.

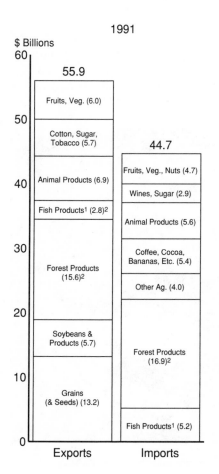

1991

$ Billions

Exports: 55.9
- Fruits, Veg. (6.0)
- Cotton, Sugar, Tobacco (5.7)
- Animal Products (6.9)
- Fish Products[1] (2.8)[2]
- Forest Products (15.6)[2]
- Soybeans & Products (5.7)
- Grains (& Seeds) (13.2)

Imports: 44.7
- Fruits, Veg., Nuts (4.7)
- Wines, Sugar (2.9)
- Animal Products (5.6)
- Coffee, Cocoa, Bananas, Etc. (5.4)
- Other Ag. (4.0)
- Forest Products (16.9)[2]
- Fish Products[1] (5.2)

More generally, commercialization efforts often involve the development of government-funded basic research by a partnership between government and a private firm. Prior to the Technology Transfer Act of 1986, private firms were reluctant to help commercialize government discoveries because the discovery was in the public domain. With this legislation, however, concerns about exclusivity have been put to rest. To obtain an exclusive license, an interested company must present a financial plan for developing the product or process and utilizing it commercially. ARS and the Forest Service have many such agreements with private companies. Most universities also provide similar protection for technologies derived from their experiments.

However, having an exclusive license is only a first step in commercializing an idea. William Carpenter, Vice President at Oak Ridge National Laboratory, said, "People usually don't realize how immature a government technology is. It will cost more than they think to develop it. It will require more management assistance than they think."

A New Structure Is Emerging

The goal is now to take the best aspects of the research-extension-farmer organization for traditional production

Plant pathologist Rick Bennett examines fungi that may be used for biological control of pernicious weeds.

Scott Bauer/USDA 92BW0719-0

agriculture and create a new structure to promote new industrial uses of agricultural materials. USDA is moving ahead in efforts to build a structure that will facilitate commercialization and thus promote rural development.

The 1990 farm bill authorizes the USDA activities in industrial uses and rural development. Specifically, the bill authorizes the establishment of the Alternative Agricultural Research and Commercialization (AARC) Center, a new entity charged with researching, developing, and commercializing new industrial uses for agricultural products. AARC's goals are to create jobs, enhance rural economic development, and diversify agricultural markets.

The AARC Center will issue grants, contracts, and cooperative agreements to carry out R&D activities. Loans, interest-subsidy payments, venture capital, and repayable grants will go to fund the commercialization efforts. Priority will be given to applications with cosponsors in the private sector and in other government agencies.

Secretary of Agriculture Edward Madigan has appointed the AARC Board of Directors, and the Center is now being put together. The Board includes a scientist, a grower-processor, a businessperson, an applied researcher, a marketing specialist, and a USDA executive. USDA's commercialization efforts are being coordinated out of the Secretary's office. The first appropriations for the AARC were made in fiscal year 1992.

USDA's new Rural Development Administration (RDA), also authorized by the 1990 farm bill, and the U.S. Department of Commerce's Small Business Administration have programs that can promote commer-

Nathan Rovy (left) and Dave Dierig of the ARS Water Conservation Lab in Phoenix, AZ, inspect this year's lesquerella crop on Rovy's farm near Parker, AZ.

Ken Hammond/USDA 92BW0697-23

cialization and help shift commercialization activities to more rural settings. Several State organizations also promote commercialization efforts.

While the AARC is new, USDA's Cooperative State Research Service (CSRS) and Agricultural Research Service (ARS) have been helping to commercialize agricultural products since the early and mid-1980's.

CSRS manages commercialization projects under the authority of the Critical Agricultural Materials Act of 1984. CSRS has entered into several agreements with private firms and universities to bring technologies to the point where they attract private investment, or at least where a totally private venture is feasible. Here are some examples:

- The kenaf demonstration project involves equipment manufacturers, newspaper publishers, potential investors, and universities to produce newsprint;
- The crambe/rapeseed demonstration project involves oil processors, testing laboratories, universities, and farmers to produce various oil and meal products;
- The biodegradable starch-polymers demonstration project involves the U.S. Department of Defense, Federal laboratories, a processor and marketer, nonprofit organizations, and universities to make degradable food containers;
- The guayule natural rubber demonstration project involved the Department of Defense, a private processor, a Native American community, consultants, and universities; and

- The taxol demonstration project involves the National Cancer Institute, Federal laboratories, growers, and universities to show the viability of obtaining this cancer-treating compound from an alternative source—ornamental shrubs.

In these projects, the cooperators work together to test products for performance, scale up prototype equipment, examine alternative uses for coproducts, meet requirements for regulatory clearance, explore recycling opportunities, and conduct precommercial runs. In other words, they are working on closing the gap between emergence of a promising technology and creation of a new market for U.S. farmers.

Elsewhere in USDA, ARS has two keys to moving research results from agency laboratories to industry: (1) cooperative research and development agreements (CRADA's) authorized by the Technology Transfer Act of 1986 and (2) licensing of patents on inventions by ARS scientists. ARS has negotiated over 225 CRADA's, and is among the top Federal agencies in patent licensing. Products and processes developed through CRADA's and patent licenses include:

- Sustained-release pesticides, including biological ones, based on entrapment in modified starch carriers,
- An alternative source of taxol involving production by tissue culture, analogous to production of antibiotics and vitamins by fermentation,

- Cost-competitive inks for black and white printing based on soybean oil instead of petrochemicals,
- Oatrim, a fat substitute made from the B-glucan fraction of oat gum, which reputedly lowers blood cholesterol, and
- Improvements in cotton ginning technology to increase the efficiency of this crucial processing step and enhance the quality of cotton products.

Outside USDA, the Departments of Commerce and Energy and the Environmental Protection Agency (EPA) have the authority to promote the commercialization of agricultural materials for industrial uses. Commerce's Small Business Administration has the authority to help by targeting its grant and loan programs to small businesses wanting to commercialize agricultural materials. Also, the Commerce Department's National Information System and its Private/Public Advance Technology Program can help commercialize agricultural materials. EPA has expressed interest in commercializing products that use renewable resources. The U.S. Department of Energy funds research-oriented projects on renewable fuels.

Outside the Federal Government, activities that support commercialization include:

- State and Regional Economic Development Corporations in Kansas, Minnesota, and the Northern Regional Agricultural Utilization Consortium;
- Commodity group efforts, such as those of the National and State Corn growers and the Soybean Growers, which last year invested $1.7 million and $1.5 million, respectively, on research and development of nonfood uses;
- State matching funds at State Agricultural Experiment Stations in Iowa, Nebraska, Missouri, and North Dakota; and
- Information Centers at the University of Minnesota, Cornell University, and Oklahoma State University.

The outlook for commercialization is upbeat. Increasingly, private businesses and Government are working together to develop new uses for our farmers' productive resources, and the resulting new products should help U.S. businesses and consumers protect the environment. ❏

The Power of Choice 5

by Lawrence Libby, Chair, Department of Food and Resource Economics, University of Florida, Gainesville; Daniel E. Kugler, Director, Office of Agricultural Materials, CSRS, USDA, Washington, DC; and Steven Taff, Agricultural Economist, Department of Agricultural and Applied Economics, University ofMinnesota, St. Paul

Consumer demand is a powerful force, and people can use that power as a way to put their values to work. Individuals do care about the quality of life beyond their immediate needs, and they are often willing to pay for it.

Problems such as solid and hazardous waste disposal, depletion of finite natural resources, and food safety are affected by individual choice as well as by social policies.

The real challenge is to provide meaningful options for people in their behavior choices. One of these important options is the opportunity to purchase consumer products that do not deplete or damage the environment. Time and time again, we see that consumers *do* adjust their personal preferences, and make decisions that take into account the social and community impacts of private action, if they are given the product choices and the information that allow them to do so.

Consumer demand for a safe and attractive natural environment increases with income. Those with low incomes, who do not have adequate food or shelter, have priorities different from those whose basic needs are met. Yet whether we look at the devel-oping world or the wealthy nations, economic development that abuses or destroys the environment may exchange short-term relief for long-term damage.

Addressing the World Future Society in 1989, former Secretary of Agriculture Orville Freeman asserted, "We make a potentially dangerous mistake when we assume that we must choose between serving humanity or serving the environment. It must be a priority to bring these goals of feeding the world's hungry and protecting the world's environment into harmony. They need not and they must not be mutually exclusive."

No one wants to destroy a place while seeking to improve it, at home or abroad. The public needs and deserves the chance to act on the understanding that economic improvement and environmental safety can co-exist.

At the Personal Level

In the marketplace, when a buyer selects and purchases a product, he or she is expressing an opinion which the marketplace interprets as demand. In some cases, we purchase tangible things such as cars, newspapers, or lunch. In other cases, they are intangible things such as clean air or education.

Our attitude toward market products, to the extent that it affects what we actually purchase, is an important determinant of change in what is produced. If consumers ask for change in the marketplace, the market will adjust. It is also a function of the marketplace to offer options that respond to the preferences for consumer choice. By providing information about product attributes and their impacts on human welfare, markets both respond to and help shape consumer preferences.

How do consumer preferences change? They are influenced by changes in family income, by advertising, by education, by experience, and by the relative prices of competing products.

We are bombarded with thousands of messages and experiences every day, and the information in these messages helps us to formulate and change our attitudes. More consistent and more credible messages, and those presented by more prominent or respected individuals, increase the likelihood that groups of people will arrive at some consensus of opinion or public consciousness. If the collective attitude is expressed in the market, change can occur. Individuals influence the marketplace and the marketplace influences individuals, but there must be communication between the two: a level of common understanding, a language of exchange, and a willingness to interact.

Agriculture at a Crossroads

As a Nation, we are rediscovering that "agriculture is the foundation of manufacture and commerce" (as the motto on USDA's seal suggests). We are learning that agriculture provides much more than food and fiber, that agriculture is a storehouse of renewable chemicals and materials for the Nation's industries. This role was fundamental and widely understood in the past, but now we have come to rely largely on synthetics, many of petrochemical origin, and American agriculture has devoted much of its research to the production and improvement of a few crops: corn, wheat, soybeans, rice, and cotton.

People are the marketplace. The decision to select and purchase a product expresses an opinion which the marketplace interprets as demand.
USDA 0885X940-7

Today, in another swing of the pendulum, public attention—and market demand—may be moving away from *how much* food, fiber, and other material is grown to *how* it is grown. More and more buyers are looking beyond simple price and quantity of agricultural outputs and seeking other qualities as well. Today, concerns for the environment, human health, and economic well-being are increasingly being expressed in the marketplace by consumer demand as well as by law and regulation. There is a greater sense that short-term action can have long-term effects that may be inconsistent with personal beliefs.

What does this mean for farmers and agricultural businesses? Is it no longer enough to grow corn, raise cattle, or produce cotton? Beyond assuring the public of an adequate supply of reasonably priced and wholesome food—a clear, although often unstated, policy goal for decades—agriculture is now being asked to accomplish this without generating unaccep- table levels of environmental damage or human health risk.

One way to think of the situation that American farmers face is to view a product, such as a bushel of soybeans, as a "total product." It not only contains a certain level of vegetable oil, protein, and carbohydrates, characteristics which are valued in the market, but also has embedded in it the technique used to grow the soybeans (including tillage and chemical practices), the ownership of the farm, the relative prosperity of the surrounding community, the opportunity costs of those soybeans not being produced in some other way or in some other

Agriculture in the United States provides more than food and fiber; it is a renewable chemical and materials storehouse for our Nation's industries.

Tim McCabe/USDA 0981X1234-21

place, and so forth. Now, the buyer gets all this with a bushel of soybeans.

In addition, with domestic demand for food-based products relatively stable, industrial uses are becoming an attractive alternative market for farm-based commodities. One example of a new industrial use for soybean oil is as a partial replacement for petroleum in newspaper print inks.

Demand for environmental services from agriculture will be increasingly evident throughout the world as more and more countries approach the U.S. level of national wealth. At the moment, this demand is expressed more through policy than through prices.

As the rest of the world develops, consumers in other nations may increasingly demand the same mix of food and nonfood products and environmentally benign effects that U.S. consumers now increasingly demand. If U.S. producers wish to sell in these nations, they may need to offer products with those environmental services.

New Products

Better, more informed choices can be made in the marketplace if people are aware of agricultural industrial materials and the innovative products made from them, both what they are and the benefits they can bring to the Nation. Most people do not know that "carbonless" carbon paper works because of starch-encapsulated ink, that some "paints" on soda cans are sprayable coatings made from castor oil derivatives, and that some interior car door panels are dry-formed composites made from aspen tree fibers. Even

fewer people know that the hibiscus plant kenaf can be made into high-quality newsprint for newspapers, that the vegetable oil from crambe can be made into high-performance nylon 13,13, or that some ornamental yews are a renewable source of the compound taxol, which is being used to make an anticancer drug. These products are typical of new nonfood uses of both traditional and "new" crops. They are also products that can offer environmental benefits on the farm, in manufacturing, in the end use, and in the reuse or recycle phase.

These envisioned products, whether made from traditional or "new" crop materials, are not merely raw, harvested commodities from the farm. Rather, they are value-added products; each step in their processing contributes additional economic return and

Soybeans have many uses, as they are a basic ingredient for many food and nonfood products.
Ken Hammond/USDA 91BW1995-34A

leads to the manufacture of one or several final products for sale to consumers. Over the years, many countries have succeeded in producing basic food and fiber commodities and putting them out for bid in the international market. The future international market will offer more value-added products of agricultural origin. Embedded within them will be sustainable farming practices, environmental services, and economic returns for domestic value-added processing and marketing steps.

The Challenge Ahead

The challenge ahead is to educate and stimulate both consumers and industry. Consumers need to be aware of the responsiveness of agriculture and industry to demand-driven products and markets. Consumers can make informed choices if information about products is credible and widely available. Industry needs to know that renewable agricultural materials can offer the desired quality, price, and performance characteristics necessary for current and future market products.

Household and industrial consumers are being made more aware of the new choices they can make. They are learning that those choices can benefit them personally and provide corporate advantage, while at the same time helping to achieve national and global environmental goals. Changes in attitude and market actions can signal a new era for agriculture, an era that once again represents a handshake between the tillers of the land and the captains of industry. ❏

Agricultural products such as soybeans are being considered as a total product that incorporates not only their food and commercial value, but also the techniques with which the crops are grown, such as no-till planting in wheat residue.
Gene Alexander/USDA KS-2053-32

The 1991 Yearbook of Agriculture was printed with soy ink on recycled paper. Press Foreman Gary Crawford (left) of the Arcata Printing Company in Kingsport, TN, and Warren Bell, Printing Chief for USDA, check soy-ink-printed press sheets. A particularly successful use of soybean oil has been as a partial replacement for petroleum in printing inks.
Larry Rana/USDA 91BW2248-12

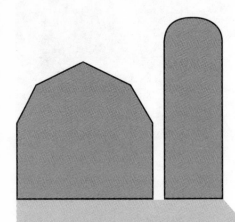

Part II.
Researching and Implementing New Products and Technologies

The Process of Research

6

by Alvin L. Young, Director, and Daniel D. Jones, Deputy Director, Office of Agricultural Biotechnology, USDA, Washington, DC, and Edward B. Bagley, Research Leader, National Center for Agricultural Utilization Research, Agricultural Research Service, USDA, Peoria, IL

For thousands of years, farmers tilled the soil for planting crops and raised animals for food and fiber. They selected high-yielding varieties of plants and animals, fashioned various tools for agricultural use, and developed rudimentary methods of pest control.

Then in the 19th century, scientific methods were first applied to agriculture on a large scale. The resulting increases in productivity allowed the United States to achieve one of the highest standards of living in the world, characterized by a great variety of abundant and high-quality agricultural products and a low percentage of per capita income spent on food.

The science of agriculture is dynamic and requires a continuing investment both in research itself and in the development of skilled people who can conduct and translate research into the products that contribute to a nation's well-being. In the United States, the establishment of an agricultural research system more than a century ago helped to ensure that education, research, and extension would contribute significantly to the Nation's food security.

The Agricultural Research System

Today, the United States has an agricultural research system that includes 72 academic institutions, 58 State agricultural experiment stations, and more than 200 Federal laboratories in a network that encompasses 15,000 scientists and 13,000 graduate students. In addition, extension agents in over 3,000 counties facilitate the communication of farmers' research needs to the scientific community, and the communication of the results of problem-solving research back to farmers.

At the national level, USDA's Agricultural Research Service (ARS), Economic Research Service, and Forest Service conduct agricultural research in their areas of responsibility. Regional research is the responsibility of the Cooperative State Research Service (CSRS), which funds extramural research at colleges, universities, and other institutions. The Extension Service administers programs for the transfer of new knowledge and processes from the scientific community to farmers and others who need the information.

Agricultural Research Goals

From its inception, U.S. agricultural research has been goal oriented. The goals of agricultural research have been many and varied and have included improved productivity, animal and crop protection, reduced costs, increased product demand, improved marketing systems, increased exports, a higher standard of living, and rural community improvement.

Today, agricultural research is directed toward the pursuit of new knowledge and technology. Solving technical agricultural problems will ensure adequate production of high-quality food and agricultural products, to help meet the nutritional needs of U.S. consumers, sustain a viable food and agricultural economy, and maintain a quality environmental and natural resource base.

In the late 20th century, our world's environment is providing special challenges and new directions for agricultural research. These include global climate change, the agricultural effects of ozone depletion and population growth, and ways to develop a sustainable and environmentally friendly agricultural production system.

Scientific Approach

Agricultural researchers, like their colleagues in other fields, rely heavily on the scientific approach for progress toward their research goals. The scientific approach starts with careful observation, then leads to a hypothesis to explain the observations. It usually results in the design and performance of experiments to test the validity and consequences of the hypothesis.

A well-designed experiment may have two possible outcomes: It may

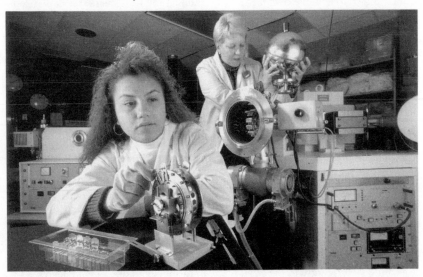

Biological aide Ellie Giron (left), a Native American student at the University of North Dakota, and ARS chemist Phyllis Johnson prepare a sample for analysis at the Grand Forks Human Nutrition Research Center in Grand Forks, ND.
Bruce Fritz/USDA 92BW1090-15

Part II. Research and Implementation

refute the hypothesis, making it necessary to develop an alternate hypothesis to explain the data; or it may withstand the experimental results and serve as a guide to further experiments. Results of experiments also may suggest other experiments to be performed or other hypotheses to be tested. Knowledge acquired by this method is provisional and subject to change when new experimental results are reported, confirmed, and accepted by the scientific community.

Choosing a Problem To Research

In addition to scientific criteria, there is a complex array of nonscientific factors that influence the selection of research problems to be addressed by agricultural scientists. This includes administrative directives, commodity interests, socioeconomic factors, and political commitments. Some of the agents of these influences include farmers, farmworkers, agribusinesses, rural residents, government agencies, international groups, commodity groups, other interest groups, legislative bodies, and the general public.

As one example, the President's National Initiative for Research on Agriculture, Food, and Environment, started in FY 1991, is providing resources for major new research thrusts. The National Research Initiative (NRI) calls for increases in funding for USDA-sponsored research to meet pressing agricultural challenges as identified by the National Academy of Sciences Board on Agriculture. The National Research Initiative was funded at $73 million in FY 1991 and

$97.5 million for FY 1992. USDA has invited the scientific community to submit research grant applications in a number of areas that it believes are particularly important for the continuing development of U.S. agriculture in a global environment.

Research and Development Cycle

The development of new products from emerging technologies traverses a range of activities, from basic research and applied research through product development, regulatory approval, and consumer acceptance. The focus of research differs significantly over this research and development cycle. In the early phases, research tends to be more knowledge oriented, and in the later phases it tends to be more product oriented.

Similarly, the nature of the investment in research changes over the research and development cycle. In the United States, most basic agricultural research has traditionally been supported by public funds. The rationale is that basic or exploratory research, while making a significant contribution to scientific knowledge, often involves financial risk. Public funding spreads this financial risk over a larger funding base. Product development, on the other hand, is usually more targeted and is supported by private funding. The private investment in product development can be viewed as complementary to the public investment in the basic research that forms the basis for later product development.

Factors Influencing Innovation and Invention

A number of factors influence innovation and invention in agricultural research (fig. 1). These include personal factors such as knowledge, observation, and commitment, as well as organizational factors such as opportunity, communication, and recognition.

Knowledge: The most productive and original scientists tend to have a vast and detailed working knowledge of their own field and a broad knowledge of science and technology in general. From this knowledge base there often grows over time an understanding and appreciation of market needs and requirements essential for significant creative innovation.

Observation: New and unexpected results can form the basis of ideas for valuable patents. Careful execution and observation of experiments are essential for innovation and, coupled with critical analysis of experimental results, can lead to new ideas, processes, and products.

Personal Commitment: Scientists often start with an idea that is rather vague and general, and that might languish without special effort. The successful inventor is the one who molds these general ideas into more concrete form and does the work required to transform the initial concept into a finished final result. Thomas Edison is reputed to have said that invention is 1 percent inspiration and 99 percent perspiration.

Opportunity: A scientist may have knowledge, experience, and commitment, but the organization must provide the opportunity to exploit ideas. An example is the development of the

Figure 1

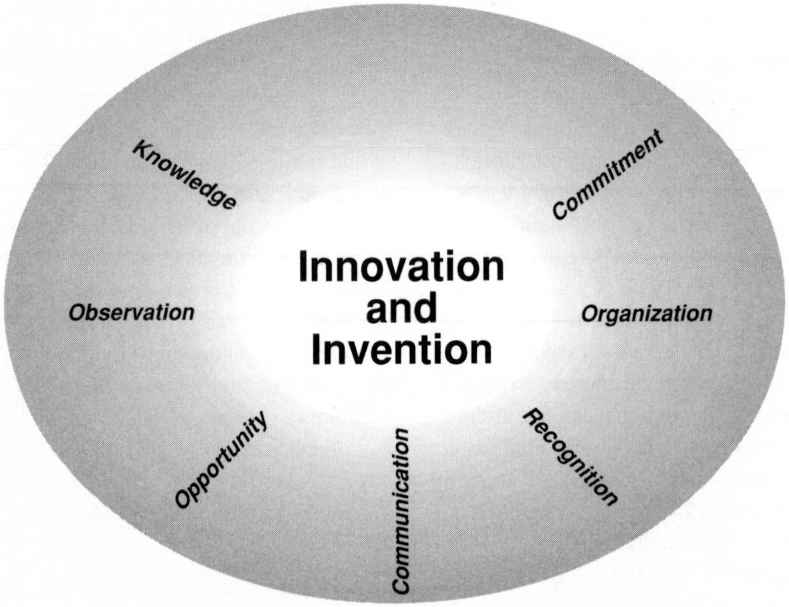

Innovation and Invention

Knowledge · Commitment · Observation · Organization · Opportunity · Communication · Recognition

process called trickle ammonia low-energy grain drying. The idea had originated with scientists at the Peoria Center of ARS and the requisite background knowledge was available. But the process itself was not developed and exploited until the necessary staff and resources became available. When they did, as a result of an urgent need to solve a problem related to toxins in grain, the commitment of the staff scientists was such that they seized the opportunity.

Communication: Agricultural problems are often multidisciplinary, requiring expertise covering a range of disciplines such as the biological and physical sciences, engineering, mathematics, and economics. A problem that may appear as insurmountable viewed from the perspective of one discipline may be amenable to elegant and original solutions when viewed by someone in another discipline. Communication is essential for this cross-disciplinary interaction so that opportunities for innovation can be recognized and exploited.

Organizational Commitment: In any large research organization, some programs are of necessity long-term and complex. For such programs, organizational commitment is critical. Time and adequate support must be provided for the team members to develop the knowledge, expertise, and appropriate industrial and academic contacts to reach the stage of technical sophistication which will permit and foster innovative developments. Organizational objectives and expectations should be made clear to all team members, and should be updated periodically as the program progresses, so that no chance will be lost through ignorance of needs. Technology transfer efforts can ensure that feedback from the private sector can be factored into program planning and execution.

Recognition: Different scientists in a research and development organization tend to have different strengths. Some scientists do excellent basic research but are indifferent to the practical implications of their work. Others have a knack for the practical but derive less satisfaction from amassing knowledge and producing manuscripts. The reward system needs to recognize those who are prolific in producing valuable patents, new products, and new processes—just as it recognizes scientists who produce fundamental information—with support, encouragement, and opportunities for promotion.

Technology Transfer at USDA

In the past, communication of the commercial potential of basic research to those with the incentive and resources to develop it has not always been timely. This has sometimes resulted in promising technologies not being fully harnessed for commercial development. In 1986, the U.S. Congress passed the Federal Technology Transfer Act in an effort to stimulate technology transfer from the scientific research community to the commercial arena.

One approach to technology transfer involves encouraging cooperative research projects between Government scientists and the private sector. USDA has developed an active technology transfer program under the authority of the Federal Technology Transfer Act of 1986, and it has entered into numerous Cooperative Research and Development Agreements (CRADA's) with private industry. Over 200 CRADA's have been negotiated between the Agricultural Research Service (ARS) and industry, plus approximately 40 more between the Forest Service and private firms.

Examples of New Products and Technologies

Developments in biotechnology are providing a breadth of examples of basic research and development of new products and technologies for agriculture.

For example, in plant systems, *basic research* is exemplified by characterization of plant germplasm and the identification of key genes that control basic plant functions. *Applied biotechnology research* on plants is beginning to make key advances in the enhancement of insect-resistance, drought tolerance, nutritional quality, and storage quality. New varieties of plants with known and precise genetic changes are being tested for agricultural performance in outdoor field plots. These include insect-resistant cotton plants and tomatoes that spoil less rapidly.

In animal systems, *basic research* is exemplified by the mapping of animal genomes and elucidation of genetic factors that control growth and reproduction. *Applied animal research* is focusing on improved growth rate, feed efficiency, disease resistance, disease diagnosis, and composition of food products of animal origin. Animal vaccines produced by the newer methods of biotechnology are already on the market and other products are likely to follow.

The Future

Presidential research initiatives are focusing on several areas of research and technology. Two areas that will directly affect agriculture include materials science and biotechnology. These Presidential initiatives recognize the critical role of these technologies in future technological strength, economic growth, and the health and quality of life for the people of the United States.

Improvements in the scientific and engineering research base of these technologies will have far-reaching effects on U.S. society and will lead to important enhancements in the quality of life as well as in agriculture, aquaculture, manufacturing, food processing, and the economic health of the Nation. ❑

New Uses for Agricultural Products: Technology Transfer for Commercialization

7

by William H. Tallent, Assistant Administrator, ARS, USDA, Washington, DC, and L. Davis Clements, Chemical Engineer, CSRS, USDA, Washington, DC

The previous chapter described how research scientists go about finding new crops as well as new uses for traditional crops. This chapter deals with the next step—converting these research results into economic benefits. We provide some clarification of widely used but often misunderstood terms and concepts. We also consider the question of what are appropriate public and private sector roles in research, development, and commercialization of new technologies. Finally, we review several new initiatives—in the United States and abroad—that are designed to turn scientific achievements into economic growth.

Commercialization and Technology Transfer

Often the terms "commercialization" and "technology transfer" are treated as if they are interchangeable. They are not. Commercialization is the process of placing a product into the marketplace with the goal of creating an economic success. Technology transfer, on the other hand, is a strategy for ensuring access to technical details that allow the production of the product being commercialized.

In order for any product to be a commercial success, at least five elements must be in place. They include a market niche, a reliable supply of raw materials, a feasible conversion technology to make products, a manufacturing facility, and a suitable business structure. Three of these elements—the supply of raw materials, the conversion technology, and the manufacturing facility—are essential for the *development* of new technologies. The sources for these new technologies may be generated from within the organization, purchased or licensed from others, or developed in collaboration with others who have complementary expertise and mutual goals.

The stages generally recognized in the conversion of fundamental scientific discoveries to commercialized products and processes are presented in figure 1.

The transition from one stage to another is usually a gradual flow, but it is helpful to describe the stages separately.

Traditionally, **basic research** has been defined as the determination of fundamental laws and properties of nature without regard to practical application of the results. This definition, however, is unpopular with mission-oriented organizations that perform research aimed at solving practical problems or at exploiting scientific advances.

Perhaps a more useful definition of basic research focuses on the *nature* rather than the *objective* of the research. This definition says that basic research is fundamental, purposeful, necessarily high risk, and often carried out at the molecular or cellular level. This definition is broad enough to include efforts that solve problems or exploit scientific opportunities for new products. Generally, basic research is more long range than subsequent stages of the research and development process.

Applied research is less risky and shorter range. It is targeted toward *specific* applications and may involve experiments designed to evaluate potential practical benefits: planting test plots of a new crop, or making sheets of paper from a new fiber. Because

---

Figure 1

The Process of Commercialization

Basic Research
➡ Applied Research
➡ Development
➡ Demonstration
➡ Manufacturing
➡ Marketing

Dr. Thomas S. Seibles, a chemist with USDA's Agricultural Research Service, views an "electrophoresis" of potato proteins. Dr. Seibles conducts basic and applied research on fruits and vegetables, including investigations of the properties of plant enzymes.
USDA 0186X013-32

applied and basic research are often conducted with the same tools and in the same kind of research facilities, the distinction between the two is not always very clear.

Development, the "D" of R&D, moves a step closer to practical application, and the risk and time involved are correspondingly reduced. Development is usually conducted using larger equipment and facilities, for example a pilot plant for a new product or a several-acre trial for a new crop. The development stage generally costs about 10 times more than the basic and applied research preceding it. The larger scale simulates full-scale production and permits better evaluation of both technical feasibility and costs.

Demonstration, the final step in establishing technical and economic feasibility, involves a 10-fold increase in cost compared to development. This step is carried out in prototype manufacturing or other commercial production facilities and may involve manufacture of prototype products. Test marketing may be conducted during the demonstration stage.

Manufacturing and marketing take place only if demonstration and test marketing give favorable results. The previous stages may or may not be conducted by private firms, but in a free market economy the private sector does the manufacturing and marketing that result in commercialization.

Two factors are important when we consider the research, development, and commercialization process. First, the survival rate of good ideas as they move from one level to the next is rather low. Typically, only 10 percent of all good ideas are seriously considered for commercialization. Out of every 10 candidates, 2 are likely to be introduced to the market, and 1 will be an economic success. The risks are very high, but they can be lessened by a broad base of innovative basic research, thorough knowledge of the markets, and appropriate sharing of the financial burdens.

The second factor in the commercialization process is cost. There is substantial government funding in the basic research enterprise and substantial commercial investment in the commercialization phase. There is a funding gap at the point where technologies are brought out of the laboratory but are not yet ready for commercial prototyping. It is at this point—when the technology has not been demonstrated in commercial practice (bridging the funding gap) and must be moved from one organization to another—that technology transfer often breaks down.

Overcoming the Gaps in Commercialization

The in-house approach to product and process development has been the preferred method in U.S. industry for many years. A joint or collaborative approach, however, may help to avoid the technology transfer gap that exists in in-house development. No single group should be responsible for creating a new technology; instead, several partners should agree to pool part of their resources to accomplish the task. The key to collaborative arrangements is that the partners should have complementary expertise and common goals and agree on the financing of their joint endeavor and the ownership of its results.

Collaborative arrangements allow an opportunity for dissimilar partners, such as private companies, government laboratories, and university researchers, to work together. These partnerships are sometimes difficult to create because of competition, lack of knowledge of capabilities, and differences in mission or institutional culture among the partners. However, there is continuing progress in developing a range of strategies to foster collaborative development efforts. Some of these strategies will be discussed in the section on public and private sector roles.

The Key Role of Patents in Technology Transfer

In an R&D program, the development, protection, and use of intellectual property are essential. The formal system for protecting intellectual property is through patents. Too often, patents are seen as guarantees of financial gain or market acceptance. They are neither.

A patent protects the rights of the inventor to the discovery and gives the inventor the right to exclude others from using it without prior agreement. A patent is a legal document that affirms that an idea is new and useful, but not that it is necessarily economically attractive. Consequently, most potential licensees are not interested in licensing a patented invention until they are convinced of its potential.

The Patent and Trademark Amendments of 1980 (Public Law 96-517) gave universities rights to inventions developed under Federal grants and contracts. Because universities could transfer or license these rights to cooperating private firms, this provided a major incentive for industry-academic interaction. Since 1980, technology complexes have evolved around major universities.

The Federal Technology Transfer Act of 1986 was designed to extend to Federal laboratories the ability for exclusive technology transfer. It not only authorizes up-front commitments for exclusive patent licenses to industrial cooperators but also provides incentives to Government scientists to protect their inventions with patents. Experience in USDA's Agricultural Research Service (ARS) and Forest Service indicates that the law is achieving its intended purpose of stimulating technology transfer.

Public and Private Sector Roles: How Much Overlap and Where?

For successful commercialization to take place, a shift in primary responsibility must occur, from research-oriented organizations and staff to those capable of competitive production and marketing. This shift should be a continuous flow that enables the technology transfer process to continue smoothly to commercialization. How best to achieve such a shift and just where in the commercialization pipeline it should take place is the subject of much study and debate. On one thing, however, there is general agreement: For researchers merely to present and publish their results in scientific meetings and journals is not enough. Industry will generally not beat a path to their door. In this regard, it should be pointed out that getting new crops and products commercialized presents a particularly complex challenge.

In commercializing agricultural products, technology transfer can be achieved only when three things occur: A farmer must grow the crop; an industrial firm must convert the harvested material to a useful product; and a supplier must market the product. During this interrelated process no one step can proceed very far without simultaneous progress in the others.

Communication is one of the major challenges in technology transfer. Those who do research are mostly interested in how things work; those in manufacturing and marketing are interested in producing a product. An important feature that affects this gap between research and production is the fact that much of the basic research is conducted and funded through public institutions (universities and government laboratories), whereas the commercialization activities are in the private sector. The private sector can acquire technical information in the form of reports and patents fairly easily, but the intimate understanding of how to make a particular product is much harder to transfer from one group to another. Some strategies for bridging this gap in understanding have been to bring in basic researchers as consultants or as full members of the development team on a temporary basis, to hire the researchers, or to acquire the company that has done the basic research.

Efforts to foster relationships that facilitate the transfer of knowledge have been increasing. We can learn from the Japanese in this area of endeavor. In Japan, the basic research for a product area is done by teams drawn from academia, industry, and government. From this research, the industry competes in bringing specific products to market. In the United States this approach has been used to some extent in industrial collaborative efforts such as those performed by the Heat Transfer Research Institute, Inc., SEMATECH, Inc., and the Engineering Research Centers developed by the National Science Foundation.

In 1985, the Commission of the European Community began an ambitious program to foster R&D collaboration among EC member nations. The main goal of the program, called the Framework Programme and funded primarily by member nations, is to develop precommercial technologies with the express condition that all projects must involve collaborations across national boundaries. The focus is on high-technology industries both because of their disproportionate contribution to economic well-being and because of their contribution to developing basic infrastructure within the community (particularly in telecommunications). Fostering cooperation between academia and industry (including small businesses) is another program goal. The 1990-94 Framework Programme includes a significant agriculture and agro-industries component.

Another European program, called EUREKA (European Research Cooperation Agency), was started in 1985. Participants in this program are primarily industrial partners. EUREKA focuses on technologies nearer to commercialization and also works across national borders; but, unlike the Japanese efforts, this program has not yet developed effective means of integrating research and commercialization.

Since the inception of the Framework Programme, there has been a change in attitude on the part of the universities from "ivory tower" aloofness to active participation. The success of integrating small and medium-size enterprises has been greater for the Framework Programme than for the EUREKA project, where the so-called Big Twelve major European corporations are still the mainstays.

The gap in the commercialization process is particularly serious for technology transfer to small businesses, many of which have neither the facilities nor the resources for the necessary developmental work. Because of the well-established economic benefit derived from small businesses, particularly in rural areas, facilitating technology transfer to them deserves a high priority in the public agricultural research establishment (that is, universities and USDA).

Public research organizations should be involved in the commercialization process at least to or through the development stage. Providing incentives for industry and Government scientists to work together in transitional phases of research and development was a major purpose of the Federal Technology Transfer Act of 1986. A strong case can be made for also promoting joint participation in the *planning* stages of the research. In fact, industry's involvement in planning can help keep the research focused on the needs of users and increase the probability that the private sector will carry the project through commercialization.

Initiatives To Commercialize New Uses for Agricultural Products

There is an increasing emphasis on fostering R&D collaboration in the production of value-added food and industrial materials from agriculture. ARS has already developed numerous products that have entered the market through licensing of patents and is currently increasing technical assistance in the commercialization of ARS research. Nonprofit groups, such as the Michigan Biotechnology Institute, collaborate with industry at both the basic research level and the process development level to develop new industrial products. Many of the land-grant universities have developed agricultural product centers that link the basic research of individual faculty members with the industry of the States and Nation. The programs in the Cooperative State Research Service's Office of Agricultural Materials are structured to create collaborative efforts among universities, Government laboratories, and private companies devoted to development of new crops and new products.

The Food, Agriculture, Conservation, and Trade Act of 1990 included a major initiative to promote the greater utilization of agricultural commodities for industrial products. This legislation calls for expanded efforts to commercialize products manufactured from agricultural materials and for the creation of an Alternative Agricultural Research and Commercialization (AARC) Center.

The AARC approach encourages closer work among private firms, Government agencies, and universities in areas of technology transfer, including technology verification, product testing, precommercial production, and regulatory approval. Moreover, resources from agencies such as the Rural Development Administration and the Small Business Administration can play a useful role in helping to bring about new industrial growth in rural areas through new uses of agricultural commodities.

Conclusion

The emphasis on agriculture as a source for new industrial products has two foundations. First, industrial products from agriculture provide a new, potentially massive market outlet for traditional and new crops. We can take full advantage of the most productive agricultural system in the world. Secondly, and possibly most important for the future, agricultural products offer the only renewable source of materials essential for everyday life throughout the world. The public has seen the need for "green" products and renewable resources; the effort to develop and commercialize industrial products from agriculture is meeting those needs. ❑

Farmers' Views 8 on Growing Crops for Industrial Uses

by Gregory Gajewski, Lewrene Glaser, and David Harvey, Agricultural Economists, Economic Research Service, USDA, Washington, DC

Why do farmers grow something different from what they've been growing? How do they decide to grow crops for industrial uses? How are the crops marketed? How do the farmers' operations change? What advice do farmers have for others who are thinking about producing these crops?

Here are some answers from nine producers who are growing industrial crops. We spoke with a diverse group, including:

- **Larry Lura**, who grows crambe in Carrington, North Dakota, and
- **Jack Montoucet**, an alligator producer in Scott, Louisiana.

We spoke with farmers producing commodities that have been around commercially for some time:

- **Jimmy Tosh**, who is growing industrial rapeseed under contract for Calgene Chemical in Henry, Tennessee,
- **Lon Pool**, who is producing feeder goldfish in Lonoke, Arkansas,
- **Bob Moody** of Newport Beach, California, who is the managing partner of a jojoba plantation in Arizona, and
- **Don Barioni, Jr.,** who grows jojoba on his plantation in the Imperial Valley of California and processes it as well.

We interviewed other farmers who are growing crops that are in the early stages of commercial development in the United States:

- **Rob Raun**, who is experimenting with milkweed in Minden, Nebraska,
- **Michael Moore**, who is helping to develop lesquerella in Waddell, Arizona, and
- **Homer Faseler**, who is growing kenaf in Edcouch, Texas, for the first time in 1992.

Diverse Farms, Diverse Acreage

Their farms are as different from each other as are the commodities. Larry Lura, for example, has 3,500 acres and 6,000 hogs. His land is about evenly split between row crops and small grains. He planted crambe on 180 acres in 1991. The oil from crambe and industrial rapeseed is used to make a slip agent for manufacturing plastic films and bags, and has the po-

tential to be used in making nylons, perfumes, plasticizers, and plastics.

The farmers growing the more experimental crops—lesquerella and milkweed—generally have fewer acres planted to those crops compared with those growing the more established industrial crops. Rob Raun has 16 acres of milkweed on his 600-acre farm. The milkweed floss, mixed with goose down, is used in comforters made in a nearby manufacturing facility. Michael Moore planted lesquerella on 10 of his 600 acres last year, and is growing only 2 acres, for plant-breeding purposes, this year. Lesquerella oil is similar to castor oil, a raw material used in products ranging from lipstick to jet engine lubricants. The meal has potential as a protein supplement in cattle feed.

For some producers with whom we spoke, the industrial (nonfood) commodity is their primary or only enterprise. Jack Montoucet, a retired fireman, uses 1.5 acres to raise 1,500 alligators a year. Lon Pool has 350 acres of goldfish ponds and has raised feeder goldfish for two decades. Feeder goldfish are used as food for other fish and animals in the aquarium industry.

Don Barioni, Jr., has a 2,000-acre joba plantation. For him, what started as 80 acres of plantings 10 years ago on part of the 10,000-acre family farm has branched off to become his own large-scale operation. Jojoba is an oilseed whose oil is used in cosmetics and lubricants, as well as in manufacturing some pharmaceuticals.

Almost all of the producers we spoke with started out with only a few acres, to get a feel for their new crop. And most are planning to continue with the same or more acres this year. A few, however, like Jimmy Tosh, the industrial-rapeseed grower, plan to scale back acreage because yields and profits have not met expectations. Tosh and other southeastern growers have had problems with hard freezes and excess rainfall. Industrial rapeseed is especially susceptible to these weather problems.

On the Lookout for New Income Sources

Why grow an industrial crop? Virtually all the farmers we spoke with said they were ultimately looking to raise their incomes. While there were wide variations in the amount of resources invested and the time until a payoff was expected, the profit motive was predominant. Most were also looking for a way to diversify their operations.

Diversification can reduce agronomic risk. Growing a greater variety of crops can improve soil biology, cut use of chemicals, and reduce the amount of output lost due to pests and extreme weather. Larry Lura, for example, described how he chose crambe to try as an alternative by describing the disease and pest problems farmers in his part of North Dakota have with sunflowers and other traditional crops. Crambe, a member of the mustard family, is not susceptible to some of the common diseases there.

Nathan Rovy, a successful lesquerella farmer in Parker, AZ, inspects his crop. Farmers growing the more experimental crops generally have fewer acres compared to those growing the more established industrial crops.
Ken Hammond/USDA 92BW0697-26A

The oil extracted from lesquerella is similar to castor oil, which is used as the basic material in products ranging from lipstick to jet engine lubricants.
Ken Hammond/USDA 92BW0697-12

Joaquin Lanz (left) and Armando Baez, University of Arizona employees, dump cattle feed mixed with lesquerella into troughs at the university's feedlot.

Lesquerella meal has potential as a supplement in cattle feed.
Ken Hammond/USDA 92BW0696-6

Part II. Research and Implementation

And crambe is not attractive to local pests.

Diversification can also cut financial risk. The revenue earned by growing crops for industrial uses does not necessarily move in tandem with the prices of traditional food and feed crops. Rob Raun, for example, said that the farm financial crisis of the 1980's showed the tremendous need to develop new crops to help farmers diversify.

In deciding what to plant each year, the outlook for relative prices plays a large role. For Jimmy Tosh, for example, the price of industrial rapeseed was high relative to wheat when he first started planting rapeseed in 1989. Now, with wheat prices up and rapeseed prices down somewhat, he is thinking about switching some acres back to winter wheat.

Which Crop To Grow?

When picking which industrial crop to produce, site, situation, and outside support governed the choices considered. The farmers stressed the need to select a crop that fits with the local ecology. Barioni, Jr., and Moody said they chose jojoba because it was indigenous to the Southwest. Barioni, Jr., went on to say that his part of the Imperial Valley presented nearly ideal

Farmers are looking to raise their incomes, as well as diversify their operations, by growing industrial oilseed crops such as jojoba.

Ken Hammond/USDA 92BW0700-11A

conditions for jojoba—a frost-free climate, a reliable and affordable supply of water from the Colorado River, and abundant seasonal labor from Mexico.

Montoucet said that alligator farming was a natural crop for Louisiana. Also, he is helping to preserve Louisiana's natural resources. In return for allowing producers to take alligator eggs from the wild, the State requires producers to return 17 percent of the grown alligators back to their native habitat. That's a higher percentage than would have survived under natural conditions.

Faseler chose to grow kenaf after he became convinced it was viable for the area based on results at a local test farm in Texas. Kenaf is used to make newsprint, carpet padding, and poultry litter, and may serve as a livestock feed supplement. Faseler chose kenaf over other crops because it does not require additional labor or equipment. He said that vegetables are an alternative, but that they are very risky and require a lot of hand labor.

In some situations, needed inputs are lacking. Montoucet initially wanted to grow redfish, but discovered that fingerlings (baby redfish) were not always available. Tosh mulled over growing canola, an edible variety of rapeseed, but chose an industrial variety because the price outlook was more favorable. Also, the Calgene representative is a friend of his. He said that Calgene, which buys his crops, has been very supportive, supplying agronomic advice as needed.

Harold Willet, of H. Willet & Associates in Jeanerette, LA, samples the fiber of a kenaf stalk. Willet designed a kenaf harvester in cooperation with USDA and Kenaf International, Inc., from combine parts that are readily available from local farm equipment dealers.
Bob Nichols/USDA 92BW0589-30

For Tosh, the new flexibility for minor oilseeds under the the the 1990 Food, Agriculture, Conservation, and Trade Act's "0/92" program (see chapter 9) gives him an opportunity to begin double-cropping industrial rapeseed with soybeans this year, considering his history of double cropping. Yet, other producers said that the programs were not flexible enough. For example, Rob Raun and some associates tried unsuccessfully to get USDA's Agricultural Stabilization and Conservation Service (ASCS) to allow him to grow milkweed for experimental purposes on land placed in the Acreage Conservation Reserve. However, ASCS says farmers may

plant milkweed on flex acres. Farmers are allowed to plant up to 25 percent of their crop acreage base to alternative crops.

Moore said he is interested in the success of crops that are not affected by USDA programs. Management decisions can then be made on market-based criteria rather than Government-regulated planting requirements.

For Lura, the North Dakota State University Research Center suggested crambe, and gave away seed for the first year, so he didn't really consider other crops. He had grown flax for a number of years, but it didn't make money. Now, the price of crambe compares favorably to that of sunflow-

The kenaf harvester is a lower and lighter version of a soldier-style sugarcane harvester. Each side of the "M" shape seen here is a pair of augers which feed the stalks back to the cutting blades.
USDA 88BW1885-14

As kenaf enters the front of the machine, it is bunched, cut, and fed to gates at the back of the machine. The stalks fall inward or outward in windrows to dry in the field.

88BW1889-35

ers, and its low input costs—about half the cost of wheat, even when he pays for the seed—makes economic sense.

Barioni, Jr., was approached by a group of investors to start growing jojoba, and didn't seriously consider other crops. The investors, many of whom were Canadian, had experience with other specialty crops, financial stamina, and the patience to wait years for a payoff. For Moody, who started as an investor and now manages a jojoba plantation in Arizona, the crop seemed to be a good profit prospect and environmentally beneficial. He didn't consider other crops either. Moody and Barioni, Jr., both said that jojoba became an option because of the basic research done at the University of California-Riverside and at the University of Arizona's Maricopa Research Center.

About Half Grow Under Contract

Research has shown that many new enterprises fold because of poor marketing. Many farmers are able to produce a commodity, only to find out that the price they can get won't cover their costs. One way to avoid this problem is to agree with a buyer on a price before beginning production. Of the nine producers we spoke with, five forward-contract to sell at least a portion of their crop.

For example, Lura signs on with National Sun Industries, Inc., to deliver crambe at a fixed price before he even puts the seed in the ground. The crop is hauled 120 miles or so to Enderlin, where National Sun crushes it in an oilseed mill used mainly for soybeans and sunflowers. While crambe is a small crop for National Sun, the company is excited about its long-term prospects. The company has been offering a favorable price, and farmers are lined up to plant crambe. However, contacts now are limited mostly to the original growers, until more of a market develops.

Michael Moore, the lesquerella grower, is paid a fixed amount per acre by Agrigenetics Company, a firm working on developing the crop. Faseler has a contract with Kenaf International for his crop.

Barioni, Jr., however, sells part of his jojoba crop under contract to independent brokers, while marketing the rest himself. His operation has become more integrated as it matures, and he has bought time at a crushing mill. While he has jojoba seed crushed locally, he sends some to Phoenix or Tucson for processing. About 80 percent of his product ends up overseas, split evenly between Japan and Europe.

Moody does not produce his jojoba under contract, preferring more flexibility to sell to processors. Recently Moody's group invested in a company that processes, refines, and markets natural oils, in order to have a reliable outlet for their own jojoba seed production.

Barioni, Jr., uses surveys of both wild and farmed jojoba to forecast prices. This helps him market the remainder of his crop. As vice president of the Jojoba Growers' Association,

he is also working to set content requirements for oil, moisture, and trash. Standards increase demand by reducing buyers' risks: they know what they are getting.

Montoucet does not use forward contracts. He sends his alligators to a local business that skins them for the hides, which he then sells to wholesale hide dealers and tannery representatives. Recently, Montoucet has started a supplementary business processing and selling the meat, so he now takes back the carcasses as well. Pool markets his feeder goldfish direct to the final buyers without using advance contracts.

Trial and Error in Growing Techniques

All of the farmers we spoke with said they began growing their new crops with strong technical support from outside sources. Most named the land-grant university-Extension system and contracting companies as key sources of technical assistance, especially in their first year of production. After the first year, they began to benefit from their own experiences. For some who have been growing an industrial crop for a few years, the information flow reverses, and the growers begin to provide new data to the universities and companies.

For example, Lura said he planted the crambe seed too early and too deep the first year. As a result, he experienced a light emergence of the seedlings and an early season weed problem that was tough to control. Also, the early planting meant the crambe was ready to be harvested at the same time the small grains were ready. By planting later and not as deep the second year, early growth was stronger, weeds were kept under better control, and the harvest was postponed.

The field-crop farmers have put the new crops into their rotation schemes. Lura substituted crambe for sunflowers, helping to break disease and pest cycles in his fields. Tosh replaced winter wheat with industrial rapeseed in his 2-year corn-wheat-soybean rotation. The rapeseed boosted the yield of his soybean crop and helped to control rye grass problems he had had in the wheat. In many cases, the industrial crop has less of an impact on the environment and uses less chemicals but

more labor than other crops. However, that's not always the case. Lura says crambe takes less fertilizer than corn, but about the same as wheat. Moore's lesquerella takes some irrigation to get a stand, but less than other crops, and less fertilizer.

Lura and Moore do not use pesticides on crambe or lesquerella because none are registered for these crops with the Environmental Protection Agency. Weed problems could be serious for lesquerella, though. Tosh says he uses Treflan, which he can't use on wheat, on some rapeseed fields to control weeds. Also, he uses more nitrogen on his rapeseed compared to other crops.

Kelly Dwyer, a member of the Jojoba Growers Association, inspects a jar of jojoba oil at the Jojoba Growers and Processors, Inc., plant in Apache, AZ. The Jojoba Growers Association is working to set content requirements for oil, moisture, and trash. Standards increase demand by reducing buyers' risks.
Ken Hammond/USDA 92BW0700-20A

Growing crambe cuts erosion on Lura's farm because it needs fewer passes with the tractor. Tosh figures substituting rapeseed for wheat really didn't change the erosion picture on his farm. Barioni, Jr., developed his own site-specific irrigation and fertilizerregimes, with conservation and profitability in mind. He also had to design much of the harvesting and processing equipment.

High Expectations Typical

Most of the farmers said that the new crop did not stand up to their initial expectations on profits. Barioni, Jr., said the early research and development costs were higher than he had initially expected, and that it took more years than he planned until revenues were able to cover costs.

Moody said that growing jojoba took financial stamina and patience—it takes 4 to 5 years before it can be harvested profitably. Raun, the milkweed grower, said that potential producers of industrial crops must be willing to take risks and be patient.

Producers who sell their crops under contract seem more satisfied with their financial returns. Lura lists the extra money as a major benefit of growing crambe. Tosh was happy with the first year, but weather problems and rapeseed's sensitivity to wetness have plagued him for the past 2 years.

Some producers can't easily switch out of their industrial crops in response to year-to-year price changes because they had to modify their operations so much. Montoucet and Pool, for example, said that the prices for their commodities were good for the first couple of years. Now, however, prices are down and input costs are up. With their investment in ponds and equipment, their focus is on long-term profitability.

Lesson Learned

For farmers considering an industrial crop, the nine growers we spoke with had the following advice:

First, get help from State and local research and Extension agencies. Then, start on a small scale, and be realistic in the returns you expect. Don't forget to develop a marketing plan. Consider growing under contract (depending on the commodity). Pick a crop that is indigenous to the area or has a good local track record.

And good luck. ❑

How Farm Programs Offer the Opportunity To Try New Crops

9

by James A. Langley, Senior Policy Analyst, Agricultural Stabilization and Conservation Service, USDA, Washington, DC

To qualify for program benefits prior to the 1990 Farm Act, agricultural producers had to comply with stringent regulations as to which crops and how many acres they could plant, regardless of market incentives.

Current farm programs, however, provide a wide range of opportunities for producers to try new crops and still be eligible for program benefits. Programs and provisions such as:

- Planting flexibility,
- Dry peas and lentils on wheat and feed grain crop acreage bases,
- 0/92 and 50/92,
- Zero-certification, and
- The integrated farm management program option

are available to producers, at their discretion, for each marketing year through 1995.

The Secretary of Agriculture may also offer additional opportunities to producers if necessary to foster development of alternative crops. This chapter briefly reviews how farm programs offer producers the potential to try new crops.

Some Basics About Crop Bases

Planting flexibility rules, and the number of acres on which producers may earn Government support payments, are defined in terms of a producer's crop acreage base. Producers are assigned a crop base for each program crop (wheat, feed grains, upland cotton, and rice) on their farm. Crop bases are calculated each year as a 5-year moving average of acreage planted and considered planted (3-year average for cotton and rice). "Considered planted" includes acres enrolled in Government programs but not actually planted to the program crop, such as reduced acres. Other types of "considered planted" acres will be pointed out below in this chapter.

Since crop bases are calculated as a moving average, producers must be careful to plant (or to be considered to have planted) their entire base each year to keep from losing base acres in later years. The only way to increase the crop acreage base for a program crop or Extra Long Staple (ELS) cotton is to not participate in the annual commodity program for any of the program crops, or ELS cotton, on the farm.

To illustrate the various parts of a crop acreage base related to planting flexibility, consider figure 1. The crop acreage base of each program crop is essentially divided into four parts: reduced acres (acreage reduction program, or ARP, factor multiplied times the base), Normal Flex Acres (15 percent of the base), Optional Flex Acres (10 percent of the base), and remaining base acres.

Producers participating in Government programs are allowed to plant the program crop on all of the base except the reduced acres. The maximum acres on which producers may receive Government support payments is the base minus reduced acres minus the normal flex acres. Let's look into the relevant provisions a little closer.

Planting Flexibility

Producers may plant an eligible crop on up to 25 percent of any participating program crop's acreage base. This acreage is known as "flex" acreage, and the plantings can be credited as "considered planted" to the program crop for base protection purposes. Planting flexibility provisions do not apply to ELS cotton.

Normal and Optional Flex Acres

The first 15 percent of the flex acreage is known as "normal flex acreage" (NFA) and the other 10 percent as "optional flex acreage" (OFA).

Normal Flex Acres are *not eligible for Government support payments*, whether or not they are planted to the original program crop, or "flexed" to another crop. When deciding what to plant on NFA, producers would need to consider, among other things, how the market returns for the original crop compare to the market returns for the alternative crop.

If **Optional Flex Acres** are planted to the original program crop, they are *eligible for Government support payments*. If "flexed" to another crop, they are not eligible for Government support payments. When deciding what to plant on OFA, producers would need to consider, among other things, how the program returns for the original crop (including Government payments) compare to the market returns for the alternative crop.

Flex Crops

Crops that may be planted on flex acreage are:

- any program crop (wheat, corn, sorghum, barley, oats, upland cotton, and rice),

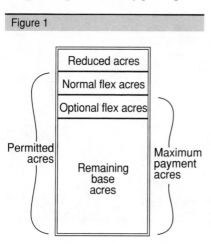

Figure 1

Government programs assign a crop base for each program crop, such as wheat, feed grains, cotton, and rice.

Wheat USDA BN-49909

Cotton

Dave Warren/USDA 067-10-28A

Part II. Research and Implementation

Feed grain (corn)   USDA 1085X1195-36A

Rice
USDA BN-40101.

- oilseeds (soybeans, sunflowerseed, safflowerseed, canola, rapeseed, mustard seed, and flaxseed),
- any industrial or experimental crop,
- mung beans, and
- any other nonprogram crop except fruits, vegetables, potatoes, dry edible beans, lentils, and dry peas.

The Secretary may, however, prohibit the planting of any crop on flex acreage. A list of prohibited crops is available in county Agricultural Stabilization and Conservation Service (ASCS) offices. Prohibited crops for 1992 include fruits and vegetables, peanuts, nuts, wild rice, trees, tree crops, and tobacco. With a few exceptions, crops planted on flex acres are eligible for any available price support loans.

Dry Peas and Lentils on Wheat and Feedgrain Crop Acreage Bases

Producers may plant up to 20 percent of their wheat or feedgrain crop acreage bases to dry peas (limited to Austrian peas, wrinkled seed, green, yellow, and umatilla) and lentils. Producers do not receive Government support payments on acres planted to dry peas and lentils; but, such acreage is credited as being planted to the program crop for planting history purposes. Acreage eligible for dry peas and lentils is in addition to flex acres. These crops are still prohibited on flex acres. This provision does not apply to upland cotton or rice crop acreage bases.

"0/92" Provision (Wheat and Feed Grains)

Wheat and feedgrain producers have the option of underplanting their permitted acres and still, under some conditions, receiving Government support payments on a portion of the underplanted acreage. Known as the "0/92" provision, this option allows wheat and feedgrain producers to leave all or a portion of their permitted acreage unplanted, or to plant a minor oilseed crop or sesame and crambe (soybeans are excluded) on the acreage that normally would have been planted to wheat or feed grains, and receive guaranteed Government support payments on the acreage.

To be eligible, the producer must devote at least 8 percent of the maximum payment acres for the program crop as conserving uses or minor oilseeds, sesame, or crambe. The maximum acreage for 0/92 payments is the difference between the acreage planted to the program crop and 92 percent of the maximum payment acreage for the program crop (see fig. 2). The 0/92 payment rate will be the higher of the projected or actual Government support rate for the crop.

Note that "minor" oilseeds, such as sunflowerseed, safflower, canola, rapeseed, flaxseed, or mustard seed, may be planted on the 0/92 acres and qualify for 0/92 payments. Producers may receive 0/92 payments on the wheat or feed grains, or price support loans on the oilseeds, but not both. There are no price support loans for sesame or crambe.

Beginning with the 1992 crop, soybeans may be planted on 0/92 wheat and feedgrain acres following a minor oilseed crop. The producer must have a history of double-cropping soybeans

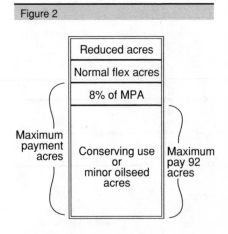

Figure 2

Part II. Research and Implementation

following any other crop on the farm in 3 out of the previous 5 years. Soybeans double-cropped on 0/92 acres are not eligible for loans.

"50/92" Provision (Upland Cotton and Rice)

A variation of the "0/92" program is available to upland cotton and rice producers. In general, the program works the same way as described above with the following exceptions. Upland cotton and rice producers must plant at least 50 percent of their maximum payment acreage to the respective crop (that is, they cannot leave the entire base not planted). Sesame or crambe may be planted on 50/92 acres, and producers still qualify for payments. However, cotton and rice producers cannot plant minor oilseeds on their 50/92 acres. The 50/92 provisions do not apply to ELS cotton.

Zero Certification

Producers who do not wish to plant any acreage of a program crop can use the "zero certification" option. This option allows them to have their entire program acreage base considered planted to the program crop for base protection purposes without planting any of the particular program crop. In this regard, zero certification may be said to offer producers 100 percent flexibility to plant alternative crops.

To qualify, producers must certify to the county ASCS office that no acres on the farm were planted to the program crop, and that they did not increase normal plantings of fruits and vegetables. "Normal" plantings are defined as the larger of the total fruits

and vegetables planted on the farm either for the immediately preceding crop year, or for an average of the previous 3 crop years. Zero certification provisions do not apply to ELS cotton.

Integrated Farm Management Program Option

In conjunction with the annual acreage reduction program, producers who wish to adopt resource-conserving crop rotations can participate in the Integrated Farm Management Program Option (IFM). IFM allows them to protect their base acreage, payment yields, and program payments, while following an integrated, multiyear farm management plan relying on resource-conserving crop rotations.

Resource-conserving crops are legumes, legume-grass and legume-small grain mixtures, and combinations of the three, as well as alternative crops if designated by the Secretary. IFM requires that a farmer devote an average of 20 percent of the total crop acreage bases on the farm to resource-conserving crops over a 3-, 4-, or 5-year contract period.

Other Potential Options

The Secretary has authority to allow producers to plant any flex crop *except program crops* on up to half of the acres removed from production under the acreage reduction program (ARP). This option has not been in force for the 1991 and 1992 marketing years. If this option were to be allowed, producers taking advantage of this option would have to give up Government support payments on an appropriate number of payment acres determined by the Secretary to ensure that this provision did not increase program cost. Hence, the economic decision regarding planting eligible crops under this "half-ARP" provision would be similar to that of planting alternative crops on optional flex acres. A producer would have to compare the potential program returns for the original crop with the potential market returns for the crop planted on reduced acres.

The Secretary may also permit all or any part of the acreage required to be devoted to conserving uses under the 0/92 or 50/92 provisions to be devoted to sweet sorghum, guar, castor beans, plantago ovato, triticale, rye, millet, or mung beans; or commodities for which no substantial domestic production or market exists but that could yield industrial raw materials that are being imported; or commodities grown for experimental purposes (including kenaf and milkweed). The Secretary may allow these crops on 0/92 or 50/92 acres only if their production is not likely to increase program costs, and if the production is needed to provide an adequate supply of the commodity or is needed to encourage increased industrial use of the raw material. Production of these crops has not been allowed on 0/92 or 50/92 acres during the 1991 and 1992 marketing years.

Producers have sufficient opportunities to produce experimental and other nonprogram crops. Any crop that may be planted under these two options may also be planted on flex acres (that is, 25 percent of each participating program crop acreage base). Based on final enrollment for 1991,

producers could have planted alternative crops on up to 33.3 million acres (20.0 million acres of normal flex and 13.3 million acres of optional flex). About 5.7 million acres (17 percent of available flex acres) were actually planted to an alternative crop. Hence, producers could have planted alternative crops on an additional 27.6 million acres and still have been within program compliance rules. The zero-certification provision adds even more acreage that may be planted to alternative crops. When public comments were requested, respondents, by a wide margin, did not favor implementing either "half-ARP" or planting experimental crops on 0/92 or 50/92 acres.

Conclusion

The 1990 Farm Act introduced numerous planting flexibility opportunities. The flexibility provisions allow producers the chance to plant alternative crops without adverse program impacts. Producers who plant on flex acres are able to take advantage of favorable movements in the market for alternative crops. They are also more at risk of unfavorable market shifts. As program crop plantings depend more on the market and less on Government payments, producers probably will need to focus more attention on their individual marketing skills to benefit from flexibility provisions. ❏

Opportunities for Rural Economic Growth

10

by Patricia A. Barclay, Confidential Assistant for Under Secretary for Small Community and Rural Development, USDA, Washington, DC

In 1890, two of every three Americans lived in rural areas, and 61 percent of these rural people lived on farms. They produced enough to feed themselves and the urban population as well. Now only 1 in every 50 Americans lives on a farm. They produce enough to feed themselves and the rest of the U.S. population, and they export huge amounts of food.

In the past, the traditional view of securing prosperity in rural America by increasing agricultural production and demand has been a focus of many Government policy decisions. If American farmers grow more crops that can be sold to an expanding number of markets worldwide, the population of rural America will prosper, the formula said.

In the 1990's, less than 2 percent of the population lives on a farm. Along with these changing demographics must come a new definition of rural prosperity—a definition that includes more than simply higher prices for more crops.

It may be time to take another look at our definition of rural prosperity.

Smelterville and Bement

Take Smelterville, Idaho, a small rural town in the Coeur d'Alene Mountains where people traditionally either worked in the mines or operated businesses that sold products to the mine workers. Then the bottom dropped out of the lead market and the price of silver dropped below $4 an ounce. Shoshone County, where Smelterville is located, now has the highest unemployment in the State.

Or take Bement, Illinois. It's a railroad town in the east-central part of the State, typical of rural America, with small shops and businesses and the grain company by the railroad tracks. Until a few years ago, Bement followed the roller-coaster farm economy.

In response to the economic problems they were facing, these two rural communities found nontraditional solutions to rural economic development that combined work done by USDA scientists and the energy and creativity of private enterprise. They demonstrate that rural America need not be held hostage to the boom and bust cycles of the traditional agricultural sector.

In both cases, small companies applied research on cornstarch, performed by scientists at USDA's Agricultural Research Service, to create new product lines.

In Smelterville, Polysorb, Inc., produces and markets a super-absorbent that can be injected into the soil to make better use of water for trees, shrubs, and other plants. The company is designing the equipment used to inject the material. It has developed fuel filters to absorb water from hydrocarbon fuels, medical absorbents for treatment and therapy, kitty litter, and a cold gel pack for chilling a bottle of wine. Employment has increased from 15 to 50 people.

In Bement, Central Illinois Manufacturing Company employs 120 people and markets fuel filters based on the same cornstarch research, which developed "super slurper."

Now that's rural economic development.

A New Equation for Economic Revival in Rural America

Now we can attack rural economic problems from two sides: Grow more crops and manufacture products using those crops in factories close to the fields where the crops are grown.

Growing more of the traditional crops to sell at home and abroad has been the traditional approach to improving prospects for rural Americans. It is still a solid technique for bringing jobs into rural areas and making it profitable for a farmer to stay on the farm. It helps Main Street businesses, and means increased employment for the grocery store, the drug store, the local car dealer, and the insurance company. More farm jobs mean more Main Street jobs—and more taxes for local government to provide better schools and parks, roads, law enforcement, and fire protection.

But during the past decade America discovered that we are dealing with a global economy and global competi-

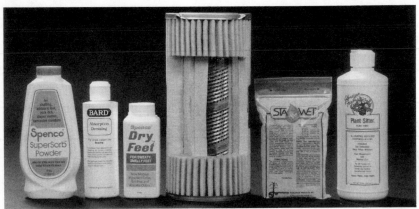

Highly absorbent Superslurper was developed from cornstarch by a team of ARS scientists. Today, it is found in body powders, absorbtion dressings, oil filters, and soil additives, as well as diapers and batteries.
Keith Weller/USDA 89BW1441-25

Part II. Research and Implementation

tion. While we can grow bumper crops of wheat, so can Australia and countries in South America. We all end up selling to the same customers. It becomes a matter of who has the lowest price—whether because of economies of scale or because of government subsidies to the farmer. Therein lies the problem. Only an expanded private sector economy in rural America can guarantee the diversity of options that rural Americans must have to succeed economically.

So now comes the second technique, an important factor in the equation for economic revival in rural America: Manufacturing!

This is the marriage of the agricultural economy with the technological revolution. It's not manufacturing on the scale of Boeing or IBM, but it can foster rural enterprises that bring 50, 100, or 200 jobs to a rural community in Idaho or Illinois. Or Iowa or Vermont or Alabama.

How does all this happen?

Smelterville and Bement are just two examples of many communities across the country. USDA scientists have developed and patented scores of uses for agricultural products that can be licensed for use by entrepreneurs who can turn them into products that fill a need in the national or international marketplace. The creativity of American enterprise allows companies and communities to combine the public sector work of USDA scientists with the private sector's ability to recognize needs, fill them, and—in the process—create jobs.

That combination could be the only permanent solution for rural America: Long-term economic development. Federal grant programs that scatter tax dollars around in some selected rural communities, without plans for long-lasting changes that improve the rural infrastructure, can't do the job. Two new techniques are being developed right now that promise to bring together Government and private enter-

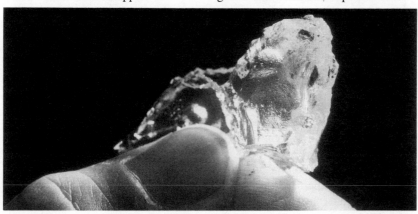

A Superslurper flake is swollen into a chunk that is over 99 percent water. Superslurper, which can be made as film, flakes, powder, or mat, absorbs about 1,400 times its own weight.
George Robinson/USDA 92BW1142

New Crops, New Uses, New Markets

prise to create long-term economic development.

One of those new ideas is the Rural Development Administration (RDA). The other is the State Rural Development Councils, part of the strategy of the President's Initiative on Rural America.

The Rural Development Administration

USDA's Rural Development Administration (RDA) will take the community and business development programs from the Farmers Home Administration and concentrate them in a single agency that deals with rural economic development. RDA will focus the Department's efforts on rural economic development into one organization that is responsible for implementing rural development programs. By bringing the existing employees and resources into a separate agency, USDA can concentrate on the specific problem of rural development without duplicating resources and effort. That single focus on rural development will give USDA a unique opportunity to improve its ability to help rural America become more competitive in the global economy.

This will be an agency whose sole interest and mission will be rural development. RDA will concentrate on improving the delivery of existing programs. It will develop specific rural development expertise to transfer the science and technology developed within USDA outside the walls of government to where people can use it. The agency can help put the science, money, and market development

that already exist in USDA at the disposal of private entrepreneurs who can use them in factories all across rural America.

RDA's employees will have expert knowledge of the programs that are available to aid those entrepreneurs with the ideas and drive to create jobs, but who need assistance, for example with financing.

State Rural Development Councils

By October 1992, 44 States are scheduled to have Rural Development Councils. These groups are part of the President's Initiative on Rural America, an interagency effort to coordinate Federal rural development policy and programs that was announced in 1989.

The State councils are composed of members from Federal, State, and local governments and the private sector who will work together to plan long-term strategies for rural economic development.

The principal rule for these councils is flexibility. The concept that the Federal Government should take tax dollars, design a program, and set rigid guidelines for its implementation is one that we now know, from experience, is not effective. Experience has proven over many years that the people who live in an area know what will work and what will not work for them.

The State Rural Development Councils bring together top officials from Federal and State agencies, local government leaders, and private sector business men and women. The councils provide them an opportunity to get to know others working toward the same objectives. One State FmHA director said that he had never had an opportunity to meet and talk seriously with the people from the State department of agriculture, let alone work with them on projects that combined the resources from all these levels.

This blend of people will yield one group that will know what the Farmers Home Administration, the Small Business Administration, or the State Departments of agriculture can provide to assist small businesses—in terms of either grants, loans, technical expertise, or market development. It is a system which can respond to the unique problems of each community. In the State Rural Development Councils, local leaders have a place to go to ask questions or provide advice.

USDA has the edge in areas of scientific discovery and development of practical uses of new discoveries. But it may not have the necessary expertise in business development or in finding venture capital to bankroll the small business owner who wants to manufacture a product. And the USDA scientist in Beltsville, Maryland, has no idea of the local issues in LaGrande, Oregon, that might enhance or impede development of a practical use for his or her discoveries.

That's what makes the State Rural Development Councils an idea whose time has come. It's a forum that brings all levels of government together. It's flexible so that the members can use what works in Idaho but may not work in Illinois.

The program started with eight pilot States whose charge was to develop and implement strategies to use the resources of government on all levels within the State. Each State council is encouraged to develop its own approach to the particular issues it faces. The complexity and diversity of rural communities call for State and local strategies to solve the problems of development within that State. These are the folks who know what will work best.

Each council's members are brought together in training sessions where they debate the most basic assumptions about rural development and the roles of various levels of government and the private sector in long-term development. The meeting and discussion result in a mission statement and goals.

The next step is to translate that statement into concrete activities:

- In Kansas, four Federal agencies (SBA, the Economic Development Agency, FmHA, and the Department of Housing and Urban Development) and the State Department of Commerce are establishing a single application process for small business loan help.
- The Maine council conducted a workshop that brought together members from Federal and State agencies and project managers from private utility companies and municipal governments to share information on rural infrastructure needs, clarify issues, and explore solutions.
- In Texas, the State council has been considering assistance and re-

sources available from State and Federal agencies to help unincorporated border communities develop public services.

The next phase of this program is to move beyond the pilot States and set up more councils. As additional State Rural Development Councils begin their work, who knows how many more projects tailored to the needs of the local rural communities can be accomplished? ❑

Setting Policies and Priorities for Public Research

11

by Patrick O'Brien, Director, Commodity Economics Division, ERS, USDA, Washington, DC

Why and how do we invest public money in agricultural research? Important research challenges face agriculture, with growing pressure to produce and market a broadening array of products more efficiently— while protecting the environment. This chapter will explore how to improve the payoff on research, both to minimize pressure to reduce funding and to increase support for activities already under way.

Two aspects of research need to be examined in order to enhance payoff. The first is to improve planning and priority setting. The second is to rethink the mix of bench science and applied research.

USDA's Research Mandate
USDA has a longstanding commitment to public support for agricultural research, defined broadly to include basic research (sometimes called bench science), applied research, education, and extension. Article 1 of the Constitution empowered Congress to act as necessary "to promote the progress of science." USDA was established in 1862 under this authority and charged with "…acquiring…preserving…and distributing…all useful information concerning agriculture in the most general and comprehensive sense which can be obtained by means of books and correspondence, and by practical and scientific experiments."

Successive acts of Congress and executive decisions have reinforced this mandate. The Agricultural Research Service, Cooperative State Research Service, Economic Research Service, and Extension Service form the core of USDA's physical and social science research program, but virtually all the other USDA agencies are involved in research as well.

The Land Grant University Act of 1862 also required that each State "establish a college of agriculture" and "the means for transmitting agricultural discoveries and related information to the public." The 1862 legislation was used as a model for establishing the 1890 colleges. The resulting network of institutions has since become a key source of public support for agricultural research.

This underlying research commitment is grounded in a sense that the payoff on public money invested wisely can be large enough and far-reaching enough to warrant the outlay of tax dollars. Also, some of the most promising research can be so costly and its benefits dispersed so widely as to rule out private investment without public support. The research payoff in question can take many different forms, resulting in more and better inputs, improved production and marketing practices, better natural resource management, enhanced nutrition, and improved operation of our rural economies.

USDA's funding of agricultural research grew sharply over time to $2.6 billion in FY 1991. This included $900 million for activities within USDA and another $1.7 billion for joint activities with other public institutions. But tightening budgets in the 1990's, combined with agriculture's declining proportion of the general economy, have renewed interest in old questions about why, how, and how much public money we invest in agricultural research.

The research challenges facing agriculture are on the rise; we are look-

ing for ways to produce and market more efficiently and still protect the environment. Funding research, however, often involves investing scarce tax dollars in long-term activities with uncertain payoff. Such activities seldom do well in the face of tightening budgets. At issue in this setting is how to improve the payoff on agricultural research? While the specifics vary widely depending on the discipline and institution in question, two general options stand out:

- *Strengthen the process of setting research priorities.* Payoff varies widely across activities, often with the outcome difficult or impossible to forecast. However, sharpening our planning and priority setting can strengthen our ability to identify potentially high payoff activities; and

- *Modify research activities to change the mix of basic research and applied research.* This change could help move more scientific discoveries through to commercial application faster.

Strengthening the Process of Setting Research Priorities

The challenge of strengthening priority setting is not new. Public research planners have struggled to combine both "micro" and "macro" elements in determining priorities. Merging the best of the two involves the difficult task of incorporating the scientist's often partial view of the world but hands-on research experience with the strategic planner's broader view but distance from research fundamentals.

Many agencies use "strategic" assessments of broad research needs as a starting point. However, the increasingly technical nature of agricultural research and expertise needed even to evaluate proposals often push priority setting away from the strategic toward the tactical or operational level—away from strategic planners toward the laboratory director and bench scientist. Moreover, the role of the laboratory director and bench scientist in shaping the perceptions of strategic planners via their reporting of research findings can reinforce this tendency.

Tactical or operational priority setting has a number of strong points. It tends to ensure that the topics invested in are "researchable"—that they are technically well grounded, with realistic expectations about results and appropriate concern about methods and review. However, it can also lead to a *technology-push* agenda, where test tube results determine priorities and staff members tend to continue working in areas where they have established expertise. This can come at the risk of less practical applicability and slowed response to changing research needs. In some cases, *market pull* can be dulled to the extent that major shocks are necessary to change the agenda.

How do we improve priority setting in this environment?

Several efforts are under way as a result of USDA and Congressional initiatives to develop a better mix of strategic, tactical, and operational priority setting. These efforts include individual agency initiatives and efforts cutting across Government and other public organizations.

The *Agricultural Research Service's National Program Staff* (NPS) is a good example of an individual agency's efforts. The NPS was established to introduce a broad national, cross-disciplinary perspective on research needs into agency planning. The NPS has lead responsibility for strategic planning and developing the 6-year implementation plan detailing the agency's research priorities. However, the NPS is also responsible for including tactical and operational input in their planning. NPS staff work with agency managers, bench scientists, and research users to plan research initiatives, set agency research priorities, and evaluate research progress. Similar, less formal efforts are under way in USDA's other large research agencies.

The 1977 Food and Agriculture Act mandated similar efforts cutting across Government, university, and private organizations. Congress instructed the Secretary of Agriculture to establish a *Joint Council on Food and Agricultural Sciences* with membership from Government, universities, foundations, and farm and agribusiness organizations. The Council's primary charge was to "bring about more effective research, extension, and teaching by improving the planning and coordination of publicly and privately supported agricultural science activities." The council reports to Congress annually on:

"(A) national priorities for food and agricultural research, extension, and teaching programs; (B) suggested areas of responsibilities for Federal, State, and private organizations; (C) levels of financial support; and (D) progress made toward accomplishing these priorities."

The council is also charged with preparing a 5-year plan for the food and agricultural sciences that reflects the coordinated views of the research, teaching, and extension communities.

The 1977 Act also created a *National Agricultural Advisory Board,* with membership from research, extension, and education users in agribusiness. The Board's functions include development of an annual report to Congress that includes:

"(A) a review and assessment of the allocation of funds for agricultural research and extension made for the Department of Agriculture; and (B) an evaluation of: (i) the effectiveness of coordination of Federal and private research initiatives; (ii) new research and extension programs that need to be conducted by the research system; and (iii) the effectiveness of the private and public research and extension system."

Parallel priority setting activities are also under way for related public organizations. The State Experiment Station directors work through *ESCOP (the Experiment Station Committee on Organization and Policy)* to develop a broader perspective on their individual and collective research agendas. A similar *ECOP (Extension Committee on Organization and Policy)* works to develop research planning links across Federal, State, and university extension programs.

How successful are these efforts at introducing a broader perspective on research needs into priority setting?

Clearly, more time is invested in strategic planning and information exchange. However, difficulties persist in efforts to link strategic planning with tactical and operational decisionmaking. Several forces are at play. The tendency to fall back on micro-level technology-push planning and priority setting is strong. Even in cases where broader assessments of research needs are available, strategic planning and recommendations are often so general that specific research projects are determined by mid-level mangers and ultimately the bench scientist. This has the advantage of minimizing the effect of the pressing but short-term needs of a particular strategic planning effort in disrupting longer term activities. However, it does so at the expense of responsiveness to real changes in research needs.

What more can we do to improve the way we set research priorities?

With the range of institutions already in place, the answer appears to be to make existing arrangements work better and, where necessary, to change basic attitudes. For example, strategic planning that stops short of translating general research needs into specific tactical priorities is of limited value. A better mix of the bench scientist's sense of what is "researchable" and the strategic planners' sense of what research is needed is critical; this improvement in the way research priorities are set could enhance public payoff.

Equally important is a change in attitude that allows us to look at agricultural research with the same critical eye that is used to evaluate other long-term investments. Agricultural research has often been seen as a good in and of itself, independent of public payoff. With added emphasis on payoff, more effort has to be put into the "investment planning" of research.

This raises the question of the extent to which agricultural research can or should be subject to the same degree of direction as other capital investments—to the same cost-benefit analysis used to assess alternative investment opportunities. Many people are hesitant to limit the freedom of the researcher, to put price tags on research findings, or to compare usefulness across activities. However, these attitudes will have to change if we are to improve strategic planning in order to enhance the public research payoff.

Research Policies

Until recently, the issue of mixing research activities to improve payoff has received little attention. Research in many State and Federal institutions tended to focus heavily on primary or bench science. This orientation was justified on several grounds. Bench science can be very costly, with uncertain outcomes; hence, public money is needed to cover at least some of the risk and startup costs. Conversely, private investment has tended to focus more on applied research.

Several factors at work in the 1980's and 1990's are bringing this paradigm, or model, into question. These include the accelerating pace of technical change and concern about who ultimately benefits from publicly funded primary research.

The first issue is largely one of timing. The traditional paradigm builds in an extended lag between primary and applied work—at a time when an increasingly competitive global market environment puts a premium on accelerated development and adoption of new technology.

As for the issue of who benefits from publicly funded primary research, the research breakthroughs developed in public laboratories are public property—available for any private agent to develop into commercially applicable technologies. More and more of this secondary work—with its patent control of new technologies—is migrating to private firms. This means that, at least in some cases, public money is funding the costly primary research that makes highly profitable applications possible. And in an increasing number of cases, this applications work and the resulting payoff occur abroad.

The ultimate question is, "Can we accelerate, and possibly enhance, public payoff to the United States with a different mix of research activities and public-private partnerships?"

Advocates of a different mix argue that payoff is potentially large enough to warrant investing more public money in applied research and developing public-private partnerships.

Agricultural feedstocks are a particularly graphic example, with both technology-push and market-pull forces at work. From a technology perspective, advances in bioprocess engineering make it possible to convert feedstocks from agricultural uses into high-value consumer and industrial products. From a market perspective, environmental problems and rising production costs suggest that an agriculture-based industry will be in a strong position to challenge the older petrochemical industry. Critics of the existing mix of research activities foresee the United States losing its technology-based competitive edge. For while the hard science basis to compete is in place, much of the applications work has yet to be done.

The time horizon is a key issue here. The private sector's applied research tends to focus on improving existing products and processes in 1 to 3 years. With public money focused on basic research, this leaves the more costly and often uncertain applications research, which often takes 3 to 10 years, underfunded. This 3- to 10-year applications work is increasingly critical with emerging technologies.

USDA has three major efforts under way to help move more basic research discoveries from the laboratory to the marketplace faster. The first involves joint research agreements developed under the Federal Technology Transfer Act. The Act allows a commercial partner to get first rights to exclusive licenses on patented inventions arising from research and development activities done in cooperation between the Federal Government and private sector researchers. ARS has over 200 such agreements in place, and the Forest Service has over 40. The idea is one of sharing risks and rewards. The Critical Agricultural Materials Act of 1984 also authorized the use of Federal funds to collaborate with private sector partners in research on developing renewable sources of

raw materials of strategic and critical value to industry.

The third effort was mandated in the 1990 Food, Agriculture, Trade, and Environment Act. The Act's *Alternative Agricultural Research and Commercialization (AARC)* sections set up a board, an advisory council, and regional centers designed to

- Fund research emphasizing the development as well as the production and marketing of new products from agriculture; and
- Work in partnership with manufacturers, financiers, universities, and private and Government laboratories in order to assist in the commercialization of new product technologies.

Experience to date has been limited but encouraging. AARC activities have been funded and several public-private partnerships are being developed. One of the most encouraging examples is a consortium including USDA, the Department of Defense, the Massachusetts Institute of Technology, the University of Hawaii, and the Warner-Lambert Company. The consortium aims to advance basic science and applied research on starch-based polymers, to accelerate the commercialization of biodegradable packaging to allow the U.S. Navy to comply with regulations on waste disposal at sea, and to expand use of U.S. agricultural resources.

Conclusions

The U.S. agricultural establishment has a longstanding commitment to supporting physical and social science research with public money. However, tightening budgets are forcing a reevaluation of the extent and nature of public investment and a search for ways to enhance research payoff. Two areas are ripe for exploration—improving priority setting and reexamining the balance between bench and applied research. Several institutions are already in place and new institutions are being set up to strengthen priority setting. USDA has also moved, with funding for the AARC, to support mixing research activities by adding more applied research.

The nascent National Research Initiative (NRI), provided for in the 1990 Food, Agriculture, Conservation, and Trade Act, recognized the need for more activity in these two areas. Con-

gress drew heavily on the assessment of publicly funded agricultural research done in 1989 by the National Research Council for the Board of Agriculture. The Act calls for both expanded research funding and a reshaping of the research system to provide for more focused research emphasizing both bench science and application.

Finally, considerable effort is being invested in improving the process of setting research priorities and of mixing bench and applied activities. Although these efforts are beginning to have an effect, the sector is still struggling to make the transition toward a more "managed" research program—a well-tended garden where a thousand blossoms can bloom. ❏

Agricultural Biotechnology and APHIS Regulations: A Pathway to the Future

12

by Charles Kastner, Senior Regulatory Analyst, Biotechnology, Biologics, and Environmental Protection, Animal and Plant Health Inspection Service, USDA, Hyattsville, MD

Biotechnology emerged as a powerful tool in the 1980's from breakthroughs in the biological sciences that had occurred during the previous decades. Biotechnology is defined as any technique that uses living organisms or substances to make or modify a prod-

uct, to improve plants or animals, or to develop micro-organisms for specific purposes.

In the 1990's, world agriculture needs the innovative potential of biotechnology to meet the dual challenges of feeding a growing human population and solving environmental problems.

The regulatory system of the Animal and Plant Health Inspection Service (APHIS) seeks to ensure the safe transfer of biotechnology from the laboratory to the farm. Through this process, APHIS acts to protect plant and animal health and acts as a catalyst for technology transfer.

A Crucial Time in Human History

The emergence of agricultural biotechnology comes at a crucial time in human history. In the past 50 years, the world's human population has increased from 2 billion to 5 billion, and demographers predict that it will rise to 6.1 billion by the year 2000. In this decade, 80 percent of this growth will take place in developing countries among the rural poor. Even now, at least 500 million people in Asia, Africa, and Latin America do not have enough food to eat, and a half billion more are at constant risk of hunger.

Over the past 50 years human beings have met the demand for increased food production by bringing new land into production and by making intensive use of new technology. In the 1990's, we find that new fertile farmland, the first part of the food production equation, is no longer available. Farmers have already now brought most of the good agricultural land into production and used nearly all of the irrigation water, and they are now rapidly depleting the ground water. In the 1990's productivity will have to come from innovation, not new land.

Biotechnology offers the chance for a new, more environmentally benign burst of productivity to meet world food needs. The alternative is to bring more marginal land into production, which would accelerate deforestation, erosion, and the loss of biodiversity, and condemn more of humanity to malnutrition.

Animal Health

Biotechnology is already playing a significant role in combatting animal diseases. Vaccines derived from biotechnology, diagnostics, and other veterinary biological products are helping to reduce diseases that rob farm production of at least 10 percent of its value each year. Examples of licensed products derived from biotechnology include subunit vaccines, gene-deleted viral vaccines, and diagnostics using monoclonal antibodies, Enzyme-Linked Immunosorbent Assay (ELISA) kits, and amplified DNA probe kits. Additional products under development include cytokines, recombinant vaccinia, and other viral vectored vaccines.

In the developing world, diagnostic test kits for rift valley fever, foot and mouth disease, and other destructive diseases offer the chance for quick intervention to reduce the spread of disease from infected animals.

Biotechnology also holds the promise of controlling complex vectorborne parasite diseases, such as trypanosomiasis, that now make large tracts of sub-Saharan Africa unusable for livestock grazing. In the future researchers may be able to provide a herd owner with a single vaccinia vectored vaccine that would immunize livestock against several different diseases.

In the developed market economies of the world, biotechnology offers improved biologics to control the spread of disease in large-scale production of livestock. For example, APHIS licensed the first amplified DNA probe kit for an animal disease. The kit dramatically reduces the time it takes to identify the bacteria causing paratuberculosis, a serious disease common in dairy cows.

APHIS licenses both biotechnologically derived and conventionally produced veterinary biological products that are sold, distributed, or manufactured in the United States, to ensure that they are pure, potent, safe, and efficacious. This assurance of product quality plays a key role in protecting America's multibillion-dollar livestock and pet industry.

Plant Health

New plant varieties developed through biotechnological techniques offer the potential to both increase the value of crops and reduce the cost of producing them. Examples include plant varieties such as tomatoes with enhanced shelf life; potatoes with a higher carbohydrate content; and corn, rice, and sunflowers with improved nutritional content.

These crops offer better nutritional value for the consumer and the potential for farmers to gain more value per unit of production. APHIS has also approved field tests of plants engineered to be herbicide-tolerant and resistant to insects and plant vi-

ruses. These plants should allow farmers to grow crops in less costly and more environmentally benign ways. In the case of cotton, growers spend millions of dollars each year for insecticides to control worm damage. Cotton plants now at the field testing stage contain genes from the bacterium *Bacillus thuringiensis* (or Bt), a protein-producing gene that is toxic to the larvae of certain insects but safe for other insects, animals, and humans. These plant varieties should help farmers reduce production costs, and also reduce the amount of pesticides put into the environment.

In the future, USDA expects to see plant varieties that make their own fertilizer by fixing nitrogen, or that can flourish under drought conditions.

Dr. Alda Giron, at DIGESEPE Laboratory in Guatemala City, Guatemala, uses a diagnostic test kit to test for foot and mouth disease. The test kits offer the chance for quick diagnosis to reduce the spread of disease from infected animals.
Laurie Smith/USDA 92BW0821

These plant varieties hold great hope for developing countries that are struggling to feed their increasing populations.

APHIS' Role

APHIS, via regulations that are based on existing statutes, ensures that plants and micro-organisms produced through biotechnology are not harmful to other plants or deleterious to the natural and human environment.

APHIS is keenly aware of its role as a regulatory pathway for agricultural biotechnology. Rational and scientific- based regulations serve the agency's primary goal: to protect U.S. agriculture. They are also necessary to ensure continued safe development of biotechnology. By providing a clear regulatory path for safe testing in the environment, APHIS acts as a catalyst for the efficient transfer of technology from the laboratory to commercial development.

APHIS regulates the products of biotechnology under its existing statutory mandate to protect animal and plant health.

The agency regulates the environmental release of certain genetically engineered plants and micro-organisms through a permit system. The approval process for veterinary biologics is different, however, in that it involves issuing a license for each commercial product to be sold for use in veterinary medicine. APHIS also uses a permit process to ensure that the importation and interstate shipment of

Dr. Victor Hugo DePaz uses a diagnostic kit to identify bacteria, in order to help control the spread of disease in large-scale production of livestock.
Laurie Smith/USDA 92BW0822

certain plants and micro-organisms, as well as all veterinary biologics, will not threaten plant and animal health or the natural or human environment.

The success of a regulatory program for technology transfer can be measured in the extent of public confidence in the safety and quality of the resulting products. The APHIS regulatory program includes a number of interrelated procedures designed to ensure safety and facilitate public confidence. By analyzing the nature of the product and the environment into which it will be introduced, APHIS evaluates any potential risks involved in field testing. APHIS coordinates its reviews with State and other Federal agencies, in order to share information on risk assessment and eliminate wasteful duplication, and it plays a major role in international efforts to harmonize regulatory oversight among nations. Finally, the agency provides timely information to the public, in the Federal Register, about the receipt, content, and approval of field test applications.

Results

By following these procedures, the United States leads the world in the safe field testing of the products of biotechnology. The approval time for field tests in the United States has decreased in the past several years; today, field test applications are typically approved within 100 days. This progress bodes well for the continued productivity of American agriculture and holds out the hope of new, more productive, and environmentally benign tools to feed the world's growing human population. ❏

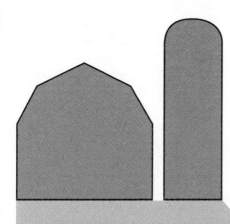

Part III.
Products From Nontraditional Crops

How Crops Can Provide Raw Materials for the Chemical Industry

13

by Shelby Thames, Distinguished University Research Professor and Professor of Polymer Science, University of Southern Mississippi, Hattiesburg; Robert Kleiman, National Center for Agricultural Utilization Research, ARS, USDA, Peoria, IL; and L. Davis Clements, Director, Agricultural Materials, CSRS, USDA, Washington, DC

Nature has produced an estimated 300,000 different plant species, of which we use only a few hundred in organized agriculture. In 1957, USDA initiated a program that collected plants worldwide from a number of sources. The idea was to take a close look at these plants chemically and see if any new and different materials in them could be useful to humanity.

About 8,000 different species were collected, most of which had never been examined before. Their chemical compositions were analyzed for potential sources of starch, protein, oil, fiber, gum, and medicinal components, as well as for any special individual characteristics. For example, researchers found over 100 different, never-before-discovered oils.

This effort to utilize new species, as well as to develop new *uses* for traditional crops, is possible because nature offers renewable, reliable "living factories" for an incredible array of chemical materials.

Agriculture in the United States is accustomed to identifying crops as specific commodities (corn, soybeans, cotton, etc.) in relation to the traditional food, feed, and fiber markets. To fully explore potential uses of a crop, we must view it not simply as a commodity but as a complex raw material that has specific functional groups suitable for producing industrial products. The utility of a given crop as a resource for the chemical industry depends upon the chemical composition and structure of the materials found in that crop.

All crops are made up of many types of materials. For example, the corn plant has starches, oil, zein (protein), and a number of lesser components in each kernel. The cobs and stalks contain cellulose (a long chain, or polymer, of sugar molecules containing six carbon atoms), hemicellulose (a polymer of sugar molecules containing five carbons), and lignin (a polymer made up of six-member carbon-hydrogen rings). Each of these materials contains chemically distinct structural units that can react with other chemical structures to form *new* materials. These reactive chemical units are referred to as the "chemical functionality" of the material.

Its specific chemical functionality is the basis for each material's use as an industrial resource. For this reason, when we consider industrial uses for both traditional and nontraditional agricultural products, we group crop resources in terms of their primary materials: starches, oils, proteins, lignocellulosics, and other natural products such as naturally derived chemicals. We will examine in more detail the functionalities and uses for three of these materials: oils, starches, and lignocellulosics.

Vegetable Oils

A major ingredient in many plants is the oil that can be extracted from their fruits or seeds. Seed oils have been used for millenia as an energy component of food—and almost as long in nonfood applications. The ancient Egyptians used castor oil in their paints and as a lubricant, and Biblical passages refer to olive oil as a source of fuel in lamps.

Seed oils from traditional crops such as soybeans, corn, cotton, coconuts, and flax provide raw materials for many of the products that we use every day. From the soap we wash with, to the grease we use to lubricate our automobiles, combines, and military equipment, vegetable oils are a prime ingredient. In addition, a number of new crops, such as crambe, rapeseed, lesquerella, and others, produce oils with unique compositions. The oil from these new crops is used

Seed oils from traditional crops, such as soybeans, provide raw materials for many of the products that we use every day—from the soap we wash with, to the grease we use to lubricate our automobiles.

USDA 067-10-2A

New crops, such as lesquerella, produce oils with unique compositions that are opening up new applications as raw materials for products from lubricants to cosmetics.
Ken Hammond/USDA 92BW0693-35

for products ranging from lubricants to plastics and from cosmetics to industrial chemicals.

Seed oils consist primarily of a chemical form called a triglyceride. These triglycerides are liquids at room temperatures and insoluble in water. Some triglycerides are stable at high temperatures because they are either saturated (nonreactive) or partially unsaturated (somewhat reactive). These oils, used in cooking, include corn oil, peanut oil, safflower oil, olive oil, and sunflower oil. Others, with high levels of chemical unsaturation, are valuable either because they are chemically reactive or because they contain unusual chemical structures.

Vegetable oils can react with other materials to form either a much thicker liquid (a lubricant) or solids.

The oils can be used directly for dust control or as carriers for pesticides. Alcohols such as methanol or ethanol can react with the oil's triglyceride to give what is called a fatty acid ester, which is useful, among other things, as a substitute diesel fuel. Vegetable oils can be converted to glycerol (used in cosmetics, synthetic fibers, explosives, etc.) and fatty acids through the chemical addition of water to the triglyceride.

The fatty acids of soybean oil and tall oil (from wood, primarily pine) are used to make materials included in hot-melt glues and in the curing component of epoxy glues, while the fatty acids in coconut oil are the major ingredient in soaps and detergents. Other uses for fatty acids include fabric softeners, cosmetics, plastics, paints, coatings, inks, antifoaming agents, minerals processing agents, and mold release agents in foundries. In short, whether we realize it or not, we use vegetable oils in our everyday life for many things we would be hard pressed to do without.

Many new uses of seed oils are now being developed to take advantage of their natural functionalities. Soybean oil has been modified to replace petroleum in inks for newspaper printing. (The 1991 and 1992 Yearbooks of Agricultue were printed with soy ink.) A number of nylons based on oils from other crops, particularly nylon-11 and nylon-13,13, are being evaluated for use as engineering plastics in the automotive industry. New, flexible coatings and paints can be made from rapeseed and crambe oils.

The functionality of each oil is unique. The fatty acids in each oil are different, and therefore each oil's ability to react is different. The unsaturated bonds in the fatty acids that make up the triglycerides are reactive; that is, they can combine with other chemicals easily. So, when we deliberately add oxygen, sulfur, or phosphorus to the unsaturated bonds in a triglyceride, we can make a lubricant, a rubber additive, or a wax. The reactivity of unsaturated bonds in fatty acids also leads to the production of raw materials necessary in the manufacture of nylons, polyesters, waxes, and other products.

The natural structure of seed oils allows us to create unique products for use in all facets of our daily lives. In some of the chapters of this yearbook, you can find more complete descriptions of how scientists are searching for new oil crops while, at the same time, pursuing new uses for several of the seed oils.

Starches

Traditionally, we view corn, potatoes, tapioca, rice, and wheat as foods for human and animal consumption, not as sources of a naturally occurring starch. But these food items are important sources of industrially useful starch, a polysaccharide ("many sugars") consisting of a long chain of individual glucose (sugar) units.

Today starch is an important raw material for the chemical industry. For instance, the paint and coatings industry has utilized starch and its derivatives as stabilizers and flow modifiers for latex paints and other water-dispersed coatings. Starch is also used as a binder in explosives, for example for fireworks and industrial applications. Starches can be acidified, dried, heated, and cooled to produce either British gums or white and yellow dextrins, which are used as adhesives. The specific nature of the product is controlled by the processing.

Unmodified starch has been used for many years to size textiles. Sizing consists of passing a yarn through a solution of starch to deposit a coating of starch over the surface of the yarn to bind individual fibers into a smooth strand. After heating to dry the sizing agent, the coated or sized yarn is ready for weaving. During weaving, a yarn is exposed to abrasion and tension, and sizing provides abrasion resistance and strength for the fibers.

Starch is commonly used in a wide

variety of adhesives, particularly those designed to bond paper to itself, glass, or other materials. It is also useful for binding mineral wool in ceiling tiles and for binding clay in ceramics. The overwhelming majority of all starch used for adhesives is used in the production of corrugated board. Other applications are in the manufacture of paper bags, bottle labels, gummed tapes, envelopes, and a variety of poster pastes or billboard-type applications. Starch-based adhesives are the materials of choice for wallpaper and other pasting operations requiring the alignment of patterns and edges.

The structure of starch can be modified or changed by a number of chemical reactions. Among them is the reaction of starch with dithiocarbonic acid to make what is called xanthated starch. Applications for xanthated starch include wastewater treatment, slow release of volatile chemicals such as pesticides, fillers for powdered rubber, and papermaking.

Modified starches are used extensively in the paper industry. The starch acts as a binder for paper to enhance its dry strength and imparts desirable water retention properties that prevent excessive dewatering during the papermaking process. Modified starch is also used to thicken coatings used on paper so that they are smooth and nonsagging. This application is similar to using starch as a thickener in cooking a stew. Starch also is the "carbon" in carbonless paper.

Starch modified with monochloroacetate is called carboxymethyl starch and is used as an absorbent in adhesives, medical poultices, papermaking, coatings, dentifrice powders, and pulp refining and for making tablets, binders, and disintegrants. Carboxymethyl starch is also used for textile printing and as a component in film-forming mixtures. Other applications of carboxymethyl starch are as a thickening agent, flocculant (to enhance settling of suspended solids), antisoil-deposition agent (to help surfaces repel dirt), and chelating agent (to combine with dissolved metals).

Modification of starch to cyanoethyl-starch provides water dispersability, resistance to swelling, excellent adhesive properties, and increased fiber absorbency. Methylstarches are used as thickeners, protective colloids, soil-suspending agents, and detergent compounds. Ethylstarches are used primarily in the paper industry as a component of sizing formulations, a pigment adhesive, and for other specialty coatings.

Plastic is so widely used in all facets of everyday life that its disposal after use has become a serious problem. Many applications—food packaging, disposable plates and utensils, and medical items such as syringes—have a fairly short useful life and are not, or cannot be, recycled. Starch-derived materials that are truly biodegradable are leading candidates to replace nondegradable petroleum-derived plastics. The chemical functionalities of starch allow it to be used in the preparation of polymers that can be formed into films or solid shapes and that can retain their properties throughout the useful life of the products. When the starch-based products must be disposed of, they can be consumed by microorganisms, for example in composting systems.

Lignocellulosics

By weight, the largest component of plant matter is lignocellulosic material—a mixture of cellulose, hemicellulose, and lignin. The relative amounts of the three lignocellulosic components depend on the type of plant and, to some extent, the age of the plant.

Traditional uses of lignocellulosic materials have taken advantage of their fibrous nature, which is a result of the long polymer chains of cellulose and hemicellulose. Common lignocellulosic materials are wood and paper pulp. In fact, paper is almost pure cellulose.

Cellulose and hemicellulose polymer chains can be hydrolyzed (a chemical process in which water is added, breaking the chains) into individual sugar molecules. These sugars can then be fermented into a number of commercially important chemicals through the action of yeasts and bacteria.

Because cellulose is a stable natural polymer, it is much more difficult to hydrolyze than hemicellulose, and its hydroxyl groups (bonded hydrogen and oxygen) react easily with other chemicals without destroying the basic polymer. This can be an advantage in making a number of important cellulose derivatives: cellulose acetate, which is used in photographic film and various coatings; rayon, which is used in textiles; and cellulose nitrates,

which are used in explosives and Ping-Pong balls.

The least utilized component of lignocellulosic materials is lignin. Lignins are highly complex polymers that consist of phenolic rings (six carbons in a ring with a hydroxyl group attached) that are connected by combinations of carbon and oxygen linkages. Lignins can react with sulfuric acid to produce a group of compounds called lignosulfonates, which are used as binders (in wallboard) and dispersing agents (in pigments).

Most of the commercially available lignin is a byproduct of paper production, which uses sulfur compounds to separate the lignin from the cellulose pulp. The lignin coproduct, called "black liquor," is used as the primary source of carbon disulfide (a chemical intermediate in making other sulfur compounds) and dimethyl sulfoxide (an organic solvent). Sadly, though there is an oversupply of lignin, the most valuable structure within the lignin, the phenol ring, continues to be little utilized. Essentially all of the phenolic compounds in industry, including most synthetic dyes, are made from petroleum or coal, not lignin.

Finally, lignocellulosic materials can be viewed as the most abundant source of carbon-hydrogen-oxygen (C-H-O) compounds that we have. Through the processes of pyrolysis/ gasification (thermal degradation in the absence of oxygen for combustion) and liquefaction (depolymerization into a variety of smaller compounds), it is possible to produce the equivalent of synthetic crude oil, synthesis gas (a mixture of carbon monoxide and hydrogen), and synthetic natural gas. These materials, in turn, provide raw materials identical to those used in the existing petrochemical industry.

In summary, lignocellulosic materials are a resource that will always be produced at the same time that we are producing crops for food, feed, fiber, or chemicals. Wood wastes, harvestable field residues, and most food-processing wastes can be collected as sources of lignocellulosics. The chemical functions of lignocellulosics permit their use either directly as chemical derivatives or indirectly as a source of C-H-O compounds for further chemical synthesis. As a category of materials, lignocellulosics are one of the cheapest per unit weight as well as one of the most abundant renewable resources that we have.

Summary
Plants contain a host of compounds that are chemically useful in making industrial products. To develop industrial products, we need to think of plants not just as commodities but as "living factories" for chemical raw materials. The major materials present in all plants are the three described here—oils, starches, and lignocellulosics—and protein and naturally derived chemicals. Together, these materials are the source of a broad range of products from medicines to newsprint, from jet engine lubricants to lipstick. ❏

Kenaf: Annual Fiber Crop Products Generate a Growing Response From Industry

14

by Charles S. Taylor, General Manager, Kenaf International, McAllen, TX, and Daniel E. Kugler, Director, Office of Agricultural Materials, CSRS, USDA, Washington, DC

"Don't put shade on it."

That is the only general crop management recommendation for the steadily increasing number of kenaf growers in areas of south Texas and southern Louisiana. They—along with newer groups of interested farmers in the Mississippi Delta, the plains of Oklahoma, the tidewaters of the Carolinas, and the valleys of California— are quickly learning that growing this annual hibiscus fiber crop is comparatively easy, requiring few inputs and little management.

But, being easy to grow is an insufficient attribute. There must be a use and a market for the crop. The necessary technologies must exist, and the crop must be economical to produce and use. Each of these attributes is important as a crop-to-product system evolves.

Kenaf, *Hibiscus cannabinus L.*, is an annual fiber crop that is now, after years of public and private research and development efforts, in the early stages of commercialization in the United States. There are those who claim that kenaf fiber has been found in the ancient pyramids of Egypt. But it is still considered a "new" crop in the Americas, where its introduction

began in the 1940's with fiber projects in Cuba, Guatemala, Mexico, and El Salvador. Nevertheless, kenaf has been and still is a major fiber crop in Africa and parts of Asia, where the long bast fibers from its bark are processed for use in various cordage products such as burlap, rope, and twine.

The principal purpose of kenaf production is to grow tall stalks that upon maturity (in about 6 months) can be cut in various lengths and ground for use in the manufacture of pulp and paper products such as newsprint or tissue.

Bast and Core
Some uses of the fiber crop require separating the two distinct fibers in the

Kenaf, *Hibiscus cannabinus L.*, is an annual fiber crop that is now in the early stages of commercialization in the United States.

David Nance/USDA 88BW1573-23A

Marvin Bagby, an ARS researcher, examines a stalk of kenaf. The long, outer bark and short, inner core fibers are processed into newsprint.
USDA 88BW1884-4

ARS soil scientist L.N. Namkin examines a stand of kenaf at Rio Farms in Texas' Rio Grande Valley. Kenaf has the potential to supplement or replace wood-based paper pulp.
David Nance/USDA 88BW1573-12A

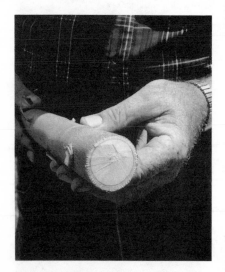

Both pulpy center and fibrous exterior of bamboolike kenaf are used to produce newsprint and other fiber products.
David Nance/USDA 88BW1576-9A

kenaf stalk—bast and core. The long, stringy bast fibers of the outer bark comprise 30-35 percent of the stalk by weight and are similar to jute in appearance and traditional applications. The bast is used to make cordage products and specialty pulps, and may be used as a substitute for fiberglass in certain applications.

The balsa-wood-like fibers of the stalk's interior, or core, have traditionally been either burned for fuel by peasant farmers in Asia or Africa or discarded. However, they can be used for a variety of products such as poultry litter, packing materials, and mulch.

Forage is another potential use for kenaf. USDA and university researchers in Oklahoma are testing kenaf's potential as a possible niche forage crop in the Southern Plains. This would require very different farming practices, growing the crop for about 60 days and chopping the immature green crop with conventional forage equipment. The potential of kenaf as a forage crop is still in the research channel, as feeding trials and continued nutritional studies are being conducted.

Kenaf Newsprint

To better understand what is driving the commercialization of this new crop, consider kenaf's potential as a source of fiber for either large-scale industrial projects (such as multi-mil-

lion-dollar newsprint mills) or smaller fiber projects (producing poultry litter and twine products). The current work by industry and USDA was triggered in the late 1970's, when newsprint prices were increasing rapidly. Publishers became interested in developing lower cost, domestic sources of fiber for the manufacture of newsprint.

A process for newsprint manufacture that was developed under the leadership of USDA led to a small first printing by the Peoria Journal Star, Peoria, IL, in 1977. Commercial-scale trials of kenaf newsprint in 1979, 1981, and 1987 involved publishers, farmers, manufacturers, and USDA. Results in the pressrooms of some of the major newspapers in the United States have greatly encouraged further work. In particular, the demonstration

One of the principal uses for kenaf is in pulp and paper products, such as newsprint.
USDA 92BW0827

project led to a full pressroom run by the Bakersfield Californian in 1987 and proved kenaf newsprint to be a market-ready commodity.

Today's environmental concerns demand that chemical use in both fields and mills be minimal. Kenaf is an annual crop fiber source, grown with minimum production inputs by local farmers (thus reducing transportation costs). Its use could serve to reduce the pressure on forest resources in some areas. Kenaf can be turned into pulp for newsprint with lower energy and bleaching requirements than those for southern pine. In fact, the Kenaf Paper Company in Willacy County, TX, has obtained permits allowing it to irrigate its fiber crop with the treated wastewaters discharged from its planned chemi-thermo-mechanical newsprint mill. In addition, research studies at USDA's Forest Products Laboratory in Madison, WI, indicate that kenaf can be blended with recycled newspapers to produce quality newsprint while also alleviating pressure on local landfills.

However, the proposed kenaf/recycled newsprint mill in south Texas has been stalled by the combined effects of a glutted North American market for newsprint, the reluctance of financial institutions to invest in a new agro-industry, and conditions in the U.S. economy. Public and private developers remain confident that the project will soon be recognized for its contribution as an economically viable, environmentally sound source of quality newsprint for regional users in south Texas and northeastern Mexico, as well as for its ability to contribute to rural development.

Other efforts to develop kenaf as a fiber source for pulp and paper mills generally have confronted the same issues. Therefore, in 1991, most of the kenaf efforts in the United States began to focus more on developing markets for separated kenaf fiber products made from bast or core.

Processing Methods

Overseas, the bark and core fibers are separated manually either before or after retting (soaking in a fetid pond or canal until bacterial action loosens the bast fibers). This age-old technology is dependent upon extremely cheap labor and very lax environmental regulations. Low and cyclical world prices, relatively small U.S. markets for imported jute, and the inability to separate the bast from the core mechanically had combined to dampen interest in exploring kenaf's potential. However, major users of imported jute fibers have initiated and maintained communication with the kenaf team as it works on gaining acceptance by the newsprint industry. These users represent a starting U.S. "niche" market for kenaf's separated and dry-processed fiber products.

Materials handling has been a problem with the earlier commercial kenaf newsprint trials, and in 1986 the Kenaf Demonstration Project (a cooperative activity between USDA and a task force of private sector interests that included Kenaf International, Andritz-Sprout-Bauer, Inc., Canadian Pacific Forest Products Limited, and the Beloit Corporation) focused on finding an effective means of introducing the unseparated kenaf fibers to the pulp mill system.

The kenaf stalks had to be reduced by a common hammermill operation in order to "flow" into the pulping system without roping and clogging. In this process, the grinding caused an initial separation of the bast and core fibers. The users of imported jute performed some tests, and work began on determining the best means of completing the separation process. This work accelerated in 1989 with a pilot plant trial supported by USDA in La Villa, TX, using a modified cotton ginning process. Unfortunately, this initial attempt proved disappointing for several reasons. Primarily, the small amount of core still mixed in the bast made it unacceptable for continuous machine runs by General Felt Industries, the main user of imported jute that was interested in kenaf. Although unsuccessful, the pilot plant trial stimulated several independent efforts to achieve a commercially viable mechanical separation in which both delivered cost and quality were satisfactory to the next-stage product manufacturer, who would use the bast fibers to make carpet padding, composite materials for interior panels, or other materials.

The first separation technology was developed by Harold Willett, who developed and successfully tested the harvesting system for the Kenaf Demonstration Project under a grant from USDA in 1987-88. Willett had observed the attempt to "gin" kenaf. He could not accept the idea that there was value only in extracting the clean bast (about 25 percent of the processing stream) and that the core could be discarded. Engineering intuition also told him that energy and capital costs had to be reduced if kenaf was to compete as a low-price natural fiber.

More New Uses

Basic economics proved Willett right on both counts. Tinkering with combine parts and focusing on getting "clean" core, he was able to design and test a process that achieves adequate separation with minimal energy and capital requirements. Furthermore, research and development work in Delaware, Texas, and California soon indicated that kenaf core had an interesting application as poultry litter. Similar potential was subsequently identified in other markets seeking low-cost, highly absorbent sources of cellulose. The core has been tested as a filter medium for fruit juices and engine oil, as a source of fiber in "lite" bread dough, as an additive to drilling mud in oil fields, as an ingredient in various horticultural products, as bedding in horse stables, and as a medium for oil spill cleanup. Business ventures are already under way in Louisiana (Natural Fibers of Louisiana), Texas (Kenaf International), Mississippi (Mississippi Delta Fiber Cooperative), California (Agrofibers), and Delaware (FiberCore).

Meanwhile, new uses have begun to be identified for the bast fiber. Some of the prospective applications have environmental as well as economic implications, as kenaf bast fiber has been successfully substituted for fiberglass in the manufacture of molded parts for car interiors. This same technology, which uses a natural fiber and produces no wastewater, is being tested in a widening range of product applications, including absorbent mats.

The Kenaf Demonstration Project began in early 1986 specifically to conduct activities that would lead to commercialization of kenaf fibers. The resulting series of collaborative activities with industry either directly or indirectly helped to build today's foundation of 8-10 kenaf businesses in the United States and kenaf research programs in USDA and universities. The successes are attributable largely to creative and innovative partnerships between public and private interests, which combine resources, ideas, and people to overcome major technical, economic, and institutional barriers.

Over time, USDA has invested more than $15-20 million of public funds into efforts to support the research, development, and commercialization of kenaf as a new fiber source for industry. While it is difficult to quantify the contributions, it is safe to estimate that the various private cooperators involved have matched USDA on at least a 3-to-1 basis. Given the projects already in operation and those soon to leap off the drawing board, it looks as though taxpayer investment in kenaf has been rewarded. ❑

Guayule Has 15 Real Rubber in It, and It Grows in the United States

by F.S. Nakayama, Research Chemist, U.S. Water Conservation Laboratory, ARS, USDA, Phoenix, AZ; W.W. Schloman, Jr., Instructor, Department of Chemistry, University of Akron, Akron, OH; and S.F. Thames, Distinguished University Research Professor and Professor of Polymer Science, University of Southern Mississippi, Hattiesburg

North and South America have two plants, hevea and guayule, that provide natural rubber for use in commerce. Many of us are familiar with the hevea tree (*Hevea brasiliensis*), a native of the Amazon region that is now grown primarily in Southeast Asia, because at present, this plant provides all of the natural rubber used in the world.

History of Guayule

The lesser known guayule shrub (*Parthenium argentatum*) is a native of north-central Mexico and southwestern Texas. In fact, the Spanish explorers saw Indians in Mexico playing with a bouncing ball made from guayule rubber. Rubber production in those days was a community undertaking; the Indians chewed the bark to separate the rubber from the rest of the plant.

The chemical composition and properties of the rubber from guayule and hevea are similar. Though guayule makes about the same quantity of resin-type compounds that have potentially valuable industrial uses, rubber removal from guayule requires special extraction procedures. The guayule plant, unlike hevea, makes and stores rubber in individual cells of the stem instead of in the stem sap.

From the early 1900's through the 1930's, guayule provided a significant amount of the rubber used to make automobile tires. During World War II, the United States made a major effort to produce guayule rubber to replace the then-unavailable overseas source of hevea. This emergency project produced large amounts of guayule rubber, reaching 10 percent of the Nation's supply and use.

The abrupt closure of the project at the end of the war resulted in the abandonment of the plant nurseries, fields, and processing facilities. Germplasm selections, breeding stock, and supplies of rubber and seeds were also destroyed. The present outlook for the commercialization of guayule is clouded because of its cyclical history of sudden spurts of interest followed by complete neglect.

Why Natural Rubber?

Modern transportation depends heavily on natural rubber, as it is the basic ingredient of tires. Natural rubber is also the ingredient of many elastic products that require high tensile strength, durability, and low heat buildup when flexed. So synthetic rubber from petroleum cannot completely replace natural rubber. In addition, natural rubber is a renewable resource, whereas petroleum reserves are not.

Properties of Rubber

Natural rubber is a polymer with a chain of thousands of isoprene molecules (C_5H_8) linked together. Plants such as goldenrod, dandelion, and milkweed manufacture a short-chain-length polymer, averaging 4,000 or fewer isoprene units. By comparison, the hevea and guayule plants can synthesize long-chain polymers of 25,000 or more units. Only the long-chain polymers have the elastic strength and durability for making tires and rubberbands.

A rubber tire encircling the desert shrub guayule symbolizes the plant's potential as a primary source of natural rubber for the United States.
Jack Dykinga/USDA 0584X711-28

Processing of Rubber

When mass production of automobiles began in the early 1900's, rubber tire manufacturing became a major industry. Guayule rubber was obtained by grinding the shrub in water and skimming off the floating rubber "worms." This flotation procedure was used during the World War II production of guayule rubber. Unfortunately, the rubber from this process contains resinous impurities that make the rubber tacky, soft, and likely to break down with time.

Efforts to improve guayule rubber quality were rekindled in the 1970's, when the petroleum crisis occurred. In the new process, resin in the worms was removed by solvent extraction.

Rubber produced in this way can make high-performance aircraft tires.

Further improvement in rubber quality and efficiency of production came about with the sequential extraction procedure. The sequential process used two different solvents: one to dissolve and remove the resin, and the other to dissolve and separate the rubber. In Salinas, CA, and Peoria, IL, USDA researchers evaluated a variety of such processes.

The latest extraction process uses only one solvent to dissolve both the rubber and the resin. Dissolved rubber in the mixture is then removed by selective coagulation and precipitation. In the late 1980's, Bridgestone/Firestone, Inc., built a pilot facility in

Rubber (top), extracted from dried guayule (bottom), at the Northern Regional Research Center, Peoria, IL. Guayule now yields about 5 pounds of rubber per 100 pounds of shrub.

Jack Dykinga/USDA 1284X1802-10

Sacaton, AZ, for extracting rubber with this process. The facility produced 5 metric tons of rubber for tire production and testing before it was closed. Resin and low-molecular-weight rubber fractions from this operation are also undergoing development and testing for possible coproduct applications.

This selective coagulation procedure can separate rubbers of different molecular weights that have different physical properties. Thus, the processor can tailor the end product to the needs of the customer.

Applications of Rubber

The demand for rubber continues to grow. Natural rubber now accounts for 31.5 percent, or 4.7 million tons annually, of the total rubber market worldwide. Petroleum-based synthetic rubber meets the remaining needs. In 1990, the United States imported over 800,000 metric tons of natural rubber, costing nearly $1 billion. About two-thirds of this natural rubber is used for tires and related products. This is not surprising, because a passenger tire is made up of 30 percent natural rubber and an aircraft tire 100 percent. The remaining one-third of natural rubber goes into making other rubber products such as V-belts, conveyor belts, storage tank linings, and hoses. A small amount ends up in footwear and adhesive products.

As expected, performance tests of guayule rubber are primarily directed to transportation. These include light- and heavy-duty truck tires, aircraft tires, military tank track pads, and motor mounts. The tensile-strength, wear, and heat-resistance characteristics of guayule products have met or exceeded those of similar products manufactured from hevea rubber.

Other nontransportation market products are available. Guayule rubber makes a nonstick base for chewing gum. Blending guayule rubber with polyolefins produces a polymer for making extruded or injection-molded products. Finally, chemical modification of guayule rubber has produced new types of polymers. These polymers have properties similar to those of existing thermoplastic elastomers for making various types of molded goods.

Guayule Coproducts

Resin-like compounds derived from the rubber extraction process add to the coproduct value of the guayule shrub. Initially, these incidental materials were considered nuisances and waste products. Now they appear to have special uses that may give them considerable value in their own right.

The coproducts of guayule consist of (1) low-molecular-weight rubber (LMWR), (2) organic and water-soluble resins, and (3) bagasse (plant residue). Some of these materials, especially LMWR, are ideal raw materials in polymer synthesis. They serve as building blocks for making more complex compounds that are useful in industry.

LMWR is a short-chain polymer averaging about 4,500 isoprene units and is thus not suitable for making tires. However, chlorinating the LMWR forms tough, flexible, and chemically resistant compounds. Be-

Performance tests of guayule rubber are directed primarily toward transportation and related products. Guayule passes a tire-scorching test at 145 miles an hour in simulated carrier landings at the Patuxent Naval Air Test Center in Maryland.
Anita Daniels/USDA 0684W917-12A

cause chlorinated rubber products resist abrasion and water, they are used in making highway stripes and marine and pool paints. Floor coating containing this material is hard and resistant to abrasion, chemicals, and impact.

Epoxy compounds of LMWR are used as toughening aids in polymer formulations. In addition, the epoxidized rubber has potential in making thickeners, adhesives, and thermoplastic polymers. The low-molecular-weight fraction of guayule is less expensive than the LMWR derived from hevea.

Hydroxylated LMWR compounds make polymer-forming raw materials used in producing polyesters, polyethers, and polyurethanes. Currently, these important materials are manufactured from petroleum sources. Guayule provides an alternative, renewable source of these important and extensively used industrial chemicals.

By modifying the LMWR, water-stable polymers are formed. These waterborne particles are used in paints that do not require volatile organic solvents. Volatile organic compounds (VOC's) in paints are being discouraged, in order to reduce solvent pollution of the atmosphere. Polymer-modified, chlorinated rubber shows promise as powder coatings that do not involve any VOC's.

In contrast to the problems with crude resinous impurities in early processing, current nonrubber compounds of guayule resin have potential useful applications in industry. When resin is chemically modified and recombined with the guayule rubber itself, rubber with high tear resistance (a desirable property in tires) is produced.

Guayule resin can be used as a plasticizer for other high-molecular-weight polymers. It can stabilize the physical properties of synthetic rubber. Protective coatings made by mixing guayule resin with epoxy material are easily stripped from the surface when needed. These coatings are useful for the temporary storage and weather protection of aircraft and motor vehicles.

The organic soluble resin, when blended with marine coatings, produces an antifouling mixture that can prevent formation of barnacles on ocean buoys and ship hulls. The material should be less hazardous to the environment than existing paint and coating compounds.

Wood impregnated with organic soluble guayule resin resists attack by marine borer, termite, and soil fungi. The resin mixture is very complex, and studies to characterize its composition are just beginning. Because the resin coproduct is a natural product, it is considered to be environment-friendly.

The bagasse, which remains after rubber extraction, is convertible to furfural, an important chemical raw material for manufacturing industrial solvents, resins, and plastics. The bagasse can also be used to make hardboard siding. The guayule-bagasse hardboard overlay is highly water repellent.

Growing Guayule

A low-growing, desert-adapted shrub, guayule can withstand extreme water stress. However, it is sensitive to hard frost. Thus, the Southwestern United States would play a major role in the cultivation of guayule.

The cultivation of guayule is similar to that of current major crops. Guayule culture initially required a large labor force, but research application of modern technology has essentially mechanized the system and better planting and harvesting equipment is now available. In addition, improved seed treatment and direct planting techniques have enhanced plant establishment and the economics of growing guayule.

The guayule shrub can be grown under irrigated or nonirrigated culture. Information is available on the water requirements and method of irrigation of the existing crop varieties. Guayule can be grown under dryland conditions, but in this situation, it needs longer growing periods than the irrigated crop. However, dryland production will provide a natural living system for storing rubber, as these plants can be maintained at a low cost and harvested, as necessary, when a special emergency arises.

To further improve guayule's economic prospect, the rubber yield of existing genetic lines of guayule must be doubled. This can be achieved

Dale Bucks, ARS national technical advisor on guayule, measures guayule plant height as the crop, grown in a marginal soil of more than 95 percent sand, is irrigated by an automated sprinkler system.

Jack Dykinga/USDA 0584X707-11

through proper selection and breeding, as was done with hevea. Guayule, unlike many of our domestic crops, produces seeds without fertilization. This is both a hindrance and a help in germplasm improvement: Plant crosses are harder to make and identify; but once a good line is developed, it can be readily maintained.

Commercializing Guayule

As with all new, alternative crops, guayule commercialization faces the proverbial "chicken or egg" problem. Farmers won't grow the crop because the rubber-processing facility is not available, and industry won't build the facility because of the lack of a reliable source of the shrub.

Yet, guayule still has great potential to become an important source of natural rubber for the United States. Not only could guayule rubber production in the United States offset the annual import of almost 1 billion dollars' worth of hevea rubber, but economists have predicted a shortage of hevea rubber in the late 1990's. Increasing the yield, decreasing the production costs, and finding new

pro-ducts of guayule will improve and hasten its chance for commercialization.

Rubber production first started in the Americas. When guayule rubber is commercially produced in the United States, the natural-rubber source will have finally returned to its place of origin. ❑

To increase the amount of rubber in guayule plants, ARS chemist Charles De Benedict sprays bioregulators on the plants.
0584X712-11A

Rapeseed and Crambe: Developing Useful Products From Oils That Are High in Erucic Acid

16

by Joseph Roetheli, Office of Agricultural Materials, CSRS, USDA, Washington, DC; Kenneth Carlson, Research Chemist, National Center for Agricultural Utilization Research, ARS, USDA, Peoria, IL; John Gardner, Superintendent, Carrington Research and Extension Center, North Dakota State University, Carrington, ND; and Kenneth Schneeberger, Director of Advancement, College of Agriculture, University of Missouri, Columbia, MO

The use of rapeseed oil dates back to antiquity. Ancient (2000 to 1500 B.C.) writing from Greece, Rome, India, and China refer specifically to oilseed rape, its medicinal value, and its use as a cooking oil. The focus of this chapter, however, is not on the edibility of oils but on the industrial use of high erucic acid (industrial) rapeseed and crambe oils.

This artist's rendering illustrates crambe, a member of the mustard family. The crop requires fewer purchased inputs and has relatively low production costs. Also, conventional wheat machinery can be used to plant and harvest crambe.
USDA 92BW0824

Until the development of the steam engine, rapeseed oil had rather limited industrial use. Then, users found that it clung to water- and steam-washed metal surfaces better than any other lubricant. But use of rapeseed oil declined when internal combustion engines that required petroleum replaced steam engines. Today, however, the extraordinary lubricating properties and other functional attributes of rapeseed oil are again gaining favor. More rapeseed oil is being used because people in developed countries are placing increased emphasis on environmental improvement and the use of renewable resources. Some bread wraps, garbage bags, and lubricants now contain rapeseed or crambe oils and therefore possess the functional properties of the oil's primary fatty acid, erucic acid. Recently, crambe has emerged as a source of high erucic acid oil.

Why the Interest in Oils High in Erucic Acid?

Considerable private sector interest exists both in use of erucic acid and in agricultural production of industrial rapeseed and crambe. Erucic acid has unique chemical properties that chemists can use to make useful products. High erucic acid oils and their derivatives have excellent lubricating properties, as well as special attributes for manufacturing nylons, paints, and coatings that do not shrink or swell with changes in moisture. These products also possess excellent electrical insulation properties, and provide good strength.

The economics of growing high erucic acid oilseed crops in the Northern Plains compare favorably with those of growing wheat, as equipment needs are similar to those used in producing and harvesting small grains. In addition, the United States has the capacity to grow and process more oilseed crops. Success in producing crambe and industrial rapeseed could decrease the need for imports.

Primary concerns affecting expanded commercialization of these crops center around improving winterhardiness in rapeseed, gaining acceptance of crambe meal as a feed, managing pest problems (including approval to use safe chemicals when necessary), developing new products that use erucic acid, and selling to existing and new markets.

Part III. Products From Nontraditional Crops

Production of Crambe and Industrial Rapeseed

Rapeseed (both *Brassica napus* and *B. campestris*) and crambe *(Crambe abyssinica)* have emerged as commercially viable alternative oil crops. Rapeseed appears to be native to the Himalayan region, and crambe is native to the arid regions of the Middle East, yet both are adapted to a broad range of growing regions in the United States and the world. Both are attractive, not only for their products, but also for their potential to diversify cropping systems, thereby reducing pest problems and conserving soil. Farmers can rotate these crops with traditional crops or with lesser known species that offer the promise of botanical diversity for the future. Nature has even provided some natural pest resistance mechanisms in crambe.

Rapeseed (industrial and canola) ranks third or fourth in volume of vegetable oil produced worldwide, depending on the year. Rapeseed is grown in northern Europe, Asia, and Canada, as well as in the U.S. Northwest and Midsouth. Except in Canada, most rapeseed grown for industrial oil (high in erucic acid) is of the winter type, which is sown in fall and harvested in summer. U.S. production of industrial rapeseed generally has remained under 15,000 acres annually.

The principal spring-seeded crop that is high in erucic acid is crambe. This crop was introduced into the United States in the early 1940's. In 1957, researchers at the New Crops Research Program of ARS in Peoria, IL, reported that up to 60 percent of the crambe seed oil was erucic acid. They also indicated that crambe ap-peared to be broadly adapted. During the next 30 years, research interest in the crop increased, but by 1985 there was no sustained commercial production because the oil cost was not competitive with that of imported rapeseed oil.

In response to a dwindling supply of petroleum, a consortium of land-grant universities and USDA's Cooperative State Research Service and ARS came together in late 1986 to expand commercial use of crops like crambe and rapeseed. Today, the consortium consists of land-grant universities in Idaho, Illinois, Iowa, Kansas, Missouri, Nebraska, New Mexico, and North Dakota; the Kansas Board of Agriculture; and several private firms. The consortium has emphasized the production and processing of crops, product development, and marketing. They have found that crambe performs better than rapeseed north of Missouri and Kansas. Rapeseed tends to be the better crop south of this line.

In 1990, a collaborative partnership was formed. Thirty-eight North Dakota farmers, National Sun Industries, and the consortium joined to share the risk of commercializing crambe. During this first year, farmers grew 2,200 acres of crambe under contract to National Sun Industries, which successfully processed and marketed the crambe. In 1991, farmers grew nearly 5,000 acres of crambe, and they planted 23,000 acres in 1992.

Processing Rapeseed and Crambe Seeds

When crambe and raspeseed are processed, the results are oil and coproduct meal. Most crambe and rapeseed are usually processed, like other high-oil seeds such as sunflower, cottonseed, and peanuts, by prepress solvent extraction methods. However, two other processing methods exist: screw pressing and direct solvent extraction.

Screw Pressing. This simple mechanical process squeezes oil from seeds using screw presses, also called expellers. Seeds are cracked, or flaked, and cooked before they enter the expeller. The meal, or press cake, contains 6-14 percent oil. This processing method generally leaves too much valuable oil in the less valuable meal to be really cost-effective. However, rapeseed press cake meal from the expeller processing can be used as a protein supplement in beef cattle rations.

Prepress Solvent Extraction. This method is most common and recovers much more of the oil than does the screw pressing method. The screw presses used to collect part of the oil do not squeeze the seed as hard in this method, so the resulting press cake then goes to the solvent extraction unit to remove the remaining oil. The solvent is recovered and recycled back to the extractor. Sometimes the resulting press oil and solvent oil are kept in separate containers because some buyers prefer press oil. Mills in Tennessee, Ohio, North Dakota, and Montana have processed rapeseed or crambe by this method. The meal, containing about 1 percent oil, provides an economical source of protein supplement for beef cattle rations.

Direct Solvent Extraction. Managers of some U.S. mills have retrofitted their facilities with extruders (similar to screw presses) to prepare oilseed for solvent extraction. These machines remove little or no oil but simply pelletize the seed material. The pellets, or collets, are highly porous and keep their integrity during direct solvent extraction, despite oil content as high as 40-45 percent for some seeds.

Most mills employing this technology crush 2,000-3,000 tons of seed per day. Thus, these mills are too large to process the small quantities of crambe or rapeseed grown to date. Researchers have processed both crops using a pilot plant extruder at Texas A&M University with excellent results. The defatted meal would be appropriate for use in beef cattle rations.

Other Processing Considerations. Crambe seed's high-fiber hull is 24 percent of the seed's weight and an even larger percentage of its volume. Hence, a bushel of crambe weighs only about 22 pounds. Commercial cracking rollers and air aspiration can remove about 85 percent of the hull material. Dehulling reduces fiber content of crambe from 20-25 percent to 8-15 percent and provides a high-protein (47-53 percent) meal. Small quantities of crambe have been dehulled on several occasions, demonstrating that this is technically feasible if it proves economically so. Rapeseed has a lower initial fiber content (7-12 percent) than crambe, so dehulling is unnecessary.

Both crambe seeds and some rapeseeds contain glucosinolates, which are undesirable substances for livestock consumption. When enzymes in the stomach come in contact with glucosinolates, they form compounds that are potentially antinutritional, especially in single-stomached animals. Hence, the meal from defatted seeds is most appropriate for use in beef cattle rations. Scientists have shown that water-washing these meals will remove glucosinolates and increase their potential as poultry feed. Research is under way to further develop this technology for removing glucosinolates, as lack of acceptance of the meal has slowed the growth of crambe and industrial rapeseed as commercial crops.

Products That Use Erucic Acid

For crambe and industrial rapeseed to succeed as crops, the use of their oils in industrial products must be expanded. Though they are currently used in several products, development is needed to transform more potential uses into marketplace realities.

Erucamide is a chemical made from erucic acid produced from industrial rapeseed or crambe oils. Plastic film manufacturers have used erucamide for decades in bread wraps, garbage bags, and sandwich bags. Erucamide lubricates the extruding machine during manufacturing of thin plastic films. After processing, the erucamide migrates to the surface of the films and keeps them from clinging together.

International Lubricants, Inc. (ILI), of Seattle, WA, markets an automatic transmission fluid (ATF) supplement and a metal-cutting oil based on derivatives of rapeseed oil. In independent third party tests where USDA's Cooperative State Research Service

was a partner, the ATF fluid supplement decreased wear by more than 50 percent when compared to the wear associated with factory-fill ATF fluid. The ATF supplement also produced 24 percent fewer acids that break down ATF fluids. The tests identified no detrimental impacts. Users of the ILI cutting fluid report that it causes much less dermatitis on workers' hands than other cutting oils, and also extends tool life. The cutting oil contains no toxic material, so it is less expensive overall and does not harm the environment.

Recently, a firm patented and introduced a low-calorie chocolate substitute that contains over 50 percent behenic acid, a derivative of erucic acid. Another firm is test-marketing this chocolate substitute in one of its candy bars.

In 1991, Mobil Oil began marketing a biodegradable, nontoxic, antiwear hydraulic fluid. Ninety-seven percent of this product is canola oil (edible rapeseed) and the other 3 percent also consists of natural materials. This fluid has environmental advantages, especially for machinery used near water such as hydraulic equipment at barge and ship loading docks and at hydroelectric plants.

A pharmaceutical product known as Lorenzo's Oil uses an extremely small volume of rapeseed oil. Lorenzo's Oil is used to treat adrenoleukodystrophy (ALD), a rare but debilitating disease in young males.

New Products Being Developed

Industrial bake-on paints using derivatives of rapeseed or crambe oils show promise. The key feature of the coatings is their increased flexibility and impact resistance. Properly formulated paints using derivatives of these oils could find a market niche. About one-third of the 1 billion gallons of paint used annually in the United States is industrial bake-on paint used on automobiles, household appliances, and machinery.

Nylon 13,13 can be made from the erucic acid in rapeseed and crambe oils. This nylon offers superior performance characteristics that enhance the likelihood of its commercialization: it absorbs only 0.75 percent moisture compared to 10.5 percent for nylon 6, a typical commercial nylon; it has excellent electrical insulating proper-

ties; and it is durable, yet flexible. Polymers such as nylon 13,13 could serve as insulators for high-voltage electrical lines, as fuel tanks and fuel lines in autos, and as lightweight yet durable parts for aerospace and marine applications.

But no one has yet commercialized nylon 13,13. A major hindrance has been the lack of a cost-effective method of achieving the first step—producing brassylic acid from erucic acid. The only commercial process for this chemical cutting of erucic acid into two fatty acids (brassylic and pelargonic acids) is a process known as ozonolysis, which is costly and potentially dangerous.

Recently, North Dakota State Uni-

Potential industrial uses of crambe, such as Nylon 13,13, may include lightweight, durable parts for aerospace and marine applications, such as the nylon gear shown here.

USDA 92BW0829

Part III. Products From Nontraditional Crops

versity chemists and University of Nebraska chemical engineers developed a new, lower cost, and safer catalytic method of making brassylic acid. This method offers new promise for commercializing nylon 13,13 and other products. Jet engine lubricants and some synthetic automobile lubricants use the coproduct, pelargonic acid.

These and other as-yet-unforseen applications for oils high in erucic acid hold great promise for the future use of crambe and industrial rapeseed. However, for a significant increase in their use to occur, that promise must be transformed into commercial reality. With persistence and dedication, opportunity exists for researchers and business specialists to expand commercial markets for industrial products that use erucic acid, and thereby reap many benefits for American agriculture and industry. ❏

Castor and Lesquerella: Sources of Hydroxy Fatty Acids

17

by Lewrene K. Glaser, Agricultural Economist, ERS, USDA, Washington, DC; Joseph C. Roetheli, Industrial Oilseeds Program Manager, CSRS, USDA, Washington, DC; Anson E. Thompson, Research Geneticist, U.S. Water Conservation Laboratory, ARS, USDA, Phoenix, AZ; Raymond D. Brigham, Associate Professor, Texas A&M University Agricultural Research and Extension Center, Lubbock, TX; and Kenneth D. Carlson, Chemist, National Center for Agricultural Utilization Research, ARS, USDA, Peoria, IL

Recorded use of castor oil dates back at least 4,000 years to when the ancient Egyptians used it in their lamps. In modern times, manufacturers have developed many products, ranging from lipstick to jet-engine lubricants, using castor oil and its derivatives.

Among commercial vegetable and petroleum oils, castor oil has unusual characteristics. Its chemical structure and hydroxy fatty acid content make it valuable for industrial applications.

During the 1950's and 1960's, about 80,000 acres of castor were grown annually on the High Plains of Texas. But domestic production decreased, and was finally abandoned altogether in 1972 when castor oil buyers and the farmer cooperative involved in crushing castor seed were unable to agree on their annual contract because of low world prices for castor oil and high local farm prices for competing crops. Since then, the United States

Castor dates back to 4,000 years ago, when the Egyptians used its oil in their lamps. In modern times, manufacturers have used it in products ranging from lipstick to jet engine lubricants.
USDA BN-13205

has imported an average of 41,200 metric tons of castor oil per year (see fig. 1).

Because of widely fluctuating world supplies and the structure of the world market, prices for castor oil vary considerably. These supply and price instabilities impose severe handicaps on users. They affect cash flow, make corporate planning difficult, and discourage investment in new products. Therefore, Union Camp Corporation and CasChem, Inc., the major U.S. buyers of castor oil, have worked with Browning Seed, Inc., scientists, and farmers to reestablish domestic castor production on the High Plains of Texas.

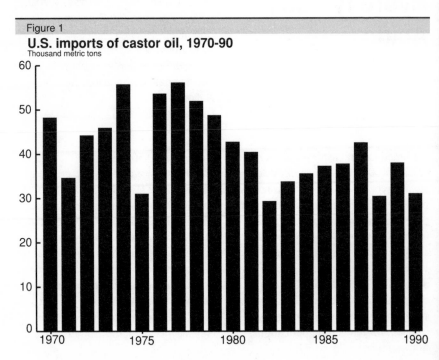

Figure 1

U.S. imports of castor oil, 1970-90
Thousand metric tons

Part III. Products From Nontraditional Crops

In contrast to castor, lesquerella has practically no history of cultivation and use. An experimental crop from the genus *Lesquerella,* it is being studied to provide U.S. manufacturers with a new domestic source of hydroxy fatty acids and U.S. farmers with a new source of income. Industry has noted the progress in crop production research and lesquerella oil's

potential as a chemical raw material. As a result, several firms have joined USDA in its developmental efforts. Small acreages are being grown in several States as part of this project.

Hydroxy Fatty Acids

Why all this interest in castor and lesquerella? It is because the primary fatty acids in castor and lesquerella oils are unsaturated hydroxy fatty acids. Because of their special chemical attributes, hydroxy fatty acids are used in a wide range of products, including high-performance lubricants, cosmetics, waxes, nylons, plastics, and coatings.

Fatty acids are the building blocks of all vegetable oils. The chain length and chemical reactivity of a fatty acid help determine its value for industrial purposes. For example, the hydroxyl group (an oxygen and a hydrogen atom) gives castor and lesquerella a fatty acids special properties, such as higher viscosity and reactivity compared with other fatty acids. Furthermore, unsaturation (one or more double bonds within the carbon chain) provides additional sites for chemical reactions to occur. Castor and lesquerella oils offer two chain lengths and two types of unsaturation for novel reactivity and strategic applications. These attributes mean more opportunities to make different products and are a prime reason for industry's interest in hydroxy fatty acids.

Crop Characteristics

Native to Africa, castor (*Ricinus communis L.*) is grown throughout the world. In temperate climates, it is an annual crop. Improved dwarf-internode varieties and hybrids developed in the United States range from 4 to 6 feet in height. Castor seeds, which contain over 50 percent oil on a dry-weight basis, are mottled brown and about the size of pinto beans. Almost 90 percent of the oil is ricinoleic acid[1]

Lesquerella is native to North America, ranging from Alaska to Alabama. The greatest concentration of species occurs in the southwestern United States and northern Mexico. Of the 23 lesquerella species scientists have studied, *Lesquerella fendleri*, a winter annual, has the best agronomic potential. Its tiny, dark-yellow seeds contain over 25 percent oil on a dry-weight basis, and about 55 percent of that is lesquerolic acid.[2]

Considerable genetic variation has been observed both within the genus and in *L. fendleri*, which appears to be highly cross-pollinated. These characteristics provide plant breeders with opportunities to improve the oil content of the seed and the amount of hydroxy fatty acids in the oil. There is also an opportunity to breed for desirable characteristics such as increased yield, erect growth, and other traits needed in a commercial oilseed crop.

Production practices for castor and lesquerella would be familiar to many farmers. Except for castor harvesting, both crops can be grown with only minor modifications to existing equipment. Special planting plates or air planters are used to handle fragile castor seeds. Planters and combines for

lesquerella should be adjusted to handle its small seed. Cultural practices for castor are similar to those for cotton, corn, and sorghum, while lesquerella can be grown in a cropping system very similar to that used for winter wheat and other small grains in the Southwest. Overall, pesticide and fertilizer use may be lower than with traditional crops. Browning Seed, Inc., has developed an improved castor harvester-huller, which will lower harvesting costs and remove a major barrier to domestic production.

Processing

Four traditional methods exist to remove oil from oilseeds: expellers (screw presses), prepress-solvent extraction, full solvent extraction, and extrusion followed by full solvent extraction. Hexane is the usual solvent. Historically, crushers have used prepress-solvent extraction for castor seed. After expellers remove most of the oil, the remainder of the oil is extracted using solvents.

All four methods can be used to extract oil from castor or lesquerella seeds. However, pilot-scale experiments indicate that extrusion followed by full solvent extraction would be the optimum procedure for noncosmetic uses. The cosmetic industry prefers expeller oils because they have not come into contact with solvents like hexane.

Extruders pressurize the seeds into a pastelike mixture. Upon release, the material rapidly expands and dries. The resulting pellets, called collets, are very porous, which allows faster solvent penetration. Increasingly,

---

[1] 12-hydroxy-9-octadecenoic acid
[2] 14-hydroxy-11-icosenoic acid

Part III. Products From Nontraditional Crops

commercial oilseed crushing plants are substituting extruders for expellers to prepare oilseeds for solvent extraction or to prepare nutritious high-energy meals for feeds.

In addition to the oil, meal is also a product of crushing oilseeds. Both lesquerella and castor meal have specific processing requirements, as do other oilseeds, because of certain components in the seed. Lesquerella seed contains glucosinolates. If the seed is not properly heat-treated, an enzyme is released during crushing that converts glucosinolates into antinutritional compounds that interfere with the animal's performance (feed consumption, weight gain, and feed efficiency). For cattle feed, the best way to maintain the quality of the meal is to inactivate the enzyme during processing, thereby preventing the breakdown of the glucosinolates. Research has demonstrated that this can be done in either cookers or extruders that prepare seed for oil extraction.

Castor seeds and meal contain a toxic protein, ricin, that can be fatal to humans if ingested, and a potent allergen, CB-1A, that can cause strong allergic reactions in sensitive people. Under a United Nations research grant, Texas A&M University perfected a system to deactivate the allergen as well as the toxin in the meal. A plant in Thailand is successfully using the process to treat 3 metric tons of castor meal per hour.

Products
Castor oil is used directly in many products such as transparent soaps, waxes and polishes, hydraulic fluids,

inks, and metal drawing oils. However, most castor oil is further processed by the chemical industry. The resulting derivatives are used in a wide range of applications. For example, hydrogenated castor fatty acids are an ingredient in lubricating greases for cars, trucks, boats, railcars, aircraft, and industrial equipment. Nylon 11, based on derivatives of ricinoleic acid, is used in engineering plastics and powder coatings. Dehydrated castor oil and its fatty acids are components of coatings, inks, and sealants. Polyurethanes made from castor oil derivatives are used in electrical and telecommunication casting resins and coatings.

Chemists have conducted only minimal research on the uses of lesquerella oil. However, those tests, along with the known properties of fatty acids, indicate that it should be a good raw material for manufacturing industrial products. Ricinoleic acid (from castor) and lesquerolic acid have similar chemical structures. This means that both common and different products may be derived from the two hydroxy acids. Where higher molecular weights are important for the chemical properties of the products, lesquerolic acid could be superior.

Besides lesquerolic acid, *L. fendleri* oil contains oleic[3], linoleic[4], and linolenic[5] acids, common fatty acids used for animal feeds and industrial raw materials. Researchers, processors, and manufacturers are faced with the

---

[3] 9-octadecenoic acid

[4] 9, 12-octadecadienoic acid

[5] 9, 12, 15-octadecatrienoic acid

challenge of finding uses that utilize the entire oil or ways to economically separate lesquerolic acid from these other fatty acids.

Treated castor meal and lesquerella meal could be used as protein supplements in livestock rations, primarily for beef cattle. During the 1960's and 1970's, when castor was grown and processed in Texas, detoxified castor meal was fed to cattle in the State. Initial feeding trials with lesquerella meal are currently under way, and preliminary results are encouraging. Meal entering interstate commerce would require approval by the Food and Drug Administration as a feed ingredient.

Future Prospects

The development of a domestic source of hydroxy fatty acids is dependent upon the advancement of castor and/or lesquerella production in the United States. Complementary opportunities exist to reestablish U.S. castor production and develop lesquerella as a new oilseed crop. Continued cooperation among industry, academia, and government—including public-private research programs and demonstration projects—is the most efficient and reliable way to make these opportunities a reality.

The immediate hurdle facing castor is the lack of a crushing facility. In 1991, plans to produce 10,000 metric tons of castor seed in the Texas High Plains stalled when negotiations for crushing the crop failed. Another problem is the perception of some processors in the area that buying food-grade corn from farmers growing castor means possible contamination of the corn with castor seed. Browning Seed, Inc., continues to search for a suitable facility, while farmers and castor-oil buyers stand ready to sign production and purchasing contracts.

Because lesquerella is an experimental crop, much work still needs to be done in its crop and product development. For example, additional germplasm collection and plant breeding may increase seed yields, the percentage of oil in the seed, and the hydroxy fatty acid content of the oil. Further refinement of cultural practices, such as planting methods, weed control, and fertilizer and water use, is needed before lesquerella can be grown on a large scale. With expanded product research, lesquerella oil may create its own markets, distinct and separate from those for castor oil, because of its own special characteristics. ❑

The cosmetics industry would be a high-priced, low-volume market to introduce a commercially viable use for lesquerella oil.

Jack Dykinga/USDA 92BW0576-30

Anson Thompson, an ARS plant geneticist, examines lesquerella at the University of Arizona experimental farm near Phoenix. Because lesquerella is an experimental crop, much work still needs to be done in its development. Further refinements in planting methods, weed control, fertilizer use, and water use are needed before lesquerella can be grown on a large scale.
Jack Dykinga/USDA 92BW0576-14.

Milkweed: The Worth of a Weed

18

by Herbert D. Knudsen, President, Natural Fibers Corp., Ogallala, NE, and Renee Y. Sayler, Associate Director of Industry Development, University of Nebraska, Lincoln

Historically, milkweed has been a weed that farmers tried to kill. Yet now, serious efforts are under way to cultivate it—and even to develop a milkweed industry.

In truth, the use of milkweed is nothing new. American Indians knew the value of floss; they used it as a soft, warm lining for their children's cradles. In 1635, the French produced silklike fabrics from milkweed fibers. Milkweed "went to war" when World War II interrupted the supply of imported kapok from Asia, and Americans picked milkweed pods so its floss could be used in U.S. Navy life jackets. Each of these uses of milkweed relied on harvesting by hand from the wild. This chapter is a case study of a current venture which seeks to grow milkweed as a cultivated crop, thereby providing a stable source of floss for commercialization.

Background

In the late 1970's, Nobel Laureate

For years, milkweed was considered a weed and farmers tried to kill it. Efforts are now under way to cultivate milkweed and develop a milkweed industry. The current venture seeks to grow milkweed as a crop, thereby providing a stable source of floss for commercial products.
USDA 92BW0811

Melvin Calvin and others were promoting the idea that billions of barrels of synthetic crude oil could be recovered from plant biomass. Standard Oil of Ohio began a milkweed research program, working with Native Plants, Inc., to produce a synthetic crude oil from milkweed biomass. Milkweed was grown, cut, dried, and baled much like hay. Analysis of that research concluded that the cost of producing the synthetic crude oil was too high and the yield of oil too low to be economically feasible.

During the course of that research project, Herbert D. Knudsen, Manager of Corporate Ventures for Standard Oil, was looking at alternative uses of milkweed. He made contact with William G. Wilson of Kimberly-Clark in Neenah, WI. Kimberly-Clark was

Milkweed

Milkweed is changing, from a worthless weed to a comfortable crop.

interested in the potential of milkweed floss for use in its disposable absorbency products. With Standard Oil's 5 years of experience growing milkweed in research plots for the synthetic crude oil project, the fit of interests seemed good. Arrangements were made for Kimberly-Clark to proceed with product development research and Standard Oil to grow milkweed.

When British Petroleum acquired Standard Oil of Ohio, they eliminated diversification efforts, so Knudsen decided to acquire the milkweed venture himself. In 1987, Natural Fibers Corp. was founded with the dream of creating a new agricultural industry, comparable in size to the cotton industry, based on milkweed.

Analyzing the Opportunity

Product development for milkweed floss has been a cooperative effort between Natural Fibers Corp., the University of Nebraska, the Southern Regional Research Center of USDA's Agricultural Research Service, and various private corporations. Based on their experience, 10 pounds of dried milkweed pods can be used to produce 2 pounds of floss, 3 pounds of seed, and 5 pounds of pod biomass. Prototype development using these components has shown that it is possible to make a number of products with milkweed floss, which can be:
- Combined with down and used as loose-fill in comforters, pillows, and clothing,
- Used to form a batt or filling for quilts, jackets, and disposable absorbency items, and

- Blended with cotton and woven to make a linenlike cloth.

In addition to the products developed from floss, milkweed biomass and the oil from the seeds have been evaluated for potential uses. Paper has been made from the bast fiber; pet litter and fireplace logs have been made from the pod biomass. The seed oil has been analyzed to determine its lubricating properties and its potential for use in cosmetics. There are undoubtedly other possible uses for milkweed. The challenge is to determine which ones are economically viable at given levels of milkweed production and cost.

To move ahead, market opportunities for milkweed were assessed in terms of volumes, prices and resources. The resources of Standard Oil were substantially greater than those of an entrepreneur, even with the cooperation and special grants funding of the University of Nebraska and USDA's Cooperative State Research Service (CSRS). While the nonwovens market was a realistic target, considering the resources of Standard Oil, it was not realistic as a startup venture for an entrepreneur. The $2 billion nonwovens market requires a minimum of 500,000 pounds of floss at less than $9 per pound. Financial projections determined that penetrating the nonwovens market would require at least $6 million of investment by Natural Fibers Corp., so it was not viewed as a viable short-term target. Instead, the goal was to find a high-value, low-volume market for the initial entry.

Market Niche

Milkweed floss has properties similar to those of goose down. In the United States, the size of the waterfowl down market is about 10 million pounds with a price range of $10 to $30 per pound. A number of loose-filled products can be made: comforters, pillows, sleeping bags, and jackets.

Knudsen's approach to product development and testing is to "put the product in the customers' hands and tell them the price. Then keep lowering the price until you cannot get the product back." With an idea of the potential retail value, one can then look at the economics of costs and revenue for the grower, the processor, the manufacturer, and the distribution system. Next, ask if you can make a profit at the price the customer is willing to pay. If the answer is "yes," you proceed to make the process as efficient as possible, from grower to consumer. For blended, loose-fill milkweed floss, the products that held the greatest potential were comforters and pillows. Thus, Natural Fibers Corp. chose these to launch their line of Ogallala Down products.

Growing Milkweed

After years of trying to kill milkweed, it now seemed that growing it was nearly as difficult. First, farmers willing to grow milkweed had to be found. Richard D. Zeller, an agribusiness professional, was hired to coordinate production activities. Robert L. Raun, former director of agriculture in Nebraska, is growing milkweed in Minden, NE. Ralph Holzfaster and Edward Perlinger, farmers from the

Ogallala, NE, area, also have fields of milkweed. In addition, a number of researchers from the University of Nebraska and one from Kansas State University have been actively involved in addressing the obstacles to growing milkweed.

Milkweed grows in the same basic regions as corn and is planted and cared for with traditional row crop equipment. A deep-rooted perennial, milkweed produces beautiful flowers that provide habitat for Monarch butterflies in mid- to late summer as they migrate south for the winter. Pods containing floss and seed are formed in the second year after planting.

The major production problems faced by milkweed farmers have been diseases, weeds, and hail. The diseases causing the most damage are a black spot fungus and a bacterial blight. University of Nebraska plant pathologist Anne Vidaver leads the efforts to control the bacterial blight, and Michael Boosalis, also a plant pathologist at the University of Nebraska, is attempting to find ways to minimize black spot. Chemical controls have not been successful; thus, variety selection may be the best recourse.

As a step in this direction, Zeller and Paul D. Nordquist have established a germplasm nursery in Ogallala. Seed from vibrant wild plants is being evaluated for yield, resistance to disease, and cultural needs such as water and fertility requirements. Test plots have been established at an experiment station in Garden City, KS. Other test plots exist at Nebraska sites near Beatrice and Scottsbluff. Average test-plot yields

for the past 5 years from all varieties and hybrids have been about 252 pounds of floss per acre.

In spite of disease and hail, Natural Fibers Corp. was able to produce 1,000 pounds of floss in 1990 and 1,500 pounds in 1991 from production fields and supplemental wild collections. While this is far short of the 500,000 pounds of floss needed to penetrate the nonwovens market, it is enough to encourage those involved to continue the effort.

Harvesting and Processing

Green milkweed pods are harvested with a modified New Idea Uni-System ear corn picker, at about 70 percent moisture, before they open to release the floss and seeds. The pods are cracked open in a roller mill and dried to about 30 percent moisture in portable tanks on the farm. The partially dried pods are transported to the Ogallala processing plant and dried to 10 percent moisture. At this moisture level, they can be safely stored and processed. The harvester was designed by Kenneth Von Bargen and the drying system was designed by David D. Jones, both of the Biological Systems Engineering Department at the University of Nebraska.

Once the pods are dried, they are pneumatically conveyed from the drying bins to the floss processing line. The processing line consists of a modified 1940 model combine, a cleaning apparatus, and a hopper. Floss is vacuum-bagged from the hopper. Milkweed floss and goose down are air-blended to produce Ogallala Down, which is manufactured into comforters or pillows using standard loose-fill processing equipment.

Commercialization

Penetrating a well-established market with a new product is not an easy task. Understanding the properties of your product, as well as the perceived needs of the end user and of the distributors with whom you will work, is essential. As milkweed floss was assessed, the following features were found to be important factors for the down market:

- A nonallergenic cellulose fiber,
- Fill-power comparable to high-quality goose down,
- White color,
- More durable than down, and
- 20 percent warmer per unit of weight than down.

In addition, as milkweed floss absorbs moisture, it continues to allow more air to move through the fibers compared to down, making it more "breathable."

End-user acceptance and promotional support were important to distributors. Promotion is a paramount concern for most startup ventures because the image created is important not only in selling the product but also in attracting investors and farmers. Natural Fibers Corp. based its 1989 promotions both on the Ogallala Sioux legend of an Indian maiden named Flame and on the Monarch butterflies. The result was sales of $20,000.

Touting comforters with milkweed floss did not create sufficient consumer demand. An attractive product name was needed. Hence, "Ogallala Down" was adopted to describe a blend of 60 percent milkweed floss and 40 percent goose down, and the slogan "Nothing Warms You Up Like Ogallala Down" was coined. Attractive, high-quality brochures, labels, and product inserts were developed. Many customers have a special interest in environmental issues. To address such issues it was pointed out that milkweed floss is a vegetable fiber produced in low-input agriculture and that use of the comforters allows the user to turn down the thermostat in the winter to save energy. (University of Nebraska and Kansas State University researchers determined that milkweed floss possesses 25 percent more insulating power than goose down.)

Selecting and recruiting wholesale distributors was also a key issue. Early sales were the result of word-of-mouth and direct marketing campaigns. To penetrate the wholesale distribution channel, it was important to convince wholesale customers to risk carrying this "new" product. Therefore, a strategy of demonstrated acceptance of Ogallala Down products by retail customers was needed. It was also important to find a wholesaler whose volume requirements fell within available floss resources. Using both direct marketing and wholesale distribution, Natural Fibers Corp. achieved a fivefold increase in sales in 1990, with nearly two-thirds of the sales in the wholesale trade.

Conclusion

In spite of the myriad obstacles, tangible, useful results have been achieved with milkweed. Many challenges remain to be conquered, but our current successes lay a strong foundation for future development of this new crop. The cooperative effort including USDA-CSRS funding resources, university research capabilities, and the entrepreneurial spirit is a model for new crop development.

How many other weeds are potentially valuable crops for use as industrial raw materials? Fewer than 300 of the estimated 300,000 plant species are used in organized agriculture; the possibilities for new discoveries, knowledge, and uses seem extraordinary. ❑

Touting comforters with milkweed floss did not create sufficient consumer demand. An attractive product name was needed. "Ogallala Down" was adopted to describe a blend of 60% milkweed floss and 40% goose down, and the slogan "Nothing Warms You Up Like Ogallala Down" was coined.
USDA 92BW0812

Peter Knudsen, director of plant operations for Natural Fibers Corp., is wearing a jacket lined with milkweed floss. Items currently on the market include pillows and comforters. Prototype products include the jacket, thread, and cloth.
USDA 92BW0813

Nature's Abundant Variety: New Oilseed Crops on the Horizon

19

by Kenneth D. Carlson, Research Chemist, National Center for Agricultural Utilization Research, ARS, USDA, Peoria, IL; Steven A. Knapp, Associate Professor, Department of Crop and Soil Science, Oregon State University, Corvallis, OR; Anson E. Thompson, Research Geneticist, Water Conservation Laboratory, ARS, USDA, Phoenix, AZ; James H. Brown, President, Jojoba Growers & Processors, Inc., Apache Junction, AZ; and Gary D. Jolliff, Professor, Department of Crop and Soil Science, Oregon State University, Corvallis, OR

"Amazing" is the word for the variety and quantity of chemicals called fatty acids that are stored by plants in their seed oils. But "difficult" is the word for the task of taking these novel oil-bearing plants to commercialization. The development of a wild species into a crop may take 10-20 years of intense, broadly based research.

The four species described here have potentially bright futures as domestically produced agricultural commodities. We predict that, together, they will have a significant impact on American agriculture in the 21st century.

Cuphea

Oleochemical producers are actively participating in research on *Cuphea* (pronounced coo´-fee-a), a genus of the family Lythraceae with about 260 species native to the Americas. Cuphea's industrial promise lies in its unique genetic ability to produce large quantities of specific short-chain saturated fatty acids (with chain lengths of 8, 10, or 12 carbons vs. 16 or 18 in most common fats and oils). These fatty acids, combined with glycerol, are stored as triglyceride oils in the seeds.

Carbon chains are like a string of pearls, with each pearl representing a single carbon atom along the chain. Common medium-chain-length saturated fatty acids in cuphea are caprylic, capric, lauric, and myristic acids, akin to necklaces with 8, 10, 12, and 14 pearls, respectively.

Currently, coconut and palm-kernel oils are the only commercial plant sources of these types of fatty acids, primarily as 12-carbon lauric acid.

Cuphea's industrial promise lies in its unique ability to synthesize large quantities of specific saturated fatty acids. Outlets for this oil include plasticizers for plastics, and synthetic lubricants.

USDA/0985X1007-33A

The United States imports more than a billion pounds of coconut oil per year and uses more than 500 million pounds of lauric acid annually, mostly for the manufacture of soaps and detergents. Because a like amount of lauric-type raw material is supplied by petroleum, cuphea industry representatives believe that demand is assured. The high capric acid (10 carbons) content of some species of cuphea suggests other outlets for this oil in plasticizers (softening and flexibilizing agents for plastics) and in synthetic lubricants. Historically, petroleum has been the source of these materials. In addition, there may be food and medicinal uses for cuphea oils.

Industry spokespersons also point to the economic and political advantages of having a stable, domestic source of medium-chain fatty acids. Coconut oil production is centered in the Philippines, Malaysia, and Indonesia, where weather, increasing domestic consumption, aging plantations, and political instability may affect the availability and pricing of coconut oil in the United States. Scientists project that 5 to 7 million acres of cuphea would meet the worldwide demand for these types of oils.

Domesticating Cuphea. Rapid progress is being made toward domesticating cuphea and eliminating its wild traits. These traits relate to seed dormancy (failure to germinate), seed shatter (preharvest seed loss from the plant), and indeterminate growth (continuous and prolonged flowering, resulting in uneven maturity of seeds).

Just recently, the basis for eliminating seed shatter was discovered by Oregon State University scientists in a population of plants resulting from crosses between two cuphea species. With these good seed-retentive cultivars in hand, indeterminate growth is of less concern.

Scientists at Oregon State University also believe that they have eliminated seed dormancy as a constraint on production. This germplasm is also autofertile, eliminating the need for pollinators. Thus, it appears that the most important biological barriers to commercial production of cuphea are well on their way to being eliminated.

Scientists are optimistic that these genetic advances will bring cuphea to the commercial test stage in the next few years through the cooperative efforts of academia, the private sector, and USDA's Agricultural Research Service (ARS). While the genetic and agronomic research continues, the work on extracting the seed oil from the seed, studying the feed value of the defatted meal, and evaluating the chemical and nutritional uses of the oil must also move forward toward commercialization.

Vernonia

Every year, substantial quantities of petroleum-derived chemicals are converted to materials called "epoxies" or epoxy chemicals, which are used in high-technology applications. A familiar use is in two-tube adhesives, where the epoxy chemical in the first tube is mixed with a chemical in the second tube and the two rapidly react to form a very strong bond. Other uses for these epoxies are in the manufacture of plastics, paints, and coatings, and in embedding materials in the electronics industry.

Although soybean and linseed oils can be chemically converted into epoxidized oils, *naturally occurring* epoxy fatty acids have been found in a limited number of plant species worldwide. One of these, vernonia (*Vernonia galamensis,* family Asteraceae), grows over a wide area of tropical and subtropical Africa. Its seeds have high quantities of a novel oil containing a unique epoxy fatty acid called vernolic acid. Two other species with seed oils containing epoxy acids are Stokes' aster (*Stokesia laevis*), a biennial native to the Southeastern United States, and euphorbia

Former ARS botanist Dr. Robert Perdue (left) and agronomist/chemist T. Nyati examine a field of vernonia in Chiredzi, Zimbabwe. Dr. Perdue is vernonia's champion, having pioneered its development for the past 10 years.
USDA/92BW0814

(*Euphorbia lagascae*), a native of Spain. Stokes' aster has received attention in the United States as an oilseed and a horticultural specimen. Euphorbia is being researched in Europe as a source of epoxy oil for industry, but it has problems of severe seed shatter and a milky, irritating sap.

Why Vernonia? ARS scientists are determining the feasibility of making vernonia a new industrial crop. Vernonia oil is not seen as a substitute or replacement for the traditional industrial applications of epoxidized soybean or linseed oils, from which it is chemically distinct. One important physical difference that can be exploited is vernonia oil's relatively low viscosity and its pourability, even below 32 °F, compared with epoxidized soybean and linseed oils.

An exciting possible new use for vernonia oil is in reformulating oil-based or alkyd-resin paints. About 325 million gallons of this type of paint are produced annually in the United States. Organic solvents (diluents) evaporate from these paints during their manufacture and use and react with other chemicals in the air, contributing to the smog that plagues many urban areas and industrial sites. It is estimated, for instance, that 22 tons per day of volatile organic compounds are released into the air from paints and varnishes in California's Los Angeles Basin alone. The Clean Air Act amendments of 1990 will require the reduction of this kind of air pollution.

Vernonia oil can replace substantial quantities of these volatile solvents and function as a "reactive diluent" in these products. Since vernonia oil functions both as a solvent and a reactant in the paint formulation, it becomes an integral part of the dry paint surface and does not evaporate to pollute the air. One pound of vernonia oil in each gallon of paint would reduce volatiles by as much as 160 million pounds per year across the Nation. Such usage alone would require at least 365,000 acres of vernonia production.

Other uses for vernonia oil may include the manufacture of new types of tough, rubbery plastics called interpenetrating polymer networks. Vernonia oil also is known to form clear, tough, yet flexible baked coatings on metals. Other new products are expected to be developed when vernonia oil becomes readily available.

Vernonia's Characteristics. There is no U.S. commercial production of vernonia, but limited acreages are being grown in tropical Africa and Central America. Many companies have received samples of the seed or oil to evaluate.

Until 1990, varieties of vernonia that would flower and produce mature seed within the United States were merely botanical curiosities. Most vernonia varieties require daylight exposures of about 12 hours to initiate flowering. In most of the United States, these plants grow during the spring, summer, and early fall months, but do not flower. Since these plants are from the Tropics, they are easily killed by even light frosts.

ARS scientists are evaluating an array of vernonia varieties collected from the wild in various parts of Africa. They have found one, given the name petitiana, that flowers readily under the long-day growing conditions in the United States. They also found that, except for flowering, petitiana and other varieties of vernonia grow well in many areas of the United States. But petitiana lacks several important agronomic characteristics needed for successful growth in a farmer's field. Plants mature unevenly, which makes mechanical harvesting difficult. Also, maturing seeds resemble dandelion seeds and are easily lost to the wind.

Scientists are now busy crossing petitiana material with other types of vernonia to combine as many desirable characteristics as possible into one new variety. These new materials are being distributed for the first time in 1992 to cooperating Federal, State, and private-sector scientists for evaluation and selection under a wide array of climatic and geographic conditions. These scientists are optimistic that new adapted varieties will be selected and tested for broad adaptation in the United States within the next 6 to 10 years.

Vernonia seed has been processed by traditional prepress solvent extraction without significant problems. Newer techniques of extrusion processing and solvent extraction are expected to work equally well for recovering oil from vernonia seed. However, further research is needed on preparing the seed for oil extraction and also on using the remaining defatted meal. This research should proceed simultaneously with the breeding, agronomic, and product development studies to move vernonia smoothly toward commercialization.

Jojoba

Jojoba (pronounced ho-hó-ba) is another example of the importance of crop champions and stubborn determination to move a wild plant to crop status. The jojoba industry was started in 1971 when Native American communities in California and Arizona, in collaboration with scientists at the Universities of California and Arizona and with support from the Federal Government, collected and processed jojoba seed from wild jojoba plants. The research investment at the time was small, but it was enough to convince a few entrepreneurs of the potential of jojoba oil for use in industrial materials.

Many investors joined the "jojoba rush" to the Southwest after the sperm whale was placed on the endangered species list, the importation of sperm whale oil was banned, and scientific evidence pointed to jojoba oil as its potential replacement in many applications. At one time, as many as 40,000 acres of jojoba were under cultivation, most planted with wild, unimproved germplasm. In the ensuing years, only a few producers of jojoba have survived. They are working to improve jojoba's germplasm, plantation management, and production practices and to develop additional markets for the oil. The existing jojoba industry has relied extensively on continuing private-sector investments.

Jojoba (*Simmondsia chinensis*) is a slow-growing perennial native to the Sonoran Desert of Arizona, California, and Mexico. Commercial seed harvest usually begins when the plants are 4 to 5 years old. Unlike other seed oils composed of triglycerides, jojoba oil is composed of liquid wax esters. These are chemicals that result from the union of long-chain alcohols and long-chain fatty acids, each having predominantly 20 or 22 carbon atoms in their chains. Oil is recovered primarily by cold pressing, and additional oil can be recovered from the press cake by solvent extraction. Although the residual jojoba meal cannot be used in feeds unless its antinutritional compounds are removed or destroyed, ARS scientists have researched a fermentation process that does this, and such meal appears to be acceptable to cattle. Its use in cattle feed, however, will require approval by the responsible State or Federal regulatory agencies.

Jojoba Production. The private sector is reported to have invested over $200 million in jojoba plantations over the past 12 years and to have established about 15 million jojoba shrubs that will produce for many years. Jojoba has been commercially harvested in the United States since 1982. Active commercial plantations also exist in South America, Mexico, and Israel, and additional plantations are being established in India, Australia, South Africa, and the Middle East. In 1990, five major U.S. processors crushed 3.5 million pounds of seed from nearly 16,000 acres of actively managed U.S. jojoba plantations. Producers received an average of $3.35 per pound for the seed, which contains about 50 percent oil. Jojoba oil prices were $56-$70 per gallon in large quantities. Over the past 15 years, jojoba has grown to be an $11 million industry at the farm gate, and about $14 million out the processor's door, with at least 70 percent of these revenues derived from export trade.

Jojoba Markets. The cosmetics industry uses more than 90 percent of the jojoba oil produced and will likely continue as the major industrial consumer over the next decade. According to Jojoba Growers and Processors, Inc., this trend of increased consumption is partly due to the industry's removal of products of animal origin and their replacement by materials of botanical origin. The specialty lubricants market would consume more jojoba oil if its cost were lower. Chemically, jojoba oil is closely related to sperm whale oil, which formerly provided high-performance, high-temperature, and extreme-pressure lubricating properties to automatic transmission fluids. The use of natural, biodegradable oils for lubricants and other applications may increase as this industry also moves

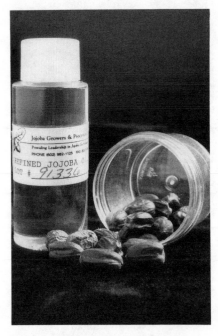

The cosmetics industry consumes more than 90 percent of the jojoba oil produced, and will likely continue as the major industrial consumer over the next decade.
Ken Hammond/USDA 92BW0810-9A

Part III. Products From Nontraditional Crops

toward environmentally friendly products.

Jojoba's Future. Once established, jojoba has deep roots and requires only about 2 acre-feet of water per year. As an alternative crop, it can help to relieve pressure on water resources in arid and semiarid regions of the world. But additional jojoba research and development are needed to develop ways of effectively and profitably using the residual meal after oil extraction and to develop new derivatives, chemicals, and products from jojoba oil to increase its markets. Agronomic and genetic research are also required to improve production yields. A strong Jojoba Grower's Association has served the industry for a decade by helping to establish industry standards for quality control of oil and seed, pesticide registration, irrigation and fertilizer research, plantation management practices, harvesting technology, and germplasm development.

Meadowfoam

Meadowfoam is the common name for species of the genus *Limnanthes* in the small North American family Limnanthaceae, which means marshflower. Meadowfoam is a herbaceous winter-spring annual wildflower native to northern California, southern Oregon, and Vancouver Island, British Columbia. One species, *L. douglasii*, was carried to England in about 1833 and later distributed widely as an ornamental in northwestern Europe and throughout North America. This suggests high adaptability for cultivation.

Meadowfoam seeds contain 25-35 percent oil. The oil is novel because over 95 percent of its fatty acids have extralong (20- and 22-carbon) chain lengths. These fatty acids are unique in having very high levels of monounsaturation (a single site of reactivity) at the number 5 and 6 carbon atoms and very little polyunsaturation. These characteristics make meadowfoam oil especially stable, even when heated or exposed to air.

The name meadowfoam derives from the appearance of a field of *Limnanthes* in full bloom, a beautiful canopy of creamy white flowers. Marvin Ringsdorf, a meadowfoam grower, tells of flying at dusk and momentarily mistaking a distant field of meadowfoam for the lighted end of an airport runway, because of the field's brilliant white appearance from the air!

Production and Markets. Meadowfoam has been grown commercially on only a small scale (less than 300 tons of seed), in the Willamette Valley of Oregon, but this production provided valuable experience in cultivation, harvesting, processing of the seed, and refining and marketing of the oil. Most of the oil was exported to Japan for use in cosmetics, personal-care items, and other high-value-added products.

Several other types of products are under investigation, including dimer acids (similar to commercial products used in coatings and adhesives) and estolides (chemicals resulting from the union of two different types of fatty acids). Potential applications for these

Meadowfoam seeds contain 25-35 percent oil. The fatty acids in meadowfoam oil have very high levels of monounsaturation and very little polyunsaturation. These characteristics make meadowfoam oil especially stable when exposed to air and heat, and one of the most stable vegetable oils known.
USDA/92BW0814

novel products are being explored with the private sector. Liquid wax esters, similar to those occurring naturally in jojoba and sperm whale oils, were synthesized and performed well in lubricant tests. Overall, meadowfoam oil still seeks a large market.

As with any new oilseed crop, the produce-the-oil-first versus develop-the-market-first dilemma is exacerbated by meadowfoam oil's relatively high cost. This cost results at least partly from inefficient seed production, but more broadly from an immature framework of production (breeding, agronomy, crop management, harvesting), processing (oil extraction and meal use), and market-

ing (oil use and product development). Since the first commercial sale in 1984, the price of meadowfoam oil has been reduced by 50 percent. Recent research results suggest that further reductions in oil cost are on the horizon.

Meadowfoam's Future. Lower production costs and higher oil yields are needed to lower the price of the oil. The Oregon Meadowfoam Growers Association and scientists at Oregon State University and ARS's National Center for Agricultural Utilization Research in Peoria, IL, are cooperating on breeding new cultivars, finding effective agronomic and cultural practices, and developing new

Part III. Products From Nontraditional Crops

products. Plant breeders at Oregon State University have developed a new, more productive cultivar that yields at least one-third more oil, and cross-pollinated experimental genetic lines have yielded more than 800 pounds of oil per acre.

In another approach, the Oregon scientists are researching the development of self-pollinating cultivars, which could revolutionize meadowfoam production if high oil yields can be obtained. This approach, if successful, could lead to the elimination of extra production and management costs associated with the current need for honeybee pollination of meadowfoam in commercial fields. Scientists agree that important biological barriers to the economical production of meadowfoam oil are being conquered, and that these advances are reducing the risks of commercialization. A competitively priced meadowfoam oil could create additional market interest and spur product development by the private sector.

The Evolution of New Crops

Forty years ago, the drive to diversify American agriculture and to develop new crops from wild species began at USDA's National Center for Agricultural Utilization Research (then the Northern Regional Research Center-ARS) with a chemical screening program on seeds from around the world. Today, the fruits of this investment are being used by many scientists worldwide. The four species discussed here, and those presented in other chapters, are but a few of the species identified in the original research that are currently wending their way to the marketplace. Dedicated scientists have persisted, and thereby ensured that 21st-century agriculture will have new crops.

Recognizing the potential regional and national impact of alternative crops, Congress authorized Alternative Agricultural Research and Commercialization (AARC) Centers in the 1990 farm bill. The goal of the AARC legislation is to foster the commercialization of new nonfood and nonfeed industrial products from American agriculture. It aims to develop an institutional mechanism that can foster technology transfer and thus help overcome barriers to commercialization. ❏

Plants and Plant Products as Sources of Pharmaceuticals

20

by James D. McChesney, Director, Research Institute of Pharmaceutical Sciences, University of Mississippi, University, MS; M.A. Wallig, Assistant Professor, Department of Veterinary Pathobiology, College of Veterinary Medicine, University of Illinois at Urbana-Champaign, Urbana, IL; and Gordon Cragg, Chief, Natural Products Branch, Division of Cancer Treatment, National Cancer Institute, Frederick, MD

Human survival has always depended on plants. Early humans relied heavily on plants for food, medicine, and much of their clothing and shelter. The botanical skills of these early people should not be underestimated; all of the world's major crops were already domesticated in prehistoric times. The Age of Discovery was fostered by Europeans' explorations to find more economical trade routes to the East to bring back plant-derived spices and other products. Indeed, the first permanent contacts between Europe and the Americas 500 years ago was a direct consequence of that effort.

Aside from their value as sources of food, drugs, or industrial raw materials, plants are also important to humankind in many other ways. One can hardly imagine modern society without soaps and toiletries, perfumes, condiments and spices, and similar materials, all of plant origin, which enhance our standard of living. The roles of forests and other types of natural vegetation in controlling floods and erosion, in removing carbon dioxide from the atmosphere, and in providing recreational facilities are of immeasurable worth.

An adequate food supply is, and always has been, one of humanity's most pressing needs. Paralleling our need for food is our need for treatments for ailments. The practice of medicine today is very different from that of earlier times. This is largely because modern doctors have available a wide array of medicines with specific curative effects.

However, we still lack specific curative agents for a number of important diseases. Some 800 million to 1 billion people, nearly one-fifth of the world's population, suffer from tropical diseases: malaria, schistosomiasis, leprosy, leishmaniasis, etc. In the United States, heart disease, cancer, viral diseases (for example, AIDS), antibiotic-resistant infections, and many other ailments still lack adequate treatment.

Progress toward cures of the serious diseases that still afflict humankind depends upon discovery of new chemotherapeutic agents (drugs) which can effectively treat them. The search for new drugs has traditionally involved evaluating preparations of organisms (particularly higher plants) to look for appropriate biological activity. This is followed by the purification and characterization of the substance(s) responsible for the desired activity.

Effect of Discovering Quinine

This approach to drug discovery became commonplace after the 1820 discovery of quinine as the active ingredient in the antimalarial *Cinchona* bark. With the discovery and utilization of quinine as a pure chemical entity (drug), the course of modern drug discovery was irreversibly altered. An analysis of the historical development of the 20 most important pharmaceuticals utilized in the United States in 1988 reveals that in each case plants contributed an essential role, supplying either the actual medicines, leads for the medicinal chemists who developed the drugs, or precursors for preparation of the final medicines.

Efforts to develop new, clinically effective pharmaceutical agents have relied primarily on one of five approaches: (1) derivatization of existing agents, (2) synthesis of compounds similar to existing agents, (3) combination therapy of existing agents with other drugs, (4) improvements of delivery of existing agents to the target site, or (5) discovery of new prototype pharmaceutical agents.

While approaches 1-4 are important and need to be continued, there is an urgent need for the development of totally new prototype agents that do not possess the same toxicities, cross resistance, or mechanism of action as existing agents. Natural products have, in the past, provided a rich source of such compounds. It is essential that the search for new drugs continue to pursue this route. The major advantage of this approach is the likelihood of identifying new prototype drugs with quite different chemical structures and mechanisms of action and, hence, lower likelihood of similar toxicities and cross-resistance. Clearly, the higher plants represent a bountiful source of new prototypic bioactive agents that must be examined.

Bioassay Is Fundamental

The fundamental element of a drug discovery program is the bioassay(s) to detect the desired biological activity. The bioassay procedure selected for searching for new prototype drugs must meet a variety of criteria. In addition to ease of operation and low-to-moderate cost, the assay must show specificity and sensitivity to minute amounts of the agent being sought. Another important requirement of the assay is its ability to serve as a guide to selecting the agents showing activity for further purification. This is especially important in the screening of substances from natural sources, since these materials are likely to be in very low concentration in very complex mixtures. Only a combination of procedures meets these demanding criteria to serve as primary screens for biological activity.

Other important program elements must be coupled to the appropriate bioassay. The probability of selection and procurement of novel sources of potential preparations must be demonstrated. Also, it must be possible to adequately purify the active materials and to determine their structure. Initially detected activity must be confirmed in subsequent trials that help define the potential clinical utility of the substance. Finally, a "portfolio" of information about the substance must be accumulated in order to make a judgement about its potential for successful development into a clinically useful agent. For example, something must be known about such factors as its general toxicity, pharmacokinetics (how drugs are absorbed and eliminated from the body), mechanism of action, and analog development (which improves the clinical usefulness of the newly discovered chemical agent).

There are continuing efforts to discover and develop cancer chemotherapeutic agents from plants. Recent results show that certain chemicals found in select plants hold exciting promise for preventing or lowering the incidence of cancer. This is a specific example of how plant-derived chemicals will continue to contribute to the well being of humankind.

Discovery and Development of New Chemotherapeutic Agents

Plants have a long history of use in the treatment of cancer, though the majority of claims made for the efficacy of such treatment must be viewed with skepticism. Cancer is likely to be poorly defined in terms of folklore and traditional medicine, making it difficult to prove a specific treatment was effective. However, the National Cancer Institute (NCI) of the U.S. Public Health Service has recognized the value of plants as sources of potential anticancer agents. In 1960, NCI initiated a systematic effort to collect and screen plants for anticancer properties in collaboration with USDA. Between 1960 and 1982, some 35,000 plants were collected by USDA in over 60 countries and screened by NCI against a range of animal tumor systems.

A large number of chemical classes of plant products have shown activity in the animal tumor screens. Several plant-derived agents are now either in regular clinical use for the treatment of cancer victims or undergoing clinical evaluation. The best known of these agents are the so-called Vinca alkaloids, vinblastine and vincristine, isolated from the Madagascar periwinkle, *Catharanthus roseus*. These drugs first became available in the 1960's, and are now used extensively, generally in combination with other agents, in the treatment of a wide variety of different cancer types.

With their use, long-term, disease-free survivals have been observed in the treatment of various lymphomas and leukemias, bladder cancer, and testicular cancer, and significant palliative benefits have been seen in patients with breast cancer, melanoma, and small-cell lung cancer. However, despite years of intensive research aimed at the viable synthesis of these agents, the cultivated plant is still the major source. Until recently, the pharmaceutical company Eli Lilly was their major producer, using plants mass-cultivated for this purpose in Texas. With the expiration of Lilly's patents on these agents, cultivation and production ventures have been initiated in other countries.

Two other agents in clinical use are etoposide and teniposide, semisynthetic derivatives of podophyllotoxin, a lignan isolated from the Mayapple, *Podophyllum peltatum*, or from *Podophyllum emodii*. These agents show clinical activity against small-cell lung and testicular cancers, as well as lymphomas and leukemias. The starting materials for semisynthesis of these agents are isolated mainly from the Asian species *Podophyllum emodii*, which grows in the wild. However, supplies of this plant are reported to be dwindling, and it is possible that cultivation will be necessary to meet the demand for these agents.

The Promise of Taxol

The most recent addition to the cancer chemotherapy armamentarium is taxol. Taxol currently is isolated from the bark of the slow-growing Pacific yew, *Taxus brevifolia*. Significant clinical activity has been observed against refractory ovarian cancer, and substantial activity has been reported recently in the treatment of breast cancer. The supply of taxol needed to treat people with these two cancers in the United States alone is at least 100 kilograms per year. If preliminary activity observed against other serious cancers, such as lung cancer, is confirmed, the demand could exceed 300-400 kg. per year. It is clear that the bark of the Pacific yew will never meet these escalating demands, but taxol and related compounds, which can be converted into taxol, can be isolated from the leaves of other *Taxus* species.

Fortunately, various cultivars of *Taxus* species are popular ornamental shrubs in the United States, and a number of nurseries cultivate them on a large scale. NCI, in collaboration with USDA, Zelenka Nurseries, the University of Mississippi, and the Ohio State University, has initiated a program for the large-scale harvesting, drying, and extraction of the leaves of a common *Taxus* cultivar. Extracts will be processed to yield taxol and related compounds. It is anticipated that this renewable source will replace the *Taxus brevifolia* bark source in the next few years. This will relieve the pressure on this old-growth forest species and provide an important new source of income for growers of ornamental *Taxus*.

Taxus species have a distinguished history, and the historical and cultural significance of these magnificent trees has been recounted in a recent book, "The Yew Tree: A Thousand Whispers," by Hal Hartzell (1991). For centuries, Yew wood was used extensively in Europe in the manufacture of the longbows which played a dominant role in English victories in famous battles such as Agincourt. It seems ironic but appropriate that the role of these legendary plants has been transformed from that of use in the manufacture of implements of war to use in the manufacture of drugs in the war on cancer.

Another plant product of significance in the cancer chemotherapy program is camptothecin, an alkaloid isolated from the Chinese ornamental tree *Camptotheca acuminata*. Clinical trials of a soluble camptothecin salt were conducted in the United States in the 1970's, but were terminated due to observation of severe toxic effects. Recently, however, several new camptothecin derivatives have entered clinical development in the United States, Europe, and Japan. Preliminary results indicate activity against leukemias, lymphomas, ovarian cancer, and various lung cancers. The derivatives are prepared by semisynthesis from natural camptothecin supplied by Chinese and Indian sources. In collaboration with USDA, NCI is initiating a small cultivation project of *Camptotheca acuminata* to provide a domestic supply of the source raw material if needed.

Other plant-derived drugs undergoing clinical trials include homoharring-tonine, an alkaloid isolated from the small Chinese evergreen tree *Cephalotaxus harringtonia*, and phyllanthoside, a terpene glycoside isolated from the Central American tree *Phyllanthus acuminatus*. Homoharringtonine, obtained from sources in China, has shown activity against various leukemias. Phyllanthoside is in early

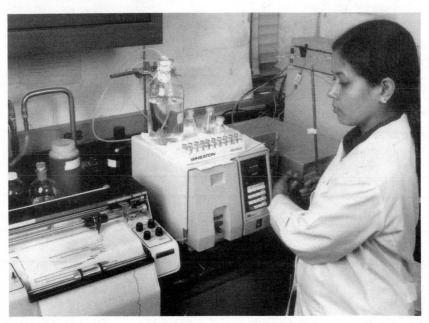

Alpana Joshi, a research associate at the Research Institute of Pharmaceutical Sciences, University of Mississippi, in Oxford, MS, manually injects a taxol sample extracted from ornamental yew clippings into a high-pressure liquid chromatography separator. The separator will analyze the sample for the amount of taxol present.
Bob Nichols/USDA 92BW0594-10

Part III. Products From Nontraditional Crops

clinical trials in the United Kingdom to determine the maximum tolerated dose in humans prior to advancing to trials against a range of cancer disease types.

Elliptinium, a semisynthetic derivative of the alkaloid ellipticine, is undergoing clinical trials in Europe. Activity has been reported against thyroid and renal cancer, and in the treatment of bone metastases resulting from advanced breast cancer. Ellipticine is isolated from species of the Apocynaceae family, including *Bleekeria vitensis, Aspidosperma subicanum*, and *Ochrasia* species.

NCI is continuing its collection program in tropical and subtropical regions worldwide, with the focus on rain-forests. The collections are being carried out through contracts with Missouri Botanical Garden (Central Africa and Madagascar), New York Botanical Garden (Central and South America), and the University of Illinois at Chicago (Southeast Asia). These collections were started in 1986, and are scheduled to continue until 1996. Over 4,000 dried plant samples per year are shipped to the NCI facilities in Frederick, MD, where extracts are prepared and tested for anticancer and anti-AIDS activity. A number of promising active compounds have been discovered, and these are being studied to determine whether they should eventually be advanced to clinical trials.

Development of Cancer Prevention Agents

At a recent university seminar on the topic of cancer chemoprevention by edible cruciferous plants, a member of the audience raised his hand and solemnly declared that he did not consider cruciferous plants like broccoli and brussels sprouts to be "edible." Even though consumption of these plants—broccoli, cauliflower, mustards, cabbage, radishes, and kohlrabi—is viewed with trepidation by some, in recent decades a strong link has been uncovered between them and decreased incidence of certain cancers. This protective effect has been confirmed in mice and rats, in which chemically induced tumors have been either reduced in number or prevented. This "chemoprotection" has been linked to an enhancement of detoxification systems in the body so that carcinogens are more rapidly metabolized and eliminated from the body.

Cruciferous plants contain substances called glucosinolates. Investigators have begun to focus their attention on the chemoprotective effects of specific glucosinolates and their breakdown products. Industrial rapeseed and crambe (see chapter 16.) are cruciferous oilseed crops grown to obtain high-erucic-acid oil. The meal remaining after extraction of the oil contains high levels (2-4 percent) of certain glucosinolates and their breakdown products, including nitriles and goitrins.

Historical Perspective

Three glucosinolate breakdown products are found at especially high levels in crambe and industrial rapeseed meals—cyanoepithiobutane (CHEB), cyanohydroxybutene (CHB), and vinyloxazolidinethione (goitrin). In the 1970's and early 1980's, meals containing *high* concentrations of these compounds were found to have adverse effects on nonruminants when fed as a high proportion of the diet. However, the "negative press" resulting from these initial studies obscured the fact that these compounds are also present at *lower* concentrations in numerous edible crucifers, including cabbage and brussels sprouts. A curious effect was also observed—these compounds helped the body eliminate toxic materials, including those with glutathione (GSH) attached. GSH is a natural metalolic substance that attaches to reactive cancer-causing compounds for inactivation and elimination from the body.

Both CHB and goitrin at nontoxic doses induce enzymes that catalyze the deactivation of toxic compounds by GSH. CHB also induces GSH synthesis, particularly in the pancreas, but also in the liver and kidneys. This effect on the pancreas is of particular interest, since there is no effective treatment currently available for pancreatic cancer, a common, rapidly developing, untreatable, and uniformly fatal cancer. The way in which these compounds and their relatives enhance the GSH detoxification pathway suggests an important role in cancer chemoprotection for the cruciferous plants that contain them.

Status of Technology

The technology for efficient removal of glucosinolates from meal is already developed, but it is not cost effective at current prices for the oil and the meal. An important use and the result-

ing high value for the glucosinolate material would help offset the cost of removal. Research is under way on inexpensive techniques for extracting glucosinolates from the meal at the time of crushing using various water/ solvent combinations.

Formation of the active breakdown products of glucosinolates is dependent on enzymes within the seed itself. Techniques have yet to be developed for large-scale extraction of these enzymes or for nonenzymatic breakdown of the extracted glucosinolates. Techniques for extraction and purification of the nitriles and goitrins exist, but must be refined for large-scale production if these compounds actually prove effective as chemopreventive or chemotherapeutic agents.

Successful technologies for cultivating, harvesting, and processing industrial rapeseed and crambe are being utilized in the few areas in the United States where these crops are now grown commercially.

Perhaps the biggest hindrance to production of pharmaceutical agents from industrial rapeseed and crambe is the long-term nature of the research that must take place before the glucosinolate products from these plants can be touted as chemopreventive or chemotherapeutic agents. Much needs to be learned about the metabolism, distribution, and mechanism of action of these compounds. Furthermore, studies are needed to ensure that these compounds themselves have no long-term adverse effects at the doses used for protection or treatment. A long-term commitment of time and funds to design and perform the required studies is needed to optimize the chances for success.

The advantages for U.S. agriculture would be in those geographic areas where land is available, but where major crops cannot be or are not grown for economic, climatic, or other reasons. The economies of scale are such that local, small-scale processing plants for cheap extraction of oil and glucosinolates could be built and local markets for the meal could be utilized, thereby decreasing bulk transportation costs and revitalizing depressed local rural economies.

The potential for domestic production of a high-value "natural" class of important preventive and therapeutic agents is present, and preliminary data are promising, but much is still uncertain about the ultimate utility of these derivatives of industrial oilseeds. If one or more of these compounds were to prove efficacious in preventing or treating cancer (in particular colonic and pancreatic cancers), an important pharmaceutical use for glucosinolates derived from crambe and rapeseed would come into being. Both cancers are among the top 10 in this country, and pancreatic cancer is unremittingly fatal.

Summary

The examples above are drawn from a variety of efforts to find preventive or chemotherapeutic agents specifically for cancer and are only illustrative of the many research and development efforts under way to find new pharmaceutical prototypes from plants for the treatment of a host of other diseases as well. Research on artemisinin from *Artemesia annua* holds promise for development of therapy for drug-resistant malaria, a major emerging disease throughout the world. Preparations of *Ginkgo biloba* are being utilized to increase peripheral and cerebral blood circulation, and they hold promise for improvement of the health status of the elderly. In Europe, materials isolated from *Echinacea purpurea* are being developed as immune system stimulants. Successful development of such agents would represent a whole new approach to treatment and prevention of infectious disease.

These are just a few examples of the many efforts to find new pharmaceuticals from natural sources and to continue the history of the contributions of plants to human survival. ❑

Natural Products: The Promise of Peanut Shells, the Value of Violets

21

by Horace G. Cutler, Research Leader and Coordinator, Microbial Products Research Unit, Russell Agricultural Research Center, ARS, USDA, Athens, GA

Around the world, many people are vitally concerned about protecting the environment while maintaining a sustained agricultural and industrial base. Both goals can be met by treating ordinary, everyday objects and substances to create safe agricultural chemicals, pharmaceuticals, flavors, and other commercial products.

Plants found in nature contain many compounds, and some of those compounds may serve as natural pesticides if resources are dedicated to their development.

In their intensive efforts to keep a steady, safe, and inexpensive supply of food and fiber available to the public, USDA scientists and others are finding agricultural chemicals that are safe for both the environment and people. These chemicals are an integral part of nature and are readily biodegraded.

Pressure To Produce

As the human population increases, resources become more strained in coping with conflicting needs for land use. Demands for food production, housing, and recreational areas (for hunting, fishing, camping, and hiking) reflect the sometimes differing values of various groups—the environmental, industrial, and agricultural interests.

After World War II, the productivity of the American farmer became the envy of the world. Never before had such a cornucopia been produced by so few. This productivity was based on three factors: canny farmers who knew their business, superior farm machinery, and pesticides (including herbicides, insecticides, fungicides, rodenticides, cotton defoliants, and plant-growth regulators).

In 1962, Rachael Carson's *Silent Spring* was published, and the widespread use of pesticides was questioned for the first time. The greatest insecticide in the history of the world, DDT, had become highly suspect because (among other things) it caused thin and brittle eggshells in birds. It was discovered that DDT had leached from the fields into the streams and rivers and had been ingested by fish.

The birds ate the fish and also the insects that had been poisoned by the insecticide, and the ecological cycle was again almost complete.

But some of us will remember the benefits of DDT during and after World War II. Refugees moving across war-ravaged Europe were stopped at checkpoints and dusted with DDT to kill lice and fleas, because fleas can carry bubonic plague (which still exists on the North American continent). In 1959, yellow fever and malaria in Trinidad, West Indies, had just been eradicated by the control of the carrier mosquito. My wife and I were living there at the time, and we found our luncheons regularly disturbed by a man with a sprayer full of DDT. He would announce in his best Trinidadian, "We commin' in, mun!" and then thoroughly spray the inside of the house. To refuse him entry would have resulted in a hefty fine and jail sentence. If the entire island had refused the pesticide spray program, yellow fever and malaria might not have been eradicated.

But we cannot go back to things as they were. The world today is very concerned about agricultural pollution in all forms, especially pollution caused by the use of pesticides. The Green Movement in Europe, the various ecological organizations in the United States, the watchdog agencies, and even the filmmakers have strong opinions about the use of pesticides and the results of their residues on land and in food crops. Sometimes the criticism is absolutely correct and sometimes it is a little distorted. All sorts of facts, figures, and extrapolated data come into the discussions. But one thing is certain: Because of registration costs, many of the agricultural chemicals presently on the market will eventually be withdrawn by chemical companies. It is quite possible that during the next 5 years many, if not all, of the fungicides in use today will no longer be available. Although many of the synthetic agricultural chemicals do not pose a hazard, the question of their persistence in the soil or in food commodities is of paramount importance to the public welfare.

Can we grow crops without the use of chemicals? The answer is mixed. It may be possible to grow pesticide-free crops (organically grown) in specific environments on a small scale, but it is almost impossible to do so on a large scale in humid semitropical areas (such as Southeastern United States) and in the Tropics. The incidence of weeds, insects, and disease seems to explode in warm climates.

The Promise of Natural Products

A middle ground between concentration on synthetic pesticides and use of none at all involves the use of natural products that possess biological activity. These natural products are organic compounds that nature regularly sees, recognizes, and handles by taking them apart easily. They are derived from plants, micro-organisms (fungi and bacteria), and insects and can be used as agrichemicals. Their characteristics are as follows:

- They have very high specific activity so that only fractions of an ounce are used per acre.

- They are target-specific and are not broad spectrum (that is, nontarget life is unaffected).
- They are biodegradable and do not persist in the environment.
- Some may be transformed in biological systems (by refermentation) to give new biologically active compounds with different activities.
- Some are both agrochemicals and pharmaceuticals.
- They come from highly renewable resources. Certain plants may be new high-cash crops for rural areas.

An intensive search is under way by USDA's Agricultural Research Service (ARS) to discover natural products for utilitarian use. In one project, USDA-ARS scientists are developing an inexpensive product from peanut shells, called Gostar (patent pending). This is primarily intended to produce, by the fermentation of a *Penicillium* (fungus), a natural product having both antitumor properties (for use as a pharmaceutical) and plant growth regulating properties (for use as an agrochemical). The goal is to produce large quantities inexpensively.

Gostar is now being used to inexpensively make a compound called 6-pentyl-α-pyrone (PAP) from the fungus *Trichoderma*. In its relatively pure state, PAP kills fungi that attack fruit trees and also other objectionable fungi in stored food products. The latter include such organisms as *Aspergillus flavus*, which produces aflatoxins that are potent inducers of liver cancer. Obviously, a nontoxic

ARS scientists have developed a process that can use peanut shells to produce a natural product with pharmaceutical and agrochemical properties.
Jack Dykinga/USDA 91BW1970-36

fungicide would be very useful in eliminating this problem, especially because (as stated earlier) most of the presently available fungicides may be removed from the market. PAP, which has also been found in the natural essence of peaches, was originally produced on a small scale for use as flavoring in baked goods; it has a buttery, cakelike flavor, and has been fed to humans on taste panels.

Violets Versus Fungi

A second example of a natural product being sought for utilitarian use relates to flowers. In the play and movie *My Fair Lady*, Eliza Doolittle, the flower vendor in Covent Garden, sold Devonshire violets. These English violets look identical to their American cousins; both are deep purple. But the English violet differs in that it grows in a cool, moist climate and it exudes a pleasant, penetrating perfume. The perfume, a natural product, is β-ionone.

Some years ago in midsummer in southern Georgia (in the United States), when the temperature was 95 °F and the humidity was also high, I wandered into the laboratory of a chemist colleague. Without thinking, I exclaimed, "Where did you get the English violets?"

Then I recovered and said, "That's a silly question; it's too hot, and they don't grow in the South. In fact, I don't know of any scented violet in the States."

My colleague told me that he had the violets because he was working with β-ionone (a compound used in the perfume industry worldwide) in conjunction with another scientist because the natural product has antifungal properties. That work led to a joint patent by USDA-ARS and the University of Georgia for the use of β-ionone as a fungistatic agent.

These and other natural materials not only can be safe for the environment but also can have international use as agrochemicals and pharmaceuticals, thus promising a profitable presence for the United States in the global marketplace. ❑

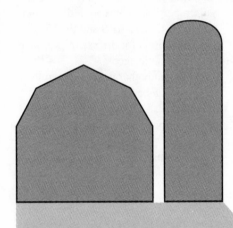

Part IV.
New Products
From Traditional
Crops

New Uses for Starch

22

by William M. Doane, Plant Polymer Research Leader, National Center for Agricultural Utilization Research, ARS, USDA, Peoria, IL

Interest in natural products as annually renewable raw materials for industry has greatly intensified, especially during the past two decades.

Much of this interest can be attributed to the oil embargo of the early 1970's. However, another reason for this interest is the increased abundance resulting from agricultural production that has more than satisfied available markets, and that has generated an oversupply of many commodities. Thus, there is increased interest in using such commodities as raw materials for industry, either to develop new products or to replace those products now made from nonrenewable sources such as petroleum.

Corn is one of the commodities produced in excess of available markets, and since the corn kernel consists of about 70 percent starch, it is one of the natural materials that is receiving considerable attention as a renewable resource.

Starch is one of the most abundant materials produced in nature, is easily recovered from plant organs holding it, is relatively low in cost, and is readily converted chemically, physically, and biologically into useful chemicals now derived from petroleum. More than 200 billion pounds of petroleum chemicals are produced annually in the United States.

Starch: Occurrence and Availability

Although starch occurs in many plant tissues, commercially it is mostly recovered from seeds, roots, and tubers. In the United States, cereal grains, such as corn and wheat, provide the major source of starch. The average yearly U.S. corn crop contains about 300 billion pounds of starch, with only about 15 percent of the crop being processed to separate the starch or starch-protein (flour) component from the corn kernels. The corn processing industry is expanding, doubling the amount processed during the past decade, and has both the interest and the capability to further expand as market opportunities increase. Of course, increased processing translates into more jobs and an improved economy.

Starch has played an important role in the human diet since before recorded history, and it also has a long history of use in nonfood (industrial) applications such as papermaking and adhesives. Today, 5 billion pounds of starch or flour are provided in the United States for industrial (nonfood) uses. About 3.5 billion pounds of the 5 billion are used in the paper, paperboard, and related industries, where starch serves a variety of adhesive functions. In addition, the starch in nearly 400 million bushels of corn was converted into ethanol in 1991.

Now, new technologies based on starch and new products derived from starch are emerging. Four of the most promising of these technologies are starch for biodegradable plastics, biopolymer plastics, water absorbent polymer (Super Slurper), and starch medium for encapsulation. These developments, described in this chapter, hold promise for vast new markets for starch and for consumer products that are more environmentally acceptable than many currently in use.

Starch: Role in Biodegradable Plastics

In the mid-1980's many popular and scientific articles began to appear on the need to develop biodegradable polymers to replace plastics. Plastics, the major nonenergy product of petroleum chemicals, are considered to be nonbiodegradable, or at best only slowly degradable over many years. This, coupled with the amount of plastics produced and ending up as litter or in landfills, has led to a push toward developing plastics from natural materials that would biodegrade. In the United States, about 60 billion pounds of petroleum-derived plastics are produced each year. Municipal solid waste contains 5-7 percent by weight (17-25 percent by volume) of plastic, largely from packaging materials.

Considerable local and national legislative activity, in the United States and abroad, has caused much research and development to be devoted to biodegradable replacements for currently used plastics. In some instances, certain uses for plastics have been banned and other uses are being phased out over the next few years. The types of uses given most attention

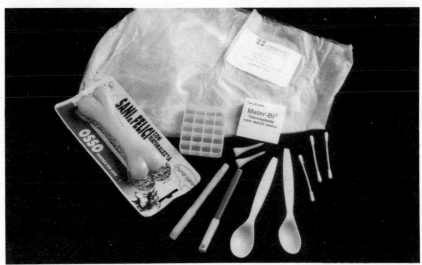

Corn is the major source of starch in the United States. Starch-based products produced by NOVAMONT North America, Inc., range from plastic bags and flatware to golf tees.
Ken Hammond/USDA 92BW0806-17A

Part IV. New Products From Traditional Crops

are those resulting in quick disposal after one-time use. Packaging films, shopping and produce bags, egg cartons, bottles, and fast-food service items are among the many plastic items targeted for replacement.

The Marine Plastic Pollution Research and Control Act of 1987 (Public Law 100-200, December 29, 1987) requires the U.S. Navy to cease disposing of nonbiodegradable plastics at sea by the end of 1993. This act has brought researchers together from academia, industry, and Government to develop plastics based on natural materials that will biodegrade in the sea into harmless components.

Plastic materials containing starch as a filler and biodegradable additive are now on the market. Polyethylene (PE) garbage and compost bags containing small amounts (generally less than 10 percent) of granular starch are now produced commercially by coextrusion of polyethylene and starch. Coextrusion, a process widely used in the food, feed, and plastic industries, allows thorough mixing and heating in a screwlike device to produce a very uniform product. Often the starch is pretreated to reduce moisture content and improve adhesion with the polyethylene to enhance strength properties of the bags. Other additives during extrusion include agents that assist in breakdown of the polyethylene to increase its degradability.

Today, we are in an early stage of a promising new technology for producing a broad spectrum of plastic products containing high levels of starch, with some consisting entirely of starch. This technology can be traced back to the 1970's, when researchers at USDA's Agricultural Research Service (ARS), National Center for Agricultural Utilization Research (NCAUR) at Peoria, IL, studied the extrusion of starch under various conditions to produce plastic films. Agricultural mulch film, containing up to 50 percent starch, was one of the resulting products.

In late 1990, an expanded (foam) packaging material containing 95 percent starch entered the marketplace, suitable as a biodegradable replacement for styrofoam "peanuts." This product made by extrusion has resilience and compressibility properties similar to those of Styrofoam, and it readily dissolves when placed in water. In 1991, companies began offering commercial quantities of starch compositions prepared by extrusion processing for use in making films and injection-molded articles. It is expected that the 1990's will see greatly expanding markets for these novel starch-based plastics.

Biopolymer Plastics via Starch Fermentation

Fermentation of starch or starch-derived sugars has long been practiced to produce a variety of alcohols, polyols, aldehydes, ketones, and acids, chemicals used in foods and beverages, paints, solvents, plastics, cosmetics, and many other products. One of the acids, lactic acid, has received considerable attention as the basis of biodegradable plastics with a host of potential industrial applications. Lactic acid is converted into a plastic by polymerization, a process by which individual units of lactic acid are joined together like links of a chain to form a long chain. Because of the high cost associated with producing and recovering lactic acid, the use of this biopolymer plastic has been restricted mostly to the medical field, where it's used in biocompatible, biodegradable, reabsorbing sutures and prosthetic devices. There is a potential market of millions of pounds yearly for commodity plastics, as research leads to improved preparation and recovery of lactic acid in the fermentation process. Companies in the United States and abroad are now pursuing this promising market.

Another biopolymer plastic known as polyhydroxybutyrate (PHB) or poly-hydroxybutyrate-co-valerate (PHBV), also made by fermenting starch, is now being used to make bottles for oil and shampoo. A 1988 product bulletin of a company producing PHBV lists several applications for PHBV in such areas as medical implants, plastic dinnerware, bottles, films for packaging, and media for slow release delivery of medicinals. The biodegradability of PHB and PHBV polymers has drawn attention to these natural polymers, as interest in replacements for nonbiodegradable polymers has grown. The polymers, which have good shelf stability, undergo microbial degradation when buried in soil.

Super Slurper

Plastics are not the only products that offer new market opportunities for starch. Research conducted by ARS

scientists to modify the properties of starch through attachment of synthetic polymers led to discovery of a unique, highly water-absorbing material, named Super Slurper. This patented development has been licensed to several companies, with commercial production resulting in several new products containing the starch-based absorbent.

The unique character of the polymer, which can be provided in film, granular, or powder form, is its ability to absorb several hundred times its weight in water without dissolving. This fluid absorbing and holding capacity has made Super Slurper useful in many personal care, industrial, and agricultural applications.

For application as an additive to absorbent soft goods such as disposable diapers, incontinent pads, bandages, hospital bedpads, and sanitary napkins and tampons, both the powder and film forms have been used. The ability of the absorbent polymer to retain most of its absorbed fluid under pressure is a desirable property for such applications. A Super Slurper product that had absorbed 648 times its weight of water still retained 409 times its weight when it was subjected to substantial pressure. Cellulose fibers, on the other hand, initially absorbed 40 times their weight and retained only 2.1 times their weight under the same pressure.

Adding some water to the powdered starch polymer provides a hydrogel especially effective in treating skin wounds of animals. The hydrogel absorbs large quantities of fluids secreted by the wounds, relieves pain, and prevents drying of subcutaneous tissue. A medical supply company also markets the product for treatment of human patients suffering from various kinds of ulcers. Skin ulcers respond favorably to the treatment; the wounds either heal completely or stay cleaner, thus causing less scar formation, fewer infections, and less odor than ulcers treated by other methods.

The most promising applications for Super Slurper seem to be agricultural applications, such as for seed and root coating and as an additive to fast-draining soils to retain water. Large-scale field trials with corn, soybean, and cotton seed coated with the polymer have shown increased germination and seedling emergence and, in most trials, increased yields. When bare-rooted seedlings are dipped in hydrated polymer before transplanting, transplant shock is overcome and survival is greatly increased. For such applications, the powder or granular form is being used.

Fuel filters containing the absorbent have been used for several years. The filters are effective for removing small amounts of water from diesel fuel and gasoline-alcohol blends. Use of these filters in connection with underground storage tanks, automobiles, trucks, tractors, and transformers is expanding to provide a sizable new market for starch. As the production of this highly absorbent starch polymer continues to increase, so too will new market opportunities.

Starch for Encapsulation

One research area that shows considerable promise for a large new industrial market is the use of starch as a material to encapsulate agricultural chemicals such as herbicides and insecticides (collectively referred to as pesticides). Improved pest control technology is needed both to reduce losses in agricultural production and to reduce the negative environmental impact of chemical pesticides.

A new technology is now available to better target pesticides and to reduce their environmental impact. Starch-based formulations provide controlled release of chemical agents, improving the effectiveness of pest control by keeping the pesticide targeted to the pest. Losses of chemicals that normally occur through volatilization, decomposition by sunlight, and leaching by water are greatly reduced when the chemicals are applied encapsulated in starch. Release of the active agent from the starch can be controlled by chemical or physical treatments, incorporation of other additives, or selection of processing conditions for the starch. Performing the encapsulation in a twin-screw extruder provides a highly efficient, versatile, and continuous process amenable to commercialization.

In 1990, NCAUR devoted considerable effort to the encapsulation of atrazine, alachlor, and metolachlor, three herbicides used in large quantities for weed control. These herbicides were selected for field evaluation to compare starch-encapsulated products with standard commercial formulations for efficacy of weed control and reduced movement of the chemicals into ground water. Laboratory studies had shown that movement of herbicide into soil was greatly reduced when applied encapsulated in starch.

Field studies conducted in 1990 indicated that downward movement of atrazine was significantly reduced with the starch-encapsulated product. From the 1991 trials, yields of corn, which are a measure of weed control, showed no significant difference between treatments with commercial formulations and starch-encapsulated products. Additional field trials and engineering studies will help researchers to design and demonstrate the commercial process for manufacturing starch-encapsulated pesticides. Commercial interest in this technology is high, and USDA is proceeding to transfer the technology to the private sector through cooperative research efforts and through licensing of the patents.

Starch in Your Future

In the future, we can expect to see emerge many more technologies and

---

Calcium Magnesium Acetate (CMA)—An Alternative Road Deicer

by R.J. Bothast, Fermentation Biochemistry Research Leader, National Center for Agricultural Utilization Research, ARS, Peoria, IL

If calcium magnesium acetate (CMA) becomes widely used as a road deicer, the demand for starch could increase. Starch can be readily fermented to acetic acid, the major chemical used to make CMA.

An alternative road deicer is needed to replace the 9 million tons of salt (sodium chloride, or NaCl) used annually in the United States. Although salt is inexpensive (1-2 cents/lb) and effective, it causes enormous economic losses each year from corrosion of vehicles, bridges, and underground utilities; from deterioration of concrete roads and bridges; from pollution of streams and water supplies; and from killing roadside vegetation. The average annual economic loss caused by salt damage in New York State alone was estimated recently to exceed $1 billion, caused by spreading about 1 million tons of salt. This is equivalent to an economic loss of more than 50 cents per pound of salt used.

Aside from the direct economic losses, the most potentially serious damage in some States is the pollution of water supplies; for example, in Massachusetts, the sodium content in drinking water in many communities already exceeds 20 milligrams per liter, the recommended upper limit for individuals on a sodium-restricted diet.

Research initiated by the Federal Highway Administration identified CMA as an acceptable deicer without the harmful side effects of salt. Compared with salt, CMA is essentially nontoxic, noncorrosive, and nonpolluting, and it new products based on starch. The great interest and need to more fully utilize our agricultural commodities as renewable resources, coupled with the capability of American farmers to produce in abundance, will catalyze and stimulate research and development efforts in this direction. Tomorrow, consumers will have a lot more starch in their lives beyond that appearing in their diet. ❑

lowers the freezing point of water by $16°C$ more than salt does. Widespread use of CMA would also help to alleviate the effects of acid rain by acting as a buffer and helping to neutralize sulfuric and nitric acids in the environment next to roadways and in streams and lakes that receive the runoff.

CMA is manufactured commercially from acetic acid, dolomitic lime ($CaO \cdot MgO$), and magnesia (MgO) and sold for about 30 cents per pound. Most of the CMA manufacturing cost is for acetic acid, which is now typically synthesized from natural gas and lists for about 29 cents per pound plus shipping.

The price of CMA is a strong incentive to find methods to reduce the cost of production, and to find techniques that can reduce the rate of application for adequate snow and ice control. Costs could be reduced substantially by fermenting low-cost materials to acetic acid. Low-cost materials that could be used include corn starch (glucose), wood (glucose and xylose), municipal solid waste (glucose and xylose), unused whey (lactose), and possibly several single-carbon compounds (CO, CO2, and methanol). Two fermentation routes are possible for the production of acetic acid. One is a standard fermentation to ethanol followed by oxidation with bacteria to acetic acid (similar to vinegar production); the second is direct conversion of sugar to acetic acid by bacteria in the absence of oxygen.

Future research and development can help reduce the cost of CMA by

• Identifying the least expensive feedstocks,

• Developing continuous fermentation processes that use bacteria which can produce acetic acid from broth containing as much as 10 percent CMA in solution,

• Developing new and more efficient recovery techniques, and

• Recovering salable byproducts.

Uses for Vegetable Oils

23

by Marvin O. Bagby, Research Leader, Oil Chemical Research, National Center for Agricultural Utilization Research, ARS, USDA, Peoria, IL

American agriculture produces over 16 billion pounds of vegetable oils each year. These domestic oils are extracted from the seeds of soybean, corn, cotton, sunflower, flax, and rapeseed plants.

Although more than 12 billion pounds of these oils are used for food products such as shortenings, salad and cooking oils, and margarines, large quantities serve feed and industrial needs. The latter applications include chemicals such as plasticizers, which add pliability to plastics and other substances; stabilizers, which help other substances resist chemical change; emulsifiers, which enable the mixing of normally unmixable liquids; surfactants, which reduce the surface tension of liquids and are commonly used in detergents; and esters, nylons, and resins, which are basic ingredients in many industrial products. Besides detergents and plastics, products that contain chemicals derived from vegetable oils include lubricants, coatings, corrosion inhibitors, adhesives, cleaners, cosmetics, water repellants, and fuels.

The three domestic oils most widely used industrially are soybean, linseed from flax, and rapeseed. The relatively low cost of soybean oil and its dependable supply make it one of the more important oils; it provides nearly 80 percent of the seed oil produced annually in the United States. Other vegetable oils widely used industrially include palm, palm kernel, coconut, castor, and tung, but these are not of domestic origin.

Nonfood uses of vegetable oils have grown little during the past 30 years. Although some markets have expanded and new ones have been added, other markets have been lost to competitive petroleum products. Public and private researchers are seeking to develop new industrial products or commercial processes. Through these efforts, vegetable oils should maintain—or even add to—their market share while petroleum, which is nonrenewable, becomes more expensive.

Research and development approaches frequently take advantage of the natural physical or chemical properties of the oils or their major constituents—fatty acids and glycerol—but it is often advantageous to modify these properties for specific applications.

Vegetable oils are too viscous and too reactive with atmospheric oxygen to establish significant markets for use in cosmetics, lubricants, and certain chemical additives. Fortunately, properties such as viscosity, pour point, freezing point, and reactivity can be decreased by chemically introducing branching groups or side chains on the straight-chained fatty acids. For example, derivatives of isostearic acid, a byproduct of commercial dimer acid manufacture, can be used in many products—textile lubricants, softeners, and antistatic agents; coupling agents; emulsifiers; greases; and synthetic lubricants—for which the unmodified oil would be too reactive.

Conversely, to make certain products, vegetable oils must be made *more* reactive. By changing a domestic oil's physical properties, it can be made to resemble—and replace—imported tung oil in coatings, resins, ink vehicles, and plastics.

Markets for these highly reactive oils are expected to grow with the increasing sophistication of consumers worldwide and with changing and more stringent product performance requirements.

Scientists at USDA's Agricultural Research Service (ARS) pioneered much of the research that established industrial markets for vegetable oils. Most ARS research on industrial uses for fats and oils takes place at the National Center for Agricultural Utilization Research (NCAUR), Peoria, IL; the Eastern Regional Research Center (ERRC), Philadelphia, PA; and the Southern Regional Research Center (SRRC), New Orleans, LA.

Epoxidized Oils and Films

During World War II, ERRC scientists developed methods for converting vegetable oils to epoxidized oils, for use as plasticizers and stabilizers. Epoxidized oils are highly compatible with commercial resins, and they are nonvolatile. They are also effective stabilizers, thus eliminating the undesirable toxic stabilizers that were previously necessary. Out of the 300 million pounds of soybean oil used annually for industrial products, nearly 122 million pounds are converted to epoxidized oil. Other oils, mainly linseed, produce an additional 15 million pounds.

Linseed oil, containing about 60 percent linolenic acid, reacts rapidly with oxygen in air to form insoluble, flexible, adherent films which are used in paints and coatings. Although its use in paints has plateaued as a result of competition from other technologies, many paint formulations still contain linseed oil because of its superior adhesion characteristics. Also, NCAUR technology has demonstrated that formulations of linseed oil may be used to cure and protect concrete.

Rapeseed oil is principally useful as a source of erucic acid, a long-chain fatty acid consisting of 22 carbon atoms. Derivatives of erucic acid are used in the plastics industry as antiblocking or antistatic agents to make plastics less sticky and self-adhering and therefore easier to work with.

Research and development begun by NCAUR in the early 1940's led to the commercial production and use of polyamide resins. Polyamides are prepared from dimer acids that have been derived from soybean and other vegetable oils and are used as hot-melt adhesives for shoe soles, book bindings, can-seam solders, and packaging. Production of dimer acids in the United States is about 40 million pounds per year; perhaps more than half of this is used for polyamides. Because polyamides have flexibility, adhesion, and resistance to chemicals and moisture, they are used in flexigraphic inks and moisture-proof coatings. Polyamides are also used to make drip- and sag-resistant paints that do not need stirring and that will not be absorbed into porous surfaces such as open-grained wood and cinderblocks. Two-part adhesives (epoxy resins and polyamide curing agents) are widely used today and are made from the polyamides developed from this ARS research.

Nylon 9

Nylon 9, a product of NCAUR research, is a plastic made from oleic acid, a fatty acid found in most vegetable oils, including soybean, cottonseed, and sunflower. Because nylon 9 has a low moisture absorption rate, it does not warp and it is a better electrical insulator than nylon 6, a commonly used, and otherwise comparable, plastic derived from petroleum. Nylon 9 is slightly stronger than nylon 11 and nylon 12, two plastics which have properties similar to nylon 9. Because nylon 9 can withstand high temperatures, it has potential as an excellent material for making molded objects that will be subjected to large variations in air temperature, for example grills on automobiles. Its low rate of moisture absorption makes it ideal for products that require electrical and water resistance, for example insulators and water pumps.

Soybean Oil Inks

Soy inks, alternatives to conventional petrochemical-based inks, were developed by the American Newspaper Publishers Association (ANPA) and were first used in 1987 by the Cedar Rapids Gazette (IA). The ink from soybeans consists of about 50-60 percent degummed soybean oil, 20-25 percent petroleum resin, and 15-25 percent pigments. This ink has gained rapid acceptance by the newspaper industry. The colored inks are especially popular. Because the black inks formulated by the ANPA were not cost-competitive with typical offset news inks they are not widely used.

The technology for making soy inks consists of a direct substitution of soybean oil for the mineral oil portion of the vehicle (the entraining and dispersing agent for the pigments and other solid substances). Therefore, other oils that have a fatty acid composition similar to that of soybean oil should be directly interchangeable. In fact, some formulators have prepared inks from mixtures of soybean and corn oils. Economic considerations and marketing strategies govern the selection of the oils used in the formulation.

At the request of ANPA and the American Soybean Association, NCAUR recently developed a technology in which the vehicle is totally derived from vegetable oils. Although soybean oil was emphasized because of its dependable supply and low cost, this new technology was demonstrated with several commodity oils. Besides

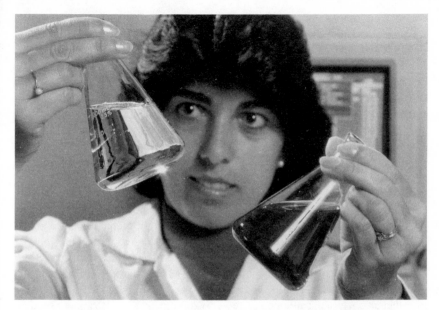

Chemist Sevim Erhan compares soybean oil with the traditional petroleum-based product used in the manufacture of printing ink. Soy oil is a much lighter colored vehicle for producing ink.

Keith Weller/USDA 91BW2345

replacing petroleum, this technology permits formulation of inks over a broader range of viscosity as well as inks that are more cost-competitive with conventional offset news inks. Further, inks formulated with this technology have rub-off characteristics equal to those formulated and marketed as low rub-off inks.

Dust Control

Although petroleum products have been used in the past as dust suppressants, environmental considerations have virtually eliminated such practices. In the 1980's, soybean oil was evaluated by ARS researchers and others for dust control in swine confinement operations and in grain

elevators. Because vegetable oils are readily biodegradable and edible, they are ideally suited for this purpose.

Diesel Fuel

Vegetable oils have potential as reliable and renewable sources of fuel for compression ignition engines (diesel)—a concept as old as the diesel engine itself. In fact, early engines were demonstrated running on peanut oil. Once cheap petroleum became readily available, the modern engine was designed to use petroleum fuel. Periodically, the alternative vegetable fuel concept has been reestablished, usually during petroleum shortages—and as petroleum shortages and prices eased, interest in alternatives again waned. Consequently, scientists do not yet understand how best to change the chemical and physical properties of vegetable oils to allow their trouble-free use as a fuel source. To fill this knowledge gap, NCAUR scientists are currently focusing on problems of high viscosity, low volatility, and incomplete combustion.

While evaluating vegtable oil fuels, NCAUR researchers have observed several characteristics that can restrict their use as motor fuels. These were grouped in two general categories, operation and durability. The former included ignition quality characteristics such as poor cold-engine startup, misfire, and ignition delay, and the latter included characteristics of incomplete combustion such as carbon buildup in the combustion cylinder and on the injectors, ring sticking, and lube oil dilution and degradation. In addition, the high viscosity of vegetable oil (more than 10 times that of number 2 diesel fuel) causes poor fuel atomization and inefficient mixing with air, further contributing to incomplete combustion. Because of their unsaturation, vegetable oils are more reactive than diesel fuel and are therefore much more susceptible to oxidative and thermal polymerization reactions that can interfere with combustion.

NCAUR researchers have been more successful in reducing viscosity than they have been in increasing volatility. Four approaches have been tried with varying degrees of success: (1) transesterification (reaction of vegetable oil to alcohols to give smaller molecules consisting of methyl, ethyl, or butyl esters), (2) dilution of vegetable oils with petroleum distillates, including diesel fuel, (3) pyrolysis (using heat to break chemical bonds and form new compounds of greater volatility), and (4) microemulsification (making heterogeneous mixtures like oil and water become a stable, homogeneous solution).

Fuels produced by each technique have been tested in engines. However, those prepared by approaches (1), (2), and (4) have received the most attention and the more rigorous engine tests. All of the techniques have provided encouraging results, and the transesterification and dilution technologies have achieved some commercial success. In Brazil, fuels developed by dilution may be used under some very specific conditions without loss of engine warranty. Warranties on some vehicles operated on esters are also honored in South Africa and parts of Europe. The oils used are those most readily available in the individual areas—soybean oil in Brazil, sunflower oil in South Africa, and rapeseed oil in Europe. NCAUR efforts are continuing to further develop the technologies and improve the combustion, cold-temperature tolerance, and cost-effectiveness of vegetable oils.

Epilogue

ARS continues in its commitment to identify and develop new nonfood uses of agricultural materials, including new uses for vegetable oils. This commitment was first made in 1938, when Congress established the four Regional Research Centers. Since then, an abundant supply of seeds from oil crops has been the driving force in encouraging research on new uses and technologies for vegetable oils and their derivatives. A major objective of such research is to expand the markets for domestic vegetable oils by producing products that use them instead of imported oils.

Discovery of economically competitive processes for converting oils to shorter chained fatty acids or more highly unsaturated or hydroxy fatty acids would markedly broaden the spectrum of specialty chemicals that can be made from U.S. agricultural surpluses. The possibilities for developing new technologies and products for plant oils are diverse and awaiting discovery. ❏

New Products From Field and Forest

24

by John Youngquist, Roger Rowell, and Debra Dietzman, Forest Products Laboratory, Forest Service, USDA, Madison, WI, and Stan Bean, Forest Products and Harvesting Research, Forest Service, Washington, DC (retired)

Each year, the sun creates abundant supplies of an inexpensive raw material—biomass. One particular class of biomass called lignocellulosics is drawing increasing interest as a potential source of new materials and an alternative, renewable source of familiar products.

Lignocellulosics are any substances that contain both cellulose and lignin. Common examples are wood, agricultural crops and residues, and grasses. When broken down into particles or fibers, lignocellulosics provide the raw material for a wide array of products.

Potential Products

Composites. Researchers are currently studying the formation of new types of composites that combine lignocellulosics with glass, metals, plastics, or synthetic fibers. The resulting products are strong, durable, and uniform. Wood-plastic composites are currently being developed for use in building materials, such as for doors, windows, walls, and floors; reuseable packaging; and other products.

In making composites from lignocellulosics, the biobased fibers or particles can be chemically modified to produce consistent properties not achievable from the raw material alone. A major goal of this research and development is to make new materials solely from renewable resources that rival or exceed the performance of products made from nonrenewable materials.

Wood chips are the source material used to manufacture building materials from re-cycled wood.

Steve Schmeiding/FS M84-0128

Samples of structural materials, including structural web "I" beams and wall panels, made of pulp composites.

Steve Schmeiding/FS M91-0248-6

Part IV. New Products From Traditional Crops

Nowoven Mat Products.
Incorporating lignocellulosics into nonwoven mats permits the creation of complex, molded shapes (such as car doors) and simple products (such as mulching material for seedlings). The technology that permits this transformation is similar to that used to make disposable diapers and other nonwoven textiles. The process starts with a mat composed of short and long fibers, such as short wood fibers and long polyester fibers. (Long-fiber agricultural plants such as kenaf can replace the polyester fiber.) The mat is drawn between two rollers and then through a needle board. The needles go into the material smoothly, but barbs on the needles catch the long fibers on the way out and pull them back through the rest of the mat. The result is a flexible fiber mat that can be combined with an adhesive, put into a press, and molded into any desired size or shape. Left into a loosely compacted form, it can be used as air or oil filters and as mulch or seeding material.

Chemicals. Biomass is also being used to produce chemicals for a variety of industrial uses. Fast pyrolysis of wood and bark wastes, followed by chemical fractionation, produces mixtures of phenolic compounds that could replace phenol in some thermosetting resins that are used, for example, in bonding-oriented strandboard, plywood, and some particle boards.

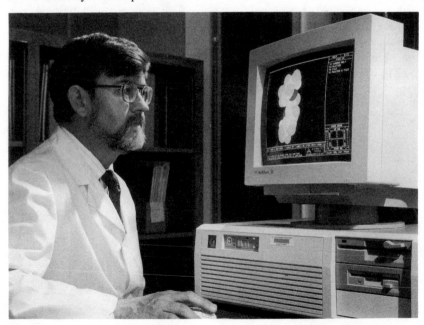

Anthony Conner, Forest Service chemist and project leader in the adhesives lab, Forest Products Laboratory, Madison, WI, views the molecular structure of adhesives.

Steve Schmeiding/FS M90-0084-17

New Crops, New Uses, New Markets

Starch, abundant in corn and other crops, yields chemicals that are now obtained primarily from petroleum. These include alcohols, polyols, and acids. Researchers are also incorporating starch in synthetic polymer films and bottles to enhance their biodegradability.

Vegetable oils are another attractive renewable resource for a broad variety of unique monamers and polymers. For example, Vernonia oil, a natural vegetable oil, could replace conventional solvents in alkyd and epoxy coatings and other applications.

Fuels. Lignocellulosics also represent a cheap feedstock for biological production of ethanol and other fuels. Researchers have found that enzymes convert cellulose to ethanol with very high yields. Some studies of the chemical conversion of cellulosic feedstocks to ethanol and other chemicals have been under way for more than 10 years.

Benefits of Lignocellulosics.
Lignocellulosics are being adapted for these many uses because they are economical and lightweight, and they require low amounts of energy for processing. In addition, they do not harm the environment and can replace nonrenewable imported oil with abundant, renewable agricultural and forest resources that are inexpensive and underutilized.

Greater biomass utilization could also help ameliorate solid waste disposal problems. About 180 million tons of municipal solid waste are generated annually in the United States. About half of that is cellulosic and could be converted to useful products.

Lignocellulosics also offer great latitude in their chemical composition, configuration, and availability. Agricultural crops and residues have unique fiber properties and chemical compositions, but they may be available only seasonally, and they have a

Tom Custer, a researcher at the Forest Products Laboratory in Madison, WI, using an electron microscope to view the fiber structure of a wood sample.

Steve Schmeiding/FS M90-0088-15

Part IV. New Products From Traditional Crops

low fiber yield per unit density. On the other hand, wood fiber can be harvested at any time of year and has a high fiber yield per unit density, but its fiber may be too short for some applications.

Outlook

The current interest in biomass utilization is reflected in national legislation that would push greater use of agricultural byproducts. This initiative involves commercialization of agricultural commodities for nonfood uses. The resulting new markets for corn, agricultural wastes, and other lignocellulosic materials could help us reduce our dependency on foreign oil and create economic opportunities for farmers and other agricultural commodity producers.

Lignocellulosics will be used in the future to produce a wide spectrum of products ranging from very inexpensive, low-performance composites to relatively expensive, high-performance materials, chemicals, and fuels. The wide distribution, renewability, and recyclability of lignocellulosics will encourage development of more markets for low-cost renewable materials. Markets for high-performance composite materials will result as cell-wall-modification chemistry creates the dimensional stability and moisture resistance required of these products.

Research continues on combining lignocellulosics with other resources to develop a product with properties that are much better than those of its individual components. This strategy takes advantage of the unique properties of all types of resources and permits the design of new products that meet consumer requirements while minimizing cost and environmental impact.

The future for expanded use of field and forest products seems promising for many environmental and economic reasons. ❑

The Forest Products Laboratory in Madison, WI, operates a number of exposure sites that test a variety of wood and varnish formulas.

Leif Ersland/FS M130-978

New Industrial Uses of Dairy Products

25

by Robert G. Bursey, Senior Vice President for Dairy Foods and Nutrition Research, National Dairy Promotion and Research Board, Arlington, VA

Milk, as it comes from the cow or is delivered from the farm, represents a complex mixture of ingredients and biochemicals which, if separated and/or modified, have chemical properties and functional attributes that lend themselves to a wide array of nonfood applications.

In many respects, raw milk from the cow is analogous to crude oil that is extracted from the earth, cracked, and separated into vinyls, acrylics, gasoline, motor oil, grease, and other fractions that can be further processed and used as components in any number of consumer goods. Petroleum is today more than just a source of energy to power an engine. It is a feedstock (raw material) used to make literally thousands of products that touch

Milk, as it comes from the cow or is delivered from the farm, represents a complex mixture of ingredients and biochemicals. These components lend themselves to a wide array of nonfood applications.

USDA 014-33-23

almost every facet of our lives. The same is possible with milk. Unlike our knowledge about petroleum, however, our understanding of the full potential of nonfood uses of the ingredients in milk is still in its infancy.

The list of nonfood uses of the components of milk that have already proved to be both technically achievable *and* commercially feasible is long and varied. The potential would appear almost endless, constrained only by the limits of our imagination, the availability of resources to explore and develop them, and the economic reality of exploiting them.

Continued efforts to identify and develop nonfood uses for all agricultural commodities are critical. As non- or less-renewable natural resources become increasingly scarce, the need to define agricultural products as substitutes for these resources becomes even more important. The need to invest in developing these technologies today is critical because of the lengthy time typically required to deliver an innovation to the marketplace economically.

The next few pages suggest just a few of the many possible nonfood uses for each component in milk. Milk and other dairy products are complex mixtures of biochemicals, minerals, water, and combinations of these compounds. The biochemicals in dairy products can generally be classified as carbohydrates, proteins, and fats. Nonfood uses of compounds derived from each of these three biochemical fractions are already products of commerce and the list of such applications continues to grow.

Carbohydrates

The major carbohydrate found in milk is lactose, or milk sugar. Considered a simple carbohydrate, lactose is similar to table sugar in chemical composition but is much less sweet. For some time, and to some extent even today, lactose has been considered a byproduct or potential waste product from the processing of many dairy items such as cheese. Exploration of nontraditional commercial uses of lactose was hampered by the low cost of sugar, which could often be substituted for lactose in many of its more novel applications as a potentially useful surplus commodity.

However, lactose has for many years been used by the pharmaceuticals industry as an excipient and diluent for drugs. Often, the active ingredients in pharmaceuticals, the actual medications, cannot be used in their pure forms. In addition, drugs must be released under proper conditions and over a regulated time period to have their greatest effect. Similarly, the effective dose of a drug is often quite small and sometimes tastes bad. Lactose dilutes the active ingredient in a medication to help ensure that a uniform dose is being ingested, and that the medication is delivered in a form that is convenient and agreeable (in size, shape, and taste) for the user. It also establishes the appropriate conditions and time-release qualities to make medication as effective as possible.

Lactose is also split into its constituent simple sugars, glucose and galactose, which may be further biologically or chemically modified to form alcohols, lactic or acetic acids, or more complex products such as penicillin. In these applications, lactose must compete with the less expensive sugars and starches that become the commercially preferable feedstocks. However, the economics of these relationships often change, leaving such uses as potential future opportunities. (One is reminded of the increase in the use of ethanol in motor fuels as the cost of petroleum soared during the 1970's.) The alcohol and aldehyde derivatives of lactose appear to offer great promise for commercial application in the chemical industry, where the competition is less plentiful and the finished-product cost higher.

Chemical derivatives of lactose, the lacticol esters (the alcohol form of lactose to which a fatty acid has been attached), are known to have potential as surface active agents and emulsifiers. These fatty acid derivatives of lactose can be used in toothpaste and other toiletries because they are derived from natural ingredients and tend to be nontoxic. Their use has also been demonstrated as quenching agents in the hardening of steel.

Lacticol has been used as a raw material for the production of polyurethane foams. These foams have demonstrated their effectiveness as home insulating material as well as for use in packaging. Lacticol has also demonstrated potential in the manufacture of urea formaldehyde resin adhesives. This compound has even been dried and pressed into briquettes for use as fireplace logs. The commercial viability of these applications is again limited by the relative cost of lactose compared to other agricultural sources of fibers, starches, and sugars.

Proteins

Although the current and potential uses of the carbohydrates in milk are numerous, the potential commercial nonfood applications of the protein components in milk appear to be even greater. The ability of dairy proteins to act as surfactants and to stabilize emulsions has been demonstrated in a wide array of food applications. In addition, these properties of proteins are beginning to find application in nonfood systems such as personal hygiene and cosmetic products.

A new vista of future nonfood applications for dairy proteins follows the recent discovery indicating that microparticulation (the physical splitting of large particles of proteins into small ones) of dairy proteins creates a variety of novel textural and functional attributes previously unseen in protein. Microparticulation of dairy protein is currently being used in producing replacements for fat in foods. The potential of this technology in nonfood systems is just now beginning to be explored.

Casein, the protein found in greatest quantity in milk, has had nonfood commercial applications for some time. It has been used in specialty adhesives, premium paper coatings, the manufacture of biodegradable plastics, and even material that substitutes for ivory. Recently, special "high-clarity" casein has been used in the manufacture of television screens. In a similar capacity, it is currently being used as a component of the light-sensitive emulsion on some photographic film.

Within the past 3 years, scientists have demonstrated that casein, as well as the whey proteins in milk, can be made into a clear filmlike packaging material. Unlike traditional packaging films, those made from milk proteins are both edible and readily biodegradable. Possessing many of the properties of conventional packaging materials, the results of this technology appear to have great potential for use in both the food and pharmaceuticals industries, where the unique edible property can be especially useful. Perhaps one day in the near future, home cooks will be able to spray a freshly cut onion or block of cheese with an edible protein film before returning it to the refrigerator and, several days later, use it with the assurance that it has not lost its taste or nutritional quality.

Since the beginning of time, milk from mammals has provided their newborn not just with the nourishment of its food value, but also with some protection from infectious disease because of the antibodies (immunoglobulins) it contains, especially in the early days of lactation. The transfer of immunological protection has been recognized as an essential feature in the synthesis of formulas for newborn calves. It has also been recognized that the lactating cow is a potential source of large quantities of antibodies for use against a host of animal diseases and possibly some diseases of humans. Today, lactating cows are being used to produce antibodies that are subsequently harvested and used as antibiotic preparations for the treatment of many animal diseases. Cows have become potential factories for producing pharmaceuticals used in veterinary medicine.

It may be feasible to transfer this technology to applications in human disease. The antimicrobial properties of dairy proteins might also be used in other consumer product applications such as personal hygiene products and cosmetics.

In laboratory tests, derivatives of many dairy proteins—either existing in raw milk, developed during natural fermentation processes, or created by *in vitro* hydrolysis—exert a number of biological effects, such as blood pressure regulation. The potential of these substances to be useful pharmacological agents for humans is being studied in several laboratories in this country as well as abroad.

Milk is also a source of lesser amounts of many other protein components that may have commercial potential for the pharmaceuticals and personal health care product industries. Proteins such as lactoferrin (an iron-building protein) and several enzymes (such as lactoperoxidase) have been studied for their potential application in these industries, but much remains to be accomplished in developing this technology.

Fats

The potential nonfood uses of components of the fat, or lipid, portion of milk are less well defined at this time but are nonetheless sizeable. Use of dairy lipid derivatives as industrial lubricants has been demonstrated, but their use is currently constrained by less expensive alternatives. Dairy lipids may also be converted to waxlike substances for use as water repellants. Derivatives of fats found in milk have also been shown to have potential as emulsifiers, surfactants, and gels. The nonfood applications of these properties are only now being explored. Other lipids derived from milk have been reported to have antioxidant, antimicrobial, and antitumor properties, each of which holds promise for commercialization in the pharmaceuticals industry. The use of dairy fat as a feedstock for producing biomass for animal feeds or energy production has been proposed. At present, such proposals are not cost-effective.

Conclusion

This chapter is intended to provide merely a brief "look under the tent" at the promising current and future nonfood uses of some of the ingredients in milk. Much research is under way to expand on some of the applications noted above, as well as to identify new nonfood uses of these and other components in milk and other dairy items. As the supplies of less-renewable natural resources begin to shrink and the economics of many of the identified applications shift to support their further development, many of the more innovative potential uses of dairy ingredients may come into commercial use. ❏

New Technology for Animal Hides, Wool, and Cotton

26

by William N. Marmer, Research Leader, Hides, Leather, and Wool Research Unit, Eastern Regional Research Center, ARS, USDA, Philadelphia, PA, and Noelie R. Bertoniere, Research Leader, Textile Finishing Chemistry Research Unit, Southern Regional Research Center, ARS, USDA, New Orleans, LA

When we think of nonfood agricultural commodities produced in this country, cotton surely comes to mind as a source of fiber for clothes. Nevertheless, two major byproducts of the meat industry are also major sources of nonfood products for apparel: sheep give us wool, and the hides of sheep, pigs, and cattle give us leather.

You might guess correctly that cotton is overwhelmingly the most significant natural fiber crop in this country. We meet all our national needs for the raw fiber from the domestic crop. Even when cotton in finished products is included, we are a net exporter as well. The scope of USDA-ARS cotton research covers the full breadth of the cotton industry, including such diverse areas as cotton growth, ginning, marketing, spinning and weaving, and textile finishing. Much of the program has been centered at the Southern Regional Research Center (SRRC) of the Agricultural Research Service (ARS) in New Orleans.

In terms of wool, we meet a third of our needs for raw wool fiber from the domestic clip, but when wool in imported garments is factored in, that figure drops to 13 percent. Australia and New Zealand, the world's major exporters of wool, raise their sheep primarily for fiber. American wool, on the other hand, is truly a byproduct of the lamb industry. The current ARS program in wool research is a small one, functioning out of the ARS Eastern Regional Research Center (ERRC) in Philadelphia. The aim of the current program is to add value to the domestic wool clip, which suffers in its market return relative to its foreign counterparts.

Regarding hides and leather, the United States produces more animal hides than its tanning industry can convert to leather, so our hide *export* market is a $2 billion-a-year industry. We are also net exporters of unfabricated leather, but when shoes and other fabricated products are factored in, we are overwhelmed by imports. ARS research in hides and leather is also centered at ERRC and focuses on all aspects of research, from hide quality and preservation through tanning and finishing.

This chapter concentrates on some new technological developments from all of these ARS programs. Research is directed toward making quality

products, making the domestic products more competitive with their foreign counterparts, making our products more durable and easy to care for, and assisting the producers and users of these commodities in working within increasingly stringent environmental controls.

Wool: Bleaching Stained Fibers and Black Hairs

Raw wool carries with it such a tremendous amount of extraneous material that the true wool yield may be only half the original weight of the fleece. Most of the contaminants, such as grease, are washed out during "scouring." However, two contaminants particularly problematic in some domestic wools are stubbornly persistent—heavily stained fibers and black hairs. Stained fibers give wool a yellow cast that is particularly noticeable when the end product is a white or pastel-dyed garment. As for black hair, just a few enmeshed in the thousands of white fibers in a piece of fabric are amazingly conspicuous.

Stained fibers are traditionally bleached with hydrogen peroxide, an oxidative bleach. Once oxidative bleaching is done, it may be followed with reductive bleaching (another class of bleaching agent) to achieve the whitest products. Such combined or "full" bleaching is an expensive process because it involves the preparation and heating of two separate bleach baths and the rinsing of the product in between. In general, full bleaching is not practiced.

ARS scientists in Philadelphia looked at full bleaching and

discovered that the two processes could be combined into one sequential procedure in the same bath. In the new process, the two parts are accomplished in a clever way by chemical manipulation of the peroxide left over after the initial oxidative bleaching. Instead of discarding that bath, the peroxide is chemically converted to a reductive bleach by addition of thiourea to the bath. The result is extra whiteness.

Bleaching black hairs and stained fibers simultaneously is particularly difficult. The textile industry uses a variation of peroxide bleaching that requires—specifically for the black hairs—treatment of the wool with iron salts. When the new ARS process is coupled with the iron-salt method, the elimination of the rusty discoloration that sometimes results from residual iron is an added benefit.

Followup work is now permitting the single-bath full-bleaching concept to be extended to allow subsequent dyeing in the same bath. ARS scientists have been granted four patents to cover the bleaching process in all its variations. These scientists have worked to transfer this technology to the private sector by assisting woolen mills in experimenting with the system in their plants. One license has already been granted, a partially exclusive license for one niche of the woolen market.

Hides and Leather

Hide Preservation. When a hide comes out of the packing plant, it usually has to be preserved for a long period during shipping to and storage at the tannery. Almost all hides are preserved through curing in a concentrated salt brine. Needless to say, this is a large generator of salt pollution. ARS scientists in Philadelphia have looked at an unconventional way of preserving hides without using salt.

Irradiation by a beam of electrons is currently used to sterilize small items such as surgical bandages and scalpels. It is very effective so long as the item is enclosed in sterilized packaging. In 1986, a number of hides were sealed in plastic with a small amount of bactericide, then irradiated with an electron beam. Some of those

Chemist Frank Scholnik (left) and research associate James Chen examine the results of experimental treatments for leather. The Agricultural Research Service has designed an environmentally friendly way to sterilize hides with electron-beam irradiation rather than salt brine curing.
Scott Bauer/USDA 92BW0839

hides were soon tanned to leather, and the properties of the resulting leather were compared to those of leather from brine-cured hides. Differences were inconsequential. More impressive, however, was recent experimentation on the remaining hides in which tanning was delayed; *5 years later*, samples were removed from their packaging and tanned to leather of excellent quality. The private sector is showing renewed interest in such preservation, and new research is under way.

Recycling of Solid Tannery Waste. Tanneries generate a tremendous amount of solid waste during the multistep conversion of hides into leather. Much of this waste is chrome-containing solid waste from the 90 percent of hides that are chrome tanned. This waste, mostly destined for landfills, amounted to over 50,000 metric tons in the United States in 1988 alone.

The tanning industry appealed to ARS scientists in Philadelphia to look into chrome waste. Landfill expenses were skyrocketing, and environmental concerns were rising over potential hazards from this waste. Although the chrome in this waste is not the toxic variety and is legal in landfills, questions have been voiced over the long-term fate of the waste in landfills.

ARS responded by developing a process that allows the chrome to be separated from the waste. The recovered chrome can be recycled back into the tanning operations, and the balance of the material, now chrome-free, can be used for fertilizer or as an additive for cosmetic products or animal feed. The ARS process has been patented, and worldwide interest has led to initial licensing activity.

Computer Modeling of Hide Protein (Collagen). Why would such a theoretical item as collagen modeling be included in a chapter on new technology? The computerized molecular model of collagen is being developed and refined, and new changes to the model are continually made available to the world's research community through the Protein Data Bank of the Brookhaven National Laboratory. This ARS model is of immense value, not only for leather research but also for diverse studies of collagen's role in human skin and bone tissue.

A lot of tanning technology has been developed from experience or observation, with no real understanding of why it works. This is particularly true for chrome tanning. Why is chrome tanning so effective? It is because chrome (or its substitutes) interacts with collagen, the backbone molecule for hide tissue. Collagen is a complex molecule that forms bundles seen under the microscope as fibers.

The computer model, a detailed map of every atom of these fibers, will be used to learn how chemicals such as chrome neatly fit into the molecular structure of collagen during tanning. In response to increasing pressure for investigation of "environment-friendly" chrome alternatives, the model will be used to test the ability of chrome substitutes to "dock" with collagen. Followup studies in the lab and tannery will be used to confirm the effectiveness of these chrome alternatives as tanning agents.

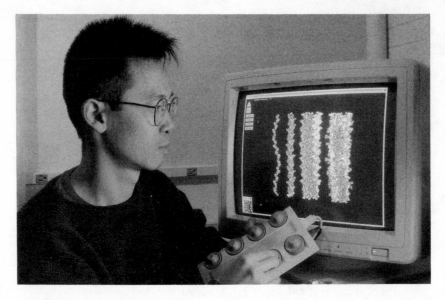

Research Associate James Chen studies the stages in which collagen (hide protein) models interact to form larger microfibril units. The computer model is a detailed map of every atom of these fibers. The model will be used to see how chemicals fit into the molecular structure of collagen during tanning.
Scott Bauer/USDA 91BW2138-6

Solvent-Free Finishes for Leather. Did you know that there is a polymeric finish on the surface of most leather? This is particularly obvious in the case of patent leather. Traditionally, finishes are applied to leather by spraying it with materials dissolved in organic solvents. This method is increasingly coming under attack because of the environmental hazards associated with those solvents. Elaborate recovery systems must be used to prevent these solvents from entering the atmosphere.

ARS scientists looked at a solvent-free approach—finishes cured by exposure to ultraviolet (UV) light. UV-cured finishes are used today on many nonleather products (such as metal cans and paper). Over several years,

ARS learned how to apply UV-cured finishes to leather while still maintaining the necessary durability and flexibility. UV-curing was found to be applicable to intermediate-and top-coating of leather, including patent leather finishing and color coating. Considerable effort by ARS has brought together the leather industry and suppliers of chemicals and equipment for the UV-curing sector. Commercialization is expected soon, with new interest in the process being shown both in the United States and abroad.

Cotton

Formaldehyde-Free Durable-Press Treatment. Most chemical agents used today to impart easy-care properties to cotton fabrics are derivatives of formaldehyde. These chemicals are inexpensive and are used to produce cotton fabrics that require little or no ironing. However, since regulations of the Occupational Safety and Health Administration mandate low levels of formaldehyde in the workplace, textile mills incur additional expenses related to monitoring formaldehyde in the air and to assuming responsibility for the health of mill workers for an indefinite period of time. Thus there is need for a new type of compound that does not contain formaldehyde or any other substance that might require similar regulation.

ARS scientists in New Orleans have recently used new chemicals to give easy-care properties to cotton fabrics. The most successful of these chemicals is BTCA (butanetetracarboxylic acid). Citric acid, a constituent of oranges, lemons, and other fruits, is also being used. These agents do not contain any known toxic materials, and they give a resilient product that retains more strength than does conventional durable-press cotton. For now, however, they are more expensive than the formaldehyde-containing agents currently in use.

The use of these chemicals has been patented by ARS, and numerous chemical and textile companies have expressed interest in licensing them. Full commercialization will depend on cost-competitiveness and future OSHA regulations regarding formaldehyde. Potential beneficiaries include textile mills that produce durable-press fabrics that contain cotton and their mill and garment workers who would work in a better environment.

Dyeable Durable-Press Fabrics. Cotton fabrics treated for easy care cannot be dyed because the large dye molecules can no longer penetrate into the fabric fibers. For this reason, cotton fabrics are dyed before they are treated chemically to give them easy-care properties. These dyeing treatments are done on the uncut fabric, so colors must be chosen prior to garment manufacture.

Recently, there has been increased interest in dyeing finished garments as a means of reducing inventories of poorly selling colors and of providing a mechanism for quick response to

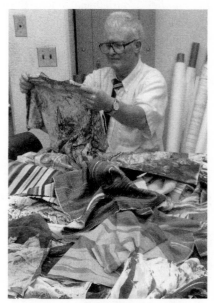

Colorful, dyeable, wrinkle-free cotton fabrics are examined by chemist Robert Harper, Jr. ARS scientists have developed processes for adding special nontoxic, dye-attracting chemicals to conventional durable-press fabrics.
Perry Rech/USDA 90BW1829-34.

fashion trends. This technique has been limited to garments made from unmodified cotton that would accept the dyes. Such dyeing results in wrinkled garments that are acceptable for some, but not all, markets.

ARS scientists in New Orleans have developed processes for adding special dye-attracting chemicals to conventional durable-press formulations. These chemicals, which contain cationic (positively charged) sites, are permanently incorporated into the durable-press fabric. It is then possible to dye this cationic durable-press fabric with dyes that contain an anionic (negatively charged) site. The most successful additives to date are choline chloride and triethanolamine, nontoxic materials used in chicken feed and cosmetics, respectively. Not only do variations in the way the cationic compound is applied lead to unusual special effects on the fabric, but garments prepared from these cationic easy-care fabrics may be dyed a variety of colors.

This technology has been patented and is available for licensing. Potential beneficiaries include the U.S. textile industry, which would be helped in its struggle with competition from imports, and various small businesses specializing in garment dyeing.

Temperature-Adaptable Fabrics. Cotton fabrics, like most substances, increase in temperature proportional to the amount of heat they experience. ARS scientists in New Orleans, however, now have altered the chemical composition of fabrics so that they do not respond proportionately to the amount of heat applied. Over certain temperature ranges, large amounts of heat are absorbed with little increase in fabric temperature. Upon cooling, this stored heat is released. These heating and cooling cycles are repeatable. Fabrics with this property are described as temperature adaptable.

To obtain this property, the fabric is treated by attaching compounds known as polyethylene glycols to cotton by means of the conventional durable-press reagent DMDHEU (dimethyloldihy-droxyethyleneurea). The temperature range in which heat is absorbed is controlled by the molecular weight of the polyethylene glycol.

Other beneficial and improved properties resulting from this treatment include resistance to abrasion and pilling (formation of fuzz balls), better oily soils release, decreased static charge, enhanced water absorption, and antibacterial activity.

Potential uses for these products are numerous, including clothing designed for both hot and cold climates. This process has been patented and has been licensed for specific uses by two companies to date. It is currently being sold as a component in skiwear and in thermal socks and thermal underwear by the two licensees. Other applications are anticipated.

Staple-Fiber Core Yarns. After numerous launderings, all-cotton fabrics, particularly those chemically modified to be durable press, show obvious damage from abrasion, such as holes at sharp creases. One solution to this problem has been to blend cotton with polyester fibers. The cotton provides the comfort and the polyester the needed strength. These fabrics, known as "intimate blends," have been in use for many years.

Cotton/polyester intimate blends are not free from problems. They are not as comfortable as 100-percent-cotton fabrics and lack some aesthetic properties. On repeated laundering, the blended material forms surface fuzz balls (pill). Also, blended fabrics

Figure 1: Cross sections of intimate-blend (A) and staple-fiber core (B) cotton/polyester yarns.

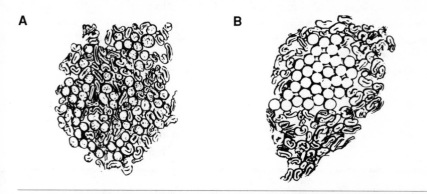

A

B

Cotton technologist A. Paul Sawheny observes the polyester staple-core/cotton-wrap spinning system, a new way to blend more cotton fiber with synthetic fiber. The yarn results in a fabric that is strong, yet comfortable.
Perry Rech/USDA 90BW1812-30

are usually difficult to treat for flame retardancy.

ARS scientists in New Orleans have developed a new type of cotton/polyester yarn that eliminates most of these deficiencies. During spinning of staple-fiber core yarns, the synthetic staple core is twisted while simultaneously being wrapped with cotton. This results in a yarn with a cotton surface and a synthetic interior. A comparison of the cross sections of intimate blend and staple-fiber core yarns is shown in figure 1.

In staple-fiber core yarns the cotton surface has a natural appearance, feels comfortable when worn, is dyeable with cotton dyes, and can be otherwise chemically modified. The synthetic interior provides strength and dimensional stability.

This process has been patented and is licensed to one company. Potential uses include apparel and home furnishing.

Conclusion

Consumers appreciate the properties of goods made from natural materials such as hides, wool, and cotton. At the same time, the public holds the manufacturers of these goods responsible for meeting ever-increasing environmental standards. ARS continues to maintain an awareness of these two needs in its research. ❑

Biotechnology 27 for Tailoring Old Crops to New Uses

by Daniel D. Jones, Office of Agricultural Biotechnology, USDA, Washington, DC, and Susan K. Harlander, Associate Professor of Food Science, University of Minnesota, Minneapolis

The new tools of molecular biology, with their capability for effecting genetic changes that are precise and rapid, can help significantly in the development of new uses for agricultural crops. As used here, the term "biotechnology" refers to these new methods of molecular biology—techniques that use living organisms to make or modify products, to improve plants or animals, or to develop microorganisms for specific uses.

The development of new products from nontraditional plants—such as kenaf, guayule, and crambe—has been proceeding for a number of years. For the most part, these plants have been produced and propagated by traditional methods of natural variation and artificial selection followed by economic assessment. These methods can be both labor-intensive and time-consuming. By comparison, the methods of modern molecular biology offer the prospect of introducing precise, well-characterized, and timely genetic changes into plants, animals, and microorganisms for the specific purpose of expanding their utilization for new food and nonfood uses.

Food Uses

In the area of new uses of crops for the food industry, biotechnology promises an impact on custom-designed ingredients, production of useful substances by plant tissue culture, and improvement of microbiologically produced enzymes used in food processing.

Custom-Designed Food Ingredients. Historically, food processors have been largely limited to purchasing the materials that are readily available at a particular time. In order to compensate for inconsistencies in the quality of these materials, they have often had to modify their manufacturing techniques, thus adding to the cost of food processing.

The tools of biotechnology offer the potential to custom-design agricultural commodities with improved nutritional or functional characteristics that make them more valuable to the processor. This allows the food processor to design and tailor products to fill a specific market niche. Examples include tomatoes with increased solids content, carrots with a longer shelf life, rapeseed with decreased levels of saturated fatty acids, and corn with increased levels of specific amino acids and altered levels of starch, protein, and oil.

With a digital refractometer, ARS scientists can measure soluble solids in field-grown crosses of high-solids variants and commercial tomatoes. This single application of biotechnology offers the potential to custom-design agricultural commodities with improved nutritional and processing characteristics.
Scott Bauer/USDA 92BW0835

Technician Louisa Ling prepares a tomato paste sample for flavor analysis by chemist Ron Buttery at the ARS Western Regional Research Center in Albany, CA. Microbiologically derived enzymes help control texture, appearance, and nutritive value, as well as flavors and aromas in food processing.
Jack Dykinga/USDA 89BW1901-23

As scientists and the public begin to understand more about the role of diet in health and disease, one can easily imagine using the tools of biotechnology to enhance the level of specific nutrients or certain components, such as soluble or insoluble fiber, or specific vitamins and minerals associated with healthier foods. The digestibility and absorption of nutrients could be enhanced, and natural toxicants or antinutrients in foods could be eliminated. Availability of fruits and vegetables with improved flavor, texture, aroma, and shelf life would lead to the inclusion of more fresh produce in the diet.

Producing Useful Substances With Plant Cell Tissue Culture. Plant cell tissue culture offers an alternative to the use of whole plants as a biological source of useful substances. Tissue can be removed from the root, stem, leaf, or fruit of plants, and the undeveloped cells can be grown in the laboratory in gels or liquid solutions containing all the essential nutrients required for growth. The useful substance can then be extracted and purified.

Plant tissue culture for production of natural food ingredients offers several distinct advantages over extraction of these components from whole plants. Seasonal variations, unfavorable weather conditions, and epidemic diseases are not problems when plant tissue is grown under well-defined and controllable laboratory conditions. Plant cell culture allows the processor to control the quality, availability, and processing consistency of the ingredients. Examples of high-value food ingredients which could be produced by plant cell suspension cultures include food colors, fruit and vegetable flavors, oils, spices, antioxidants, and non-nutritive sweeteners.

The discovery of plant cell fusion also permits the combination of plant cells of different genetic makeup to produce new hybrid plants with unique characteristics. New breeding lines have been produced between cultivated crops and closely related disease-resistant wild species. The

Part IV. New Products From Traditional Crops

hybrids produced by plant cell fusion contain a mixture of genetic information from each parent, and this opens the door to the transfer of new traits that are not accessible using conventional breeding approaches.

Enzymes Used in Food Processing. Microbiologically derived enzymes are used extensively by the food processing industry to perform many valuable functions in food systems. They help control texture, appearance, and nutritive value, as well as the generation of desirable flavors and aromas. Most enzymes are used in food processing to break down large molecules such as proteins, carbohydrate polymers, or lipids to their component parts.

Many enzymes do not perform well during food processing because of

Plant physiologist Merle Weaver examines tomatoes grown using a technique know as somaclonal variation, which can produce high-quality hybrids that have high solid content.
Scott Bauer/USDA 92BW0834

high temperatures and acidic conditions, as well as other factors. Modern techniques of protein modification provide the necessary tools for modifying the specificity, tolerance to acid, and temperature stability of enzymes, as well as their resistance to digestion by other enzymes. These improvements will expand the uses for enzymes in food processing and increase the kinds of raw materials that can be utilized as food for animals and humans.

Nonfood Uses

For centuries, products of the farm and forest have been used for purposes other than human food or animal feed. Examples include cotton for fiber and absorbants; wood cellulose for paper, cellophane, textiles, and plastics; corn and potato starch for adhesives, binders, insulating foams, textile sizing, and paper coatings; and vegetable oils for lubricants, paints, and varnishes.

With some exceptions, such as wood, cotton, flax, and oilseed crops, few crops have been grown specifically for nonfood uses. Now, however, the intentional cultivation of agricultural crops for nonfood uses is a potential growth industry, and the tools of biotechnology can help to tailor crops for such uses in ways that were not possible before.

This application of biotechnology to the development of new crops to supply industrial products or raw materials is in its infancy, but it promises broad new roles for agriculture as a provider of energy, materials, and specific chemicals.

Crops That Produce Value-Added Products. Some plants are particularly valuable for the manufacture of processed or value-added products. Biotechnology is able to alter the genetic structure of these plants, modifying their servicable components; this makes them more desirable for use as value-added products and stimulates development of new or larger markets for them as raw agricultural commodities. Oils and starches derived from plants are promising examples.

Oils. The major oils used by both food and nonfood industries are soybean, corn, cottonseed, rapeseed (canola), sunflower seed, castor bean, linseed, palm, coconut, and tung oils. Potential sources of new oils are jojoba, evening primrose, borage, blackcurrent, crambe, sal, mowrah, and mango. Promising applications of biotechnology in this area include alteration of proportions of fatty acids in current oilseed crops; production of oil containing specific fatty acids by bacteria, yeast, fungi, or microalgae in fermenters; and modification of oils by enzymes produced by micro-organisms in bioreactors.

Starch and Cellulose. Starch and cellulose are used extensively in nonfood applications. Both are very large molecules made up of simple sugar glucose units joined together in chains. For industrial uses, starch and cellulose molecules are often modified through chemical reaction. This provides a broad range of products with applications in many industries, including the chemical, food, pharmaceutical, cosmetics, detergent, paper, and petroleum industries. For example, starch, ordinarily *soluble* in water, can be modified to make it water *insoluble* so that it can be incorporated into plastic trash bags to make them biodegradable. Cellulose, ordinarily *insoluble* in water, can be modified to make it water *soluble* and useful for improved oil recovery.

Fermentation Products. Carbohydrates are a preferred source of energy for producing useful substances from fermentation (the growth of microorganisms such as bacteria and yeast in the absence of air). Thus, glucose and corn syrup (made from corn starch), sugar, and other carbohydrates are used in fermentation to make a variety of useful products. Among these are ethanol for fuel; enzymes; water-soluble gums such as xanthan, which is used in oil recovery as well as in prepared foods; citric acid, which is used as an acidulant in the food and chemical industries; and polyhydroxybutyrate (PHB), a biodegradable plastic that can be molded or made into fiber or sheets.

Pharmaceuticals From Plants. It is possible to modify plants genetically so they will produce specific proteins and peptides. This would allow high-value pharmaceutical peptides such as blood factors, growth hormones, and monoclonal antibodies to be obtained from plants. As scientists become more proficient in plant genetic engineering, it may be possible to harvest nonprotein pharmaceuticals such as the cancer therapeutic agents vincristine (periwinkle) and taxol (yew tree) from plants other than the ones in which they naturally appear.

Protoplast Fusion: Increasing Insect Resistance of Plants

To breed tomato and potato plants that are naturally resistant to insect pests is the goal of Anthony C. Waiss, Carl A. Elliger, and Judith A. Eash at the ARS Western Regional Research Center in Albany, CA.

Conventional plant breeding relies on crossing plants within a species, such as one tomato with another. But Waiss and his colleagues are examining more distant relatives that offer complete resistance to insects that ordinarily attack tomato or potato plants. They exposed a number of plants to insects such as the tomato fruitworm, then selected those plants with leaves toxic to the pest. Petunia was one plant chosen. Another was cape gooseberry.

In one experiment, the researchers combined cells from cape gooseberry with cells from tomatoes through a process called protoplast fusion. First the scientists used a chemical to remove the walls from cells of both "parent" plants. These naked cells are called protoplasts. Then they zapped protoplasts with an electric shock, causing them to fuse together. They next grew plants from the fused protoplasts.

Through protoplast fusion, the scientists have produced several hundred healthy plants that are the offspring of a cape gooseberry and a tomato or potato parent. Other plants are the progeny of a petunia crossed with a potato or a tomato. Several plants produced by fusing potato and cape gooseberry are showing very promising resistance to insects.

The Gene Gun: Taking Aim at Cereal Improvement

Unlike some plants, cereals such as corn and wheat have been very difficult to improve with the modern tools of biotechnology. To overcome that obstacle, Michael E. Fromm, formerly of the University of California/ARS Plant Gene Expression Center in Albany, CA, and now with Monsanto Company, St. Louis, IL, took aim at corn with a specially developed "gene gun" that fires DNA bullets.

The gene gun used the force of .22-caliber cartridges to fire tungsten particles, coated with DNA, into special clusters of corn cells developed by researchers at Monsanto. The DNA integrated into some of the cells to become part of their genetic code. Some of the genetically engineered cells were nurtured into full-fledged plants by the research team.

In other biotech experiments with corn, cells from corn kernels are serving as miniature labs for ARS researchers Olin D. Anderson and Ann R. Blechl at the Western Regional Research Center, Albany, CA. They are using the cells to conveniently test portions of wheat genes known as promoters. Promoters switch genes on and off. The experiments could lead to new, more powerful promoters to activate genes in wheat grains. These improved genes would confer valuable traits. One of the most sought-after traits for tomorrow's wheat? Grains that yield more nutritious flour.

Conclusion

The agricultural and forestry industries have experienced a decline in profitability because of excess production. This has provided the opportunity for product uses other than as traditional foods, feed, and fibers. These uses include feedstocks for industrial processes, as well as useful substances isolated directly from the plant material. New crops can be developed to meet specialized industrial and energy needs. Molecular genetics can direct modification of proteins/enzymes, bacteria, yeast, and molds for improved or expanded applications in food bioprocessing. The techniques of biotechnology will be very important for targeting genetic changes in food and fiber raw materials, in order to enhance their processing potential and the manufacture of value-added products. ❑

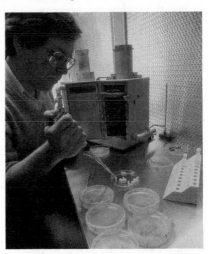

At the Plant Gene Expression Center, Albany, CA, a microbiologist uses a pipette to place the gene and tungsten mixture that will be blasted into plant cells within the gene gun.
USDA/ARS 89BW0445-32

New Medicines From Old Crops

28

by James A. Duke, Economic Botanist, ARS, USDA, Beltsville, MD, and James D. McChesney, Director, Research Institute of Pharmaceutical Sciences, University of Mississippi, Oxford

Columbus set sail 500 years ago, seeking black peppers and Asian Indians. Instead, he found red peppers and American Indians and changed the cuisines of the world. Red pepper has become the world's leading spice, used in hot cuisine from Bombay to Bangkok, Karachi to Kunming, and Sao Tome to Szechwan. It is even considered the national spice of Ethiopia. Interestingly, the compound that gives red pepper its pungency also gives it some medicinal potential.

Today, there is much interest in designing foods that can reduce the probability of diseases like cancer; they are sometimes called "designer foods," "food farmacy," "nutriceuticals," or "prandial pseudoprescriptions." Hundreds of bioactive compounds in our food crops have indicated healthful activities. A computer data base at the University of Illinois (Chicago) enumerates dozens of compounds in the peppers (*Capsicum* spp.) reported to be cancer-preventive, or antitumor compounds. Most of the compounds are rather common and can be found in many crops.

However, USDA does not encourage self-diagnosis or self-treatment with herbal medication. Despite their history as folk medicines, many of these compounds are still in need of much more clinical research. Many of these properties are not yet proven to the standards of the U.S. Food and Drug Administration.

Cancer is one of the most feared diseases in the United States, although coronary disease is the biggest killer. Because of the low incidence of stomach cancer in Latin America, where aji (*Capsicum* spp.) is the leading spice, it has been suggested that aji may prevent stomach cancer. Antioxidants (compounds that prevent the oxidative damage of free radicals) like capsaicin seem to prevent cancer, at least in experimental animals, by nullifying the cancer-causing activities of nitrosamines and other carcinogens.

Strangely, hot (pungent) compounds, once thought to cause ulcers, are among those showing signs of ulcer-preventive activities. And it is the hot compounds (capsaicin in hot peppers; a sulfur-containing compound in garlic and onion; gingerols in ginger; and isothiocyanates in conventional crops like mustards and onions) that may offer some cancer-preventive activities as well. Capsaicin is just one of several antioxidants in *Capsicum*. Antioxidants are believed to help reduce the incidence of heart disease and cancer as well as several other, more minor maladies like cataracts and some autoimmune diseases such as arthritis.

Ajo, or garlic (*Allium sativum*), may be the second leading spice in Latin America. Both onion and garlic contain interesting compounds (such as the compound ajoene) that reduce the tendency of blood to clot and somewhat improve one's odds against arteriosclerosis and heart attack. Aspirin is already recognized by the medical profession in this regard. Others also suggest that several of the compounds in onion and garlic (and also limonene from citrus) prevent cancer. Would North America be better off

adopting a salad dressing containing capsicum, garlic, and lemon juice? This recipe contains several compounds claimed to reduce the incidence of heart failure and cancer.

Capsaicin

Like garlic, ginger, and many of our conventional crops, red pepper has worked its way from the spice rack to the medicine chest. Capsaicin, the major active ingredient in red pepper, is now found in legitimate medications for such things as arthritis and herpes zoster (also called shingles). The many biological activities of capsaicin may be described as analgesic, anaphylactic, anesthetic, antiaggregant, anti-inflammatory, antineuralgic,

Garlic contains interesting compounds that reduce the tendency for blood to clot and somewhat improve one's odds against heart attack.

Ken Hammond/USDA 92BW0825-14

Part IV. New Products From Traditional Crops

antinociceptive, antioxidant, antiulcer, cancer-preventive, carcinogenic, cardiotonic, cyclo-oxygenase-inhibitory, diaphoretic, hypothermic, irritant, 5-lipoxygenase-inhibitory, neurotoxic, repellant, respirosensitizing, and sialogogue. Some of these reported activities are good, and some are bad. As with synthetic drugs, most (if not all) natural drugs have side effects and can be toxic in high doses.

Capsaicin is rarely found outside the hot pepper family. Used in South America as an anodyne (painkiller) for centuries, peppers more recently have yielded their capsaicin to therapeutic painkiller preparations such as Axsaine and Zostrix. Of the 20 percent of shingles sufferers who experience postherpetic nerve pain, 75 percent report less pain after using creams containing capsaicin.

At the Eppley Institute for Cancer Research (Nebraska), capsaicin is being studied for its potential to deplete substance P, a normal human body chemical that transmits pain messages from nerve endings in the skin to the central nervous system. Where it is applied, capsaicin inhibits the production of substance P. About 1 percent of the population suffers from cluster headache, and 80 percent of those persons are males. These patients reported dramatic relief when dilute capsaicin was applied to the nostril on the side where the cluster headache occurred, but not when applied to the other nostril. Further, capsaicin ointment prevented cluster

Red pepper has worked its way from the spice rack to the medicine chest. Capsaicin, the major active ingredient in red pepper, is now found in legitimate medications for such things as arthritis and shingles.
Ken Hammond/USDA 92BW0840-11A

headache when applied to the temples. In the 19th century, the use of a drop or two of capsicum extract was recommended for toothache. The use of capsicum preparations was even recommended to prevent thumbsucking and nailbiting.

Capsaicin is known to inhibit pain-inducing inflammation (for example, in arthritis) by blocking the release of a substance called neurokinin, but it is not effective when taken orally. Capsaicin analogs (chemical compounds that differ structurally) were developed, which proved to be orally active anti-inflammatory analgesics. These work differently from the way conventional, nonsteroidal anti-inflammatory drugs work. Capsaicin has thus functioned as a prototype in the development of a new approach to treat the inflammation of arthritis.

Steroids

Corticosteroids are also recommended for some cases of arthritis. Few Americans realize that steroids represent about 15 percent of modern medicinal prescriptions. The medicines loosely called steroids are widely used to treat arthritis, achieve contraception, etc. At first, steroids were obtained from animal urine. Then it was discovered that a compound called diosgenin, from yams (*Dioscorea* spp.), can be converted to steroids. A burgeoning industry of steroid contraceptives soon followed. Gradually, however, wild yams became more and more unpredictable as steroid sources. Today, most steroids are made from natural compounds called sitosterol and stigmasterol, byproducts of soybean

processing. Assuming that the world pharmaceutical market has a value of $150 billion and that steroids capture 15 percent of that market, the soy byproducts called steroids are worth more than $20 billion in their final pharmaceutical form. This is a significant example of adding value by processing, since the byproducts themselves are relatively low-cost.

Soybeans made new headlines in March 1990 as a result of research at the University of Alabama in Birmingham. Soybeans contain several compounds called phytoestrogens that have mild estrogenic activities. Researchers believe that many breast tumors need the hormone estrogen to grow, so doctors often treat breast-cancer patients with an antiestrogen drug known as tamoxifen. It is speculated that phytoestrogens may behave as tamoxifen does (but more weakly) by inhibiting tumor development. When injected with a carcinogen, rats fed a soybean diet developed up to 70 percent fewer tumors than rats not fed soybeans. Asian women who eat soybean-rich diets are up to eight times less likely to develop breast cancer than are American women. Daughters of Asian immigrants who eat an American diet lose this advantage and have the same breast-cancer incidence as Americans. So soybeans, America's $12 billion crop, may have potential in the pharmaceuticals market.

Ginsenosides

North America exported 75 million dollars' worth of ginseng in 1990. Some of it was cultivated, and some of it was wild-harvested. Ginseng goes largely to Orientals who believe in its healing properties. Like those of many herbal medications, these properties are still not proven to the standards of the U.S. Food and Drug Administration.

Dopamine and L-dopa

Persons suffering from Parkinson's disease may already know the compound called L-dopa. It is found in such conventional crops as faba beans (*Vicia faba*) and velvetbeans (*Mucuna* spp). Synthetic derivatives are gradually replacing the natural product. Still, physiologically significant doses of L-dopa may be present in some varieties of faba beans. Rightly or wrongly, some people prefer the natural product to the synthetic.

Limonene

The compound limonene has been touted as a cancer preventive and even as a bactericide, insecticide, and sedative. It occurs in citrus fruits and in such conventional herbs and spices as caraway, celery, fennel, and peppermint.

Lignans

Several lignans, related to the dangerous podophyllotoxin in the wild mayapple, have also shown evidence of activity against certain types of cancers (such as lung cancer) and viruses (such as herpes). Sales of the Bristol-Myers Squibb drug Etoposide, used for lung and testicular cancer, totaled more than $100 million in 1990. Mayapple is not a conventional crop today, but may become so tomorrow if demand for it continues. Closely related lignans

occur in more conventional crops like chervil and flax.

Tryptophan

The amino acid tryptophan is found in all plants and animals. Although tryptophan produced through biotechnology was blamed for several deaths in 1990, those deaths were apparently caused by an impurity, not by tryptophan itself. Some people have grown to rely on tryptophan as a sedative and are seeking natural alternative sources. Better sources of "natural tryptophan" include crops such as bean sprouts, fenugreek, pumpkin, lablab bean, sesame, spinach, watercress, and the relatively new winged bean and evening-primrose (*Oenothera biennis*).

Dr. James Duke, an economic botanist with the Agricultural Research Service in Beltsville, MD, examines an evening-primrose. He has studied many unique plants in an effort to find new uses. Of the 2,800 plants in Maryland, he has found published folk medicinal uses for 700.
Bob Nichols/USDA 90BW1076-26

Solasodine

Australians claim to have developed a cure for skin cancer from eggplant, apparently based on the plant's content of the compound solasodine. One compilation from the U.S. National Cancer Institute indicates that poultices of eggplant were used to treat cancer as early as 1761. Belgians used the leaves to fight cancer, and Antilleans used the fruits. It is reported that some Costa Ricans, Colombians, and Venezuelans apply mashed ripe eggplant fruits in olive oil directly to tumors. A new Australian medicine contains solasodine, but it has not yet been approved in the United States because solasodine could pose some risks. Solasodine can also be an alternative starting material for the steroids mentioned above.

Conclusion

Although plants have a long and varied history of use as folk medicines, many of them are still very much in need of more clinical research to prove their efficacy and verify their safety for human use. The University of Mississippi has established the Center for the Technological Development of Natural Products. It builds on the successes in research and development of medicinal plants at the Research Institute of Pharmaceutical Sciences and the academic departments of the School of Pharmacy. Through the Center, USDA's Agricultural Research Service and Cooperative State Research Service and other Federal laboratories are entering into a partnership with the University of Mississippi and private-sector pharmaceutical companies to discover, develop, and commercialize pharmaceuticals derived from higher plants. The work will come full circle when the plant sources of these products are developed into alternative high-value cash crops for American farmers. ❑

Barnyard Biotechnology May Soon Produce New Medical Therapeutics

29

by Vernon G. Pursel, Caird E. Rexroad, Jr., and Robert J. Wall, Research Physiologists, Gene Evaluation and Mapping Laboratory, Livestock and Poultry Sciences Institute, ARS, USDA, Beltsville, MD

Farm animals may soon play an important role in providing new lifesaving medical products for treating a variety of human diseases. This is certainly not a new role for farm animals. Thousands of people have benefited from biomedical products derived from farm animals. Notable examples include replacement heart valves, insulin to treat diabetes, and oxytocin to induce labor during childbirth.

However, a number of biologically important hormones, enzymes, blood coagulation factors, and immunological agents that are vital to medical therapy are sufficiently different among species that nonhuman sources are simply not effective. In some cases, these rare proteins can be isolated from human blood and tissues, but this isolation procedure is extremely expensive. Also, these materials' limited availability does not meet their demand, and they carry the risk of transmitting infectious diseases such as hepatitis B and AIDS.

In recent years, the genetic codes of a number of these medically important proteins have been deciphered. Using recombinant DNA techniques, copies of the human genes responsible for encoding these proteins can now be transferred into micro-organisms or mammalian cells. In many cases, micro-organisms and cells "transformed" in this manner can read the genetic code of the human gene and produce the desired protein. Some of the less complex hormones, such as growth hormone, are being commercially produced in micro-organisms. Although some of the more complex proteins *can* be successfully synthesized by mammalian cells, maintaining living mammalian cells in large quantities in the laboratory is technically difficult and extremely expensive and, in many instances, even cultivated mammalian cells cannot faithfully produce the desired product.

A potentially more cost-effective means of producing human pharmaceuticals is to actually produce them *in* farm animals. This can be achieved by introducing a copy of the gene for the human pharmaceutical into the farm animal's genome. Animals that contain copies of these genes are called "transgenic animals." Genetically engineered farm animals would be a particularly attractive production system if the gene could be engineered so that the pharmaceutical is secreted into blood, milk, urine, or tissue. This would allow for easy "harvest" of the product.

Gene Transfer Methods

The primary method used to produce transgenic animals is actually quite simple, in principle. Copies of the cloned genes are transferred into embryos through a finely drawn glass capillary tube inserted into the pronucleus of a recently fertilized egg. Microinjection is done under a microscope with the aid of special optics and a micromanipulator to hold the egg and guide the insertion of the tube. After the injection, the eggs are transferred into the oviduct of a foster mother to develop.

For reasons still unknown, only a low percentage of treated eggs incorporate a transgene into one of the chromosomes. However, genes have now been successfully transferred into cattle, goats, pigs, and sheep. In farm animals, about 10 percent of these injected embryos result in a birth, and about 10 percent of the newborn are transgenic. Only about half of these transgenic animals have transgenes that function properly (express the transgene). When these transgenic animals mature and produce offspring,

usually about half of them will inherit the transgene.

Targeting Gene Expression to Specific Tissues

To obtain human proteins from transgenic livestock, the DNA sequences encoding the chosen protein must be linked to the promoter/regulatory DNA sequences known to function specifically in the desired tissue. Although some of the necessary information about how promoter/regulatory DNA functions has already been established through fundamental research with mice, considerable research on gene regulation in farm animals is essential because genetic controls differ among species. For example, when a growth hormone gene was transferred into mice, only low levels of expression were detected, whereas when the same gene was transferred into sheep, extraordinarily high concentrations of growth hormone were produced. To further complicate matters, microinjected genes seem to integrate into chromosomes randomly. This is a problem because it appears that nearby genes can influence the function of the transgene, and consequently the level of gene expression can vary greatly from one transgenic animal to the next.

Mammary Gland as Bioreactor

Many scientists consider synthesis of human proteins in animals' mammary glands to be the most promising alternative to production of proteins in tissue culture. Milk proteins are synthesized by the mammary gland and secreted into milk in large quantities.

The average protein content of milk in dairy cattle and goats is 3.1 percent, while sheep and pig milk average 6.8 and 5.9 percent protein, respectively. A number of the milk proteins are synthesized exclusively in the mammary epithelial cells. Thus, use of promoter/regulatory sequences from the genes for these milk proteins will confine expression of human proteins to mammary glands and should avoid exposing the animal's whole body to the human proteins.

In addition, use of the mammary gland for biosynthesis of human proteins offers the advantages of simplicity for collection of large volumes of raw materials on a continual basis, a relatively low maintenance cost of the four-legged bioreactor after the initial transgenic animals are produced, and the ability to produce numerous progeny if the demand for the therapeutic protein should require it.

Mammary-Specific Expression of Transgenes

The promoter/regulatory sequences that have been investigated for their potential to direct expression of foreign proteins to the mammary gland include sheep beta-lactoglobulin (BLG); cow alpha-S1-casein; rabbit, rat, and cow beta-casein; and mouse whey acidic protein (WAP). Since the casein proteins comprise the majority of protein content in milk, one might expect casein promoter/regulatory sequences to be the most effective for transgenes. So far, this assumption has proven incorrect, possibly because several casein genes are clustered together, which may make their

regulation more complex than for single genes.

Recently, the mouse WAP gene, normally found only in rodent species, was transferred into swine and sheep to test whether it might be effective for expressing transgenes in the mammary glands of livestock. Milk from six lines of transgenic pigs and two transgenic sheep has been evaluated. Mouse WAP made up about 3 percent of the total milk proteins in the transgenic sows and ewes, thus demonstrating that it is possible to produce high levels of a foreign protein in the milk of pigs and sheep.

The mouse WAP promoter/regulator has subsequently been used to control the expression of human protein C in several transgenic pigs at Virginia Polytechnic Institute and State University, Blacksburg, VA. High concentrations of protein C were produced in pig milk, making it commercially feasible to extract and purify this human protein. Protein C plays an important role in the regulation of hemostasis; people with low levels of protein C have recurrence of thrombosis (intravascular blood clots). When sufficient quantities are available, it is anticipated that protein C will prevent blood clot formation in septic shock patients and those who have elective hip replacement surgery. According to projections of the American Red Cross, as soon as a dependable source and clinical effectiveness of protein C have been established, the estimated U.S. market could run as high as 96 kilograms annually with a market value of $960 million.

The mouse WAP promotor/regulator has also been used to express human tissue plasminogen activator (TPA) in a transgenic goat at Tufts University, North Grafton, MA, but only low concentrations of TPA were found. Expression of human TPA, an anticlotting agent currently used to treat patients immediately after a heart attack, had no adverse effect on milk production or general health of the transgenic goat.

The promoter/regulator for beta-lactoglobulin, a major whey protein in the milk of ruminant animals, has been extensively studied by scientists at the Agriculture and Food Research Council, Institute of Animal Physiology and Genetics, Edinburgh, Scotland. In initial studies, only low levels of alpha-1-antitrypsin (AAT) were produced in the milk of transgenic sheep. However, after adding the noncoding regions (sequences known as introns) of AAT, high levels of AAT in milk were obtained from four transgenic sheep. Almost one-half of the protein in the milk of one ewe was AAT, which was a totally unexpected finding.

AAT is being investigated for its potential to treat the more than 20,000 people in the United States who are afflicted with a common hereditary deficiency in AAT that predisposes them to life-threatening emphysema. Currently, AAT is extracted from human blood plasma, but the large quantity needed per patient (about 200 grams per year) makes that source inadequate and expensive—a year's supply costs about $22,000 per patient.

Synthesis of Human Hemoglobin

Hemoglobin is one of several biomedical proteins that cannot be synthesized by the mammary gland but could be produced in other organs of transgenic animals and recovered from the blood. In crisis treatment, hemoglobin would be superior to either whole blood or concentrated red blood cells for transfusions because it does not require refrigeration. Hemoglobin would be particularly useful on the battlefield and for major natural disasters because, unlike red blood cells, it lacks antigenic components and would be compatible with all blood types.

Scientists at the DNX Corporation, Princeton, NJ, have recently reported producing three transgenic pigs that harbor the human alpha and beta globin genes. In these transgenic pigs, about 15 percent of the red blood cells are producing human hemoglobin instead of pig hemoglobin.

After extraction from the red blood cells, the human and pig hemoglobin are separated by ion exchange chromatography. The purified hemoglobin must then be chemically modified so that the protein chains are crosslinked or polymerized. This chemical alteration is critical; otherwise the globin chains would be unstable and incapable of releasing oxygen to the tissues when used for a transfusion.

Previous clinical trials with chemical modification of human hemoglobin, which had been extracted from human donor blood cells, proved to be unsuccessful. Thus, DNX scientists do not expect the human hemoglobin produced from these particular transgenic pigs to be useful for transfusion. However, information gained from studying them will be extremely useful for designing subsequent experiments. The next step is to alter human globin genes in such a way that they are crosslinked and have reduced oxygen affinity, enabling them to readily release oxygen to the tissue. A number of laboratories are currently researching this complex problem.

Problems Remain

Even though several human therapeutical proteins have now been successfully produced in the milk and blood of transgenic animals, some difficult problems must be solved before these products are approved for use. Product safety is an important issue. These products will require the same rigorous scrutiny as the products extracted from animal tissue, produced by tissue culture, or synthesized by other recombinant techniques. Products from transgenic animals must be purified to remove all nonhuman proteins that might cause allergic reactions. In addition, it is still not known whether the complex human proteins produced in transgenic animals have the identical structure and biological activity as the natural proteins produced by the human body.

While scientists are confident that the technical and regulatory challenges can be overcome, few people are willing to predict how long it will take to work out these problems and complete the clinical testing that will be required to obtain Food and Drug Administration approval for marketing. ❑

Innovative 30 Uses of Animal Byproducts

by John P. Cherry, Center Director, Stephen H. Feairheller, Research Leader, Thomas A. Foglia, Lead Scientist, George J. Piazza, Lead Scientist, Gerhard Maerker, Lead Scientist, John H. Woychik, Research Chemist, and Michael Komanowski, Research Engineer, Eastern Regional Research Center, ARS, USDA, Philadelphia, PA

Current Trends in Animal Fats Markets

One of the original recyclers of agricultural byproducts is the U.S. rendering industry. Renderers recycle the growing amount of waste from our huge meat, dairy, and fast-food industries, converting the millions of pounds of byproducts generated daily into not only useful, but essential, products—an estimated annual production of 12 billion pounds of rendered products including inedible tallow and grease, edible tallow and meat, and bone meal. (The terms "inedible" and "edible" refer to use as a human food.)

Edible and inedible tallow presently account for about 6.9 billion pounds of this overall annual production. In recent years, the edible tallow has ranged from 15 to 21 percent of the total output of rendered products. The growth occurred because of increased processing of carcasses at centralized packinghouses and the selective removal of fat from consumer cuts. The net effect of the latter was that the price differential between edible and inedible tallow decreased to about 1 cent per pound.

The major outlet for edible tallow has been as baking and frying fat. Recent U.S. production of edible tallow was 1.2 billion pounds, with increased exports due to decreased domestic consumption.

A large proportion of U.S. production of inedible tallow, 5.7 billion pounds, has also been exported each year; but unlike edible tallow, this amount is shrinking because of a big increase in *domestic* consumption from the use of fat in animal feed and pet food. This increased use of inedible tallow began in the 1950's when scientists at the Eastern Regional Research Center (ERRC), ARS, USDA, in Philadelphia, PA, showed the high nutritional value of these byproducts in animal feed and pet foods. Today, feed fat accounts for 60 percent of domestic usage, compared with 41 percent 10 years ago. This amounts to over 2 billion pounds of feed fat.

The other major outlets for inedible tallow are in industrial applications, such as the manufacture of fatty acids, paints, varnishes, rubber goods, plastics, and lubricants. Overall, inedible tallow's largest market percentages are 96 percent of the feed market for fats and oils; 32 percent of fatty acids as specialty chemicals; 42 percent of soaps; and 69 percent of lubricants.

Enzyme-Processed Fats

The primary constituent of fatty animal byproducts such as tallow and lard is triglyceride, a union of three fatty acids and glycerol. About one-half of the fatty acids are saturated. The other half are composed of oleic acid, a monounsatu-rated fatty acid that is much prized by both the food industry and the industrial sector; this acid converts fats into consumer and industrial products such as soaps, detergents, lubricants, and adhesives. Studies at ERRC have shown that a class of enzymes called lipases can split fatty acids from glycerol. Specific lipases have been shown to selectively split oleic acid from tallow and lard while leaving the saturated fatty acids bound to glycerol, thus giving industry a molecular tool to harvest oleic acid from animal byproducts.

To understand why an enzyme that splits only oleic acids offers such an exciting opportunity to improve on existing procedures, it is necessary to explain how processing is currently done. Large tank cars containing the fats are heated with steam. The melted fats are pumped into a fatty-acid splitter where heat and superheated steam pressure (to 850 °F) are applied. The superheated steam splits the fatty acids from glycerol. As the steam cools, it condenses to water, causing separation of water-insoluble fatty acids and water-soluble glycerol. Distillation is used to separate oleic acid from the saturated fatty acids.

This industrial process has many drawbacks. First, heated fatty acids react rapidly with oxygen in air to form a variety of unwanted side products. To reduce this problem, the entire apparatus—splitters, distillers, and reactors—is continuously flushed with nitrogen. Another current problem is the large amount of energy consumed by the industrial splitting process. This large input increases costs and dampens demand.

In contrast to the high-temperature splitting process, the enzymatic or lipase splitting of the oleic acid could be conducted at room temperature. Once the splitting is complete, oleic acid is relatively easily separated from the saturated diglycerides and monoglycerides and glycerol. In many cases, the oleic acid fraction would be pure enough to sell as is. The purity of the oleic acid fraction depends in large part on the specificity of the lipase. Work to find the most specific lipase, either through the screening of natural sources or through the wonders of molecular biology, is ongoing at ERRC.

Isopropenyl Esters From Fats
Simple fats and welder's gas can be processed in the presence of other common materials to form compounds known as isopropenyl esters, which react rapidly with paper and cotton to make them water-repellent. They can

also be used in glass coatings that reduce breakage in mechanical bottling operations. Scientists and engineers at ERRC have developed high-yield processes for preparing these chemicals.

Isopropenyl stearate, or IPS, is the most commonly prepared and used isopropenyl ester. Stearic acid, a common fatty acid, is readily extracted from tallow, or beef fat. In the presence of zinc compounds, it will react readily with the major component of welder's gas, methyl acetylene, to form IPS that is over 90 percent pure. Other isopropenyl esters are made by similar processes.

In making cotton and paper water-repellent, the stearic acid group from the IPS is transferred to the surface of these materials where it becomes chemically and permanently bound. An important benefit of this reaction is that its byproduct is an innocuous water-soluble organic solvent, acetone. Alternative methods produce byproducts that are highly acidic and corrosive compounds such as hydrochloric acid. These make quality control difficult and costly and shorten the life expectancy of the equipment used in their application. Cotton can be made water-repellent with only low levels of IPS treatment and suffers very little loss of other beneficial properties; similarly, paper treated in this manner repels water and resists feathering caused by writing inks.

Soap/Lime-Soap Dispersant Combinations
Natural soap can be used in hand and bath soaps, as well as in laundry and dish detergents, when combined with

products known as "lime-soap dispersing agents." In hard water, minerals react with the fatty acid components of tallow-based soaps to produce insoluble materials known as lime soaps that are responsible for ring-around-the-bathtub and other similar problems. Lime-soap dispersing agents selectively and effectively combine with the materials in hard water responsible for the formation of lime soaps but, unlike soap itself, they remain in the solution. Furthermore, they are easily made from the same raw materials as the soap and share its ready biodegradability. Thus, soaps and laundry detergents made with these compounds are safe and easy to use for personal care, as well as being environmentally advantageous.

Scientists at ERRC developed processes for making these lime-soap dispersing agents from readily available tallow, beef fat, and other fatty materials. These compounds are anionic, or negatively charged, surfactants called sulfonated methyl esters of fatty acids. Their basic chemical structure is a sulfonated ester of fatty acids, a compound that has both water soluble and insoluble properties. The water-soluble portion is the sulfur-containing portion of the molecule, and the fatty acid is the water-insoluble portion. Hence, these compounds have the ability to interact with oily grime and dirt while maintaining the water solubility necessary for cleansing and for an easy flow down the drain.

Thus, consumer products that contain natural, safe, inexpensive soap can be made from animal fats and used in consumer products in place of petroleum-based synthetic detergents. In the United States, products containing lime-soap dispersing agents are

Laundry detergents containing lime-soap dispersing agents are available in several foreign countries and are under development in the United States.

Keith Weller/*USDA 92BW1156-3*

Part IV. New Products From Traditional Crops

Zest (Proctor and Gamble) and Lever 2000 (Lever Brothers). Laundry detergents containing lime-soap dispersing agents are available in several foreign countries and are under development in the United States.

Collagen Products

In the past 15 years, many attempts have been made to find new applications for the unique physicochemical properties of collagen, a protein derived from animal skins and hides. Nevertheless, gelatin and fibrous edible collagen sausage casings continue to be the two most important commercial outlets, besides leather, for this material.

Consumer products that contain natural, safe, inexpensive soap can be made from animal fats and used in place of petroleum-based synthetic detergents. In the United States, products containing lime-soap dispersing agents are Lever 2000 (Lever Brothers) and Zest (Proctor and Gamble). *Keith Weller/USDA 92BW1157-9*

Hydrolyzed collagen is incorporated in many cosmetic products. Medicinal-grade collagen is currently being marketed as soluble, injectable collagen; devices to reduce bleeding; wound dressings; and tissue repair material. These products are used in general surgery, dentistry, ophthalmology, dermatology, and other medical fields. Currently, the most publicized use is the subcutaneous implantation of soluble collagen for the correction of dermatological defects.

Research in the use of collagen has led to a wide range of applications. Chemically modified collagen for hemostatic work, for example, has enhanced the ability of this protein to absorb fluid while reducing stimulation of the immune system. In the design of fibrous collagen products, the strength of the reconstituted materials is often increased by joining the collagen fibers to each other through chemical bonds. One of the more promising techniques in medicine is the immobilization of enzymes or cells onto collagen matrices for selected removal of disease-causing tissues.

The medical applications for collagen developed in recent years are quite impressive. However, it is the basic knowledge about collagen's chemical and physical properties and the increased understanding of its interaction with human tissues that are inspiring further accomplishments in the protein's use.

Blood and Blood Fractions

Blood is a natural byproduct of the beef and pork meat industries and represents a substantial source of underused, readily digestible, high-quality protein. The plasma fraction that makes up 50 percent of the blood volume has a protein content of about 7 percent, while the red blood cell fraction contains 38 percent protein. Currently, the primary use of this blood has been in the animal feed industry. However, only a small amount of the blood has actually been used by the food industry because of the liquid's instability, its high water content, and food safety concerns. In addition, the red coloration and the smell of blood have been considered negative factors preventing a broader use by the food industry.

Today's food-processing technologies have significantly increased the potential for blood's use by the food industry. Current methods of preservation, fractionation, and drying of the plasma and red cell fractions now yield products that can be used in sausages and other processed meat products such as sandwich cold cuts. Plasma proteins have good gel-forming properties and good water- and fat-binding properties that permit plasma's incorporation into sausage products at levels up to 10 percent. Similarly, the red cell fraction can be used directly in certain processed meat products where the red color contributes a positive quality to the final product. Removal of the heme pigment from hemoglobin by chemical or enzymatic methods produces a decolorized product that can also be used in processed meat products. At present, protein fractions derived from blood are available for use by the food industry. ❑

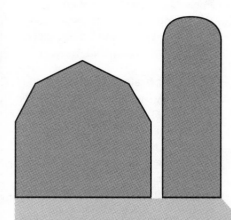

Part V.
Focus on
Renewable Fuels

Developing Biofuels: Federal Programs

31

by Roger K. Conway, Director, Office of Energy, USDA, Washington, DC; Richard Moorer, Director of Biofuels Systems Division, Office of Alternative Fuels, U.S. Department of Energy, Washington, DC; and Mark Dungan, Executive Assistant to the Secretary, USDA, Washington, DC

One of the most promising nonfood markets for farm commodities is transportation fuels.

Concern for the Nation's environment and energy security is growing. Through the 1990 Clean Air Act amendments and the President's National Energy Strategy, President George Bush has urged the Nation to step up its development and use of domestically produced biofuels because they improve environmental quality, reduce dependence on foreign oil, and strengthen national security.

USDA is committed to assisting the President's pursuit of these goals by establishing a cost-competitive, stable supply of environmentally beneficial biofuels. USDA recently developed a biofuels initiative for FY 93 and beyond. And USDA is not alone. The U.S. Department of Energy (DOE), the Environmental Protection Agency, farmers, and industries are important participants in seeing the President's goals fulfilled. For example, USDA and DOE recently signed a Memorandum of Understanding that will greatly facilitate cooperation between the two departments in this area.

USDA Biofuels Initiative

The USDA Biofuels Initiative reflects Secretary Madigan's strong interest in and commitment to helping farmers by increasing the demand for agricultural commodities. Oil imports exacerbate the U.S. trade deficit and reduce energy security, providing even more incentive for an expanded biofuels industry using domestically produced feedstocks.

The initiative focuses on the two primary biofuels: ethanol and biodiesel. The goal of the initiative is to facilitate work on all aspects of biofuel development, including feedstock development, biofuel production, and utilization. To achieve this goal, the initiative identifies three major components: research and development, economic analysis, and information and education.

Research and Development

USDA proposes a major research and development plan to provide the basis for economically viable biofuel production. The research and development areas include: feedstock, conversion, coproducts, product evaluation, and technology transfer.

Most of the feedstock research, which is primarily sponsored by DOE, has focused on biomass, particularly woody and herbaceous crops. An expanded research effort will include oilseed crops. Conventional and biotechnological techniques offer the opportunity to develop plants with potential for producing more fuel. Improved production, harvesting, and storage technologies would also reduce feedstock costs.

Research is progressing in improving technology to convert feedstocks to fuel. Genetic engineering of microorganisms holds promise for improving yields, reducing fermentation times, eliminating undesirable coproducts, and improving separation efficiencies. Improved distillation and dehydration will reduce processing time and energy needed to produce biofuels.

Moreover, making new conversion technologies commercially viable in existing or proposed new facilities requires research to determine what is cost-effective. Several technologies make biodiesel technically equivalent to diesel fuel, but long-term testing also is needed to assess biodiesel engine performance and durability.

Coproduct research focuses on developing a broader range of marketable high-value coparoducts, including food uses and high-volume industrial products, such as biopesticides, building materials, glues, and solvents. Coproduct development is a very important factor in lowering the cost of producing biofuels.

Marvin Bagby, an ARS scientist, demonstrates the viscosity difference in various alternative fuels produced from oilseed crops. USDA is committed to pursuing a cost-competitive, stable supply of environmentally beneficial biofuels.
USDA 0487X390-9

The research and development program reflects the joint planning and information exchange with DOE during the budget process.

Economic Analysis. The economic viability of a new technology must be assessed to determine whether it will be commercially viable. This assessment includes analysis of the feedstock market, as well as the market for products produced. As demand for biofuels increases, the price of feedstocks will rise and farm resources will be reallocated to energy crop production. This response raises two points: Enough additional feedstock must be produced to maintain the cost-competitiveness of the new technology; and sufficient agricultural resources must be available to meet the Nation's other food and fiber demands.

Regarding resources, particular interest has been given to land. Although some cropland may be replaced with energy crops, the precise effect is unclear because nonfood energy crops can be grown on a wide range of lands, such as pasture or forest lands that are in abundant supply. Economic analysis also includes assessing the expansion of feedstocks on rural economies.

Analyzing biofuel markets is another component of economic analysis. With the expanding oxygenate market, analysis will address how future biofuels could compete with high-oxygen fuels made from petroleum. Moreover, another important task will be to identify key economic factors to develop a new market for biodiesel.

Information and Education. Initially, the information and education element of the plan will be directed toward educating the public, decisionmakers, American agriculture, fuel suppliers, and engine manufacturers about biofuels, especially ethanol. A primary goal of the information and education program is to spread the word about the economic and environmental benefits of biofuels.

Enhancing the transfer of technology will be another important component of the information and education program. As new crops and production technologies are developed, it is anticipated that USDA's Extension Service and Soil Conservation Service will put into place proven programs to test and adopt new technology.

Coordinating and Implementing the Initiative. The following organizational structure will be used to provide overall policy and technical guidance and to ensure coordination of research and development,information and education, and economic, environmental, and social analysis efforts:

USDA's Office of New Uses and Energy will have the responsibility to implement the biofuels initiative. It will coordinate activity within USDA and provide the Secretary of Agriculture and the Assistant Secretary for Economics with objective and expert counsel on matters related to the initiative.

The Office of New Uses and Energy will help facilitate a high level of cooperation among USDA agencies, improve coordination with other Federal Agencies, State governments, universities, and private industries, and develop appropriate analyses for government decisionmakers. A primary focus of the Office will be to monitor and evaluate the activities carried out under the research and development, analysis, and information and education plans to ensure that work is focused on high-priority issues. The Office also will provide greater visibility for the Biofuels Initiative by clearly articulating the goals, priorities, and accomplishments of the research and technology program.

DOE Biofuels Program
Research and development and economic analysis are the principal areas where USDA and DOE resources will be coordinated. DOE has been actively engaged in developing new feedstocks for biofuels. Under the direction of DOE's National Biofuels Program, the Terrestrial Energy Crops research activity at Oak Ridge National Laboratory in Oak Ridge, TN, is developing methods to increase the amount of biomass available for energy production.

New technology is also needed to convert these energy crops into fuels. The Department of Energy (DOE) is placing a high priority on developing technologies that convert cellulosic feedstocks, such as grasses and fast-growing trees, to ethanol at a competitive cost. The National Renewable Energy Laboratory of DOE is developing biological systems that use micro-organisms to convert cellulose and hemicellulose into sugars. Cellulose and hemicellulose, the two principal components of wood and grasses, can

be converted to sugars and then fermented to ethanol.

Some cost estimates have been made for using cellulosic feedstocks. In 1979, DOE estimated that the cost of ethanol from biomass would be $3.60 per gallon. Successful research and development have reduced the estimated cost to $1.35 per gallon. The overall goal of DOE's Ethanol Research Program is to further reduce this cost to $.67 per gallon by 2005.

Memorandum of Understanding
In January 1991, DOE and USDA signed a Memorandum of Understanding (MOU) to provide a coordinated framework for a collaborative research and development effort between the two departments to develop renewable energy. The MOU will facilitate joint research efforts between USDA and DOE in feedstock development, conversion techniques, environmental and economic considerations, coproduct development, utilization, and testing.

Consistent with the Administration's National Energy Strategy, each department will mutually support the formulation and execution of research and development programs. Collaboration under the MOU includes information exchange and consultations, exchange of specialists, organization of workshops, and joint projects. The MOU is administered by an Interagency Coordinating Committee consisting of four full-time Federal employees. The MOU will remain in effect for 6 years and may be extended or modified by mutual written agreement.

Activities are already under way. Researcher interaction between the two agencies is continuing on issues related to the cost of producting biofuels, economic analysis, and emissions research. USDA and DOE are coordinating budget activities for biofuels research.

Integrated Biofuels Program Boosts the Rural Economy

Developing a viable biofuels industry, with diversified sources of feedstock and processing facilities, can provide opportunities for rural economic development. An expanded biofuels industry would increase the demand for agricultural commodities, encourage higher value products, enhance farm income, reduce farm program costs, and utilize idle agricultural resources. In addition, crop diversification provides farmers with more planting options and more opportunities to develop an economically integrated and environmentally sustainable production system.

USDA's Economic Research Service estimates that increasing ethanol from present levels to 2 billion gallons annually by 1995 could create almost 19,000 additional jobs, and that increasing production to 5 billion gallons by 2000 could provide 100,000 jobs. A majority of these jobs will be in the feedstock production areas. Since many of the areas include small and medium-size cities, most of the jobs should be available to rural residents.

The biofuels effort will cut across a number of agencies and departments and will involve a high level of coordination and cooperation. USDA will consult, coordinate, and cooperate with DOE and industry and will facilitate the exchange of useful information. Most importantly, with good coordination in a time of budgetary restraint, USDA and DOE can make dollars count to enhance the competitiveness of biofuels.

The potential payoff to agriculture and the Nation is evident from our preliminary analysis. USDA will focus its research and development efforts to further enhance those benefits. ❑

Feedstocks for Biofuels

32

by John McClelland, Agricultural Economist, Office of Energy, USDA, Washington, DC, and John Farrell, Physical Scientist, Office of Alternative Fuels, U.S. Department of Energy, Washington, DC

The term "biofuels" defines a broad range of materials that are biological in nature and used to produce energy. Biofuels include wood for burning, ethanol, and diesel substitutes we will call biodiesel.

Many different types of plant and animal products can be used to produce liquid biofuels for the U.S. transportation sector. Raw materials used to produce liquid fuels are referred to as biofuels feedstocks. In this chapter, we will identify some of the most promising feedstocks, discuss the potential for growing them on a widespread basis in the United States, investigate the economics of biofuels feedstock production, and look at future opportunities for farmers to get involved in the biofuels industry.

In 1991, the United States used almost 120 billion gallons of gasoline and 25 billion gallons of diesel fuel for transportation. The petroleum we use in the transportation sector accounts for about 60 percent of oil we use, and the U.S. transportation sector is 97 percent dependent on petroleum. In 1990, the United States imported an average of 7.2 million barrels of oil per day. Our production of motor gasoline on an average day in 1990 was also 7.2 million barrels, which means that we use all of our imported oil plus some of our domestically produced crude oil to meet daily gasoline demand. The average price of imported crude oil in 1990 was slightly less than $22 per barrel. Our daily oil imports add $158 million to the U.S. balance of trade deficit. About one-third of our imported oil comes from the Middle East and another one-third comes from Latin America and Africa. These factors make oil supplies vulnerable and prices uncertain. Within the past 20 years, the United States has sustained three major oil price shocks.

One solution to the problems posed by our oil supply situation is "home-grown energy." While this sounds good, in practice home-grown energy is a tremendously complex undertaking that will require a lot of work and experimenting. Fortunately, USDA and the U.S. Department of Energy (DOE) have been devoting considerable resources to develop existing and new crops that can be grown and processed into liquid fuels to replace gasoline and diesel.

Dave Tolsted, a Forest Service forestry research technician, samples hybrid poplar chips at the Harshaw Forestry Research Farm, North Central Forest Experiment Station, Rhinelander, WI. One of the potential uses for the wood chips is fuel. The development of new tree species can make it possible to produce significant quantities of liquid fuels from their cellulose and hemicellulose.
Bob Nichols/USDA 92BW0733-34A

Corn

Corn has been the primary feedstock for producing fuel ethanol for more than 15 years. During that period, we have had good supplies of corn with yearly average production in excess of 7 billion bushels. This year, USDA expects farmers to plant nearly 80 million acres of corn, and if yields are good we can expect the 1992 crop to exceed 8 billion bushels.

Corn has several advantages as a biofuels feedstock. Corn is a major agricultural crop. We already know how to grow it, haul it, handle it, and process it. Within the last 50 years, we have made great strides in all of these areas; our yields have increased from about 40 bushels per acre in 1950 to more than 118 bushels per acre in 1990. New processing technologies have made it possible to process corn into starch products such as sweeteners and ethanol, thus expanding the market for corn beyond its conventional use as an animal feed. In 1991 we had about 5 million acres idled in the annual Acreage Reduction Program for corn, and nearly 4 million acres of corn land in the long-term Conservation Reserve Program. In addition, farmers elected to place in conserving use another 2.6 million acres of corn land. This means that if there is significant expansion in corn utilization, we have ample land on which to expand production.

Cellulosic Feedstocks

While the corn-based ethanol industry has grown to nearly 1 billion gallons of annual production over the last 15 years, it is unlikely that corn-based ethanol can supply all of our liquid fuel needs. Therefore, it is important that we look for other sources of agricultural biomass from which renewable biofuels can be produced at a reasonable cost with available resources. Cellulosic energy crops are probably the best alternative for producing ethanol. Conversion of cellulose into ethanol will be discussed in chapter 33, but before conversion can take place, we need to be able to produce ample supplies of feedstock. Crops that produce large amounts of cellulose can be categorized into two groups, herbaceous species and woody species.

Herbaceous Crops. Herbaceous energy crops have more variety and greater versatility then woody energy crops. Some are annual crops such as sweet sorghum or rye, while others are perennials such as switchgrass or reed canarygrass. Depending on conditions, herbaceous energy crops can be either grown in monoculture or interseeded with more than one species in a stand. They can also be double-cropped with other energy crops or with conventional agricultural crops.[1]

A number of grasses and legumes are being evaluated for their potential as energy crops in the DOE Herbaceous Energy Crop Program. Grasses include bahiagrass, bermudagrass, eastern gamagrass, Johnsongrass, napiergrass, reed canarygrass, rye, sudangrass, switchgrass, tall fescue,

---

[1]A.F. Turhollow, J.H. Cushman, and J.W. Johnson, *Herbaceous Energy Crops Program: Annual Progress Report for FY 1988*, U.S. DOE, ORNL, Nov. 1990.

timothy, and weeping lovegrass. Legumes being investigated include alfalfa, birdsfoot trefoil, crownvetch, flatpea, clover, and sericae lespedeza. Field testing is taking place at a number of sites around the country; we will discuss a small sample of these results.

Trials done by Auburn University at four Alabama Agricultural Experiment Station sites examined the performance of bahiagrass, bermudagrass, energy cane, Johnsongrass, napiergrass, sericea lespedeza, switchgrass, sweet sorghum, and weeping lovegrass. Drought in the area during the trial period caused some species to fail to establish. When double cropped with rye, combined yields ranged between about 3 dry tons per acre for bermudagrass at the Sand Mountain

Station to slightly more than 7 dry tons per acre for sweet sorghum in the Upper Coastal Plain. Switchgrass was a consistent performer at all locations, with yields ranging from 3.25 dry tons per acre at Sand Mountain to 4.7 dry tons per acre in the Upper Coastal Plains.

Switchgrass also produced good results in tests conducted by Virginia Polytechnic and State University, yielding as much as 5.7 dry tons per acre. Sericea lespedeza was the best performing legume in these trials, with yields at two sites in excess of 3.75 dry tons per acre. Weeping lovegrass also performed well at two of the Virginia sites, as did crownvetch.

Trials conducted at various New York sites by Cornell University showed alfalfa-bromegrass mixtures to

The Forest Service is researching species of trees, such as hybrid poplar, that are suitable for conversion to ethanol. To be effective, the trees must produce large quantities of wood in a short growing period.

Such species are known as short-rotation woody species, because they are grown and harvested within 3 to 8 years.
Bob Nichols/USDA 92BW0733-20A

be the most productive on the sites where they were planted, with yields of up to 4.8 dry tons per acre. Flatpea also performed well at selected areas, producing as much as 3.75 dry tons per acre. The best producing grasses were reed canarygrass and switchgrass, with maximum yields of 3.4 and 2.9 dry tons per acre respectively.

Studies were also conducted at Geophyta, OH; Purdue University; Iowa State University; and North Dakota State University. (Results of these trials and details of the studies discussed here are available in Turhollow and others.) In general, switchgrass, reed canarygrass, and sweet sorghum appear to perform the best over all geographical regions, with alfalfa being the best performing legume. However, as with trees, some species of grasses and legumes perform better in certain climates and soil types, making species selection very site-specific.

There are advantages and disadvantages to growing herbaceous crops for energy production. The obvious advantage is that many of these crops are already familiar to farmers. Production practices and the equipment used to produce both grasses and legumes are already part of the farmers' knowledge and capital base. Some farmers will be able to choose which energy crops to grow without greatly changing their existing farm plans. Some energy crops will also offer farmers additional opportunities to control erosion, and to fallow or rotate fields.

The major problem with herbaceous energy crops is their bulkiness. Most are harvested in large bales that take up space and are inefficient to transport. There is also considerable loss of biomass material in the harvesting and handling processes. In addition, some of these crops require annual cultivation and other intensive practices in order to produce high yields or to be produced at all. Intensive cultivation may have adverse environmental impacts. There may be many economic tradeoffs that have to be evaluated in the context of the whole farm plan when determining which, if any, energy crops to grow.

Woody Species. Using trees to produce energy is as old as mankind. However, the development of new tree species can make it possible for us to produce significant quantities of liquid fuels from their cellulose and hemicellulose. Species that are suitable for conversion to ethanol must produce large quantities of wood in a short period of time. Scientists call such species "short rotation woody species" because they are grown and harvested within 3 to 8 years.[2] DOE and USDA are currently researching several short-rotation woody species, including hybrid poplar, black locust, eucalyptus, silver maple, sweetgum, and sycamore.

Hybrid poplar has been extensively researched as a potential source of biomass energy in many areas of the United States, including Pennsylvania, Iowa, Michigan, and Washington. Researchers have used advanced tech-

---

[2]L.L. Wright and A.R. Ehrenshaft, *Short Rotation Woody Crops Program: Annual Progress Report for 1989*, U.S. DOE, ORNL, Aug. 1990.

niques from biotechnology to improve the genetic characteristics of the hybrid poplar. For example, techniques such as clonal propagation can be used to produce genetically identical trees that can be tested for their hardiness in a variety of settings. Because growing conditions may vary considerably from site to site in rainfall, temperature, soil type, and diseases that are likely to affect the growing trees, clones that perform well at one site may do poorly at another. With patience and a little luck, researchers can take into account these environmental factors and develop trees that are adapted to specific locations.

Black locust is another promising species of short-rotation tree that has yielded good results in tests throughout the Southeastern United States. In addition to its potential as a high-yielding species, black locust also has the ability to fix nitrogen, which may reduce the need for supplemental nitrogen applications. Research on black locust has not yet determined which genetic traits are the most desirable or what the best method of propagation is. However, results have shown that there are substantial opportunities for increasing biomass yields through genetic selection. To date, the most extensive research results have been with hybrid poplar and black locust.

There are a number of unresolved issues related to short-rotation woody species that must be resolved before they become an economical source of biomass. Costs associated with site preparation and maintenance need to be reduced. One solution that would lower the cost of replanting is to de-velop species that regrow by themselves after cutting. Resistance to disease and drought are other critical factors for ensuring maximum productivity. Many species are susceptible to weed or insect pests, making pest control a high priority for most. Efficient methods for propagating new trees, as well as improvements in harvesting and handling techniques, also could reduce production costs. In addition, the composition of the wood is very important because it must have a high energy content to be economical. Genetic selection will play a major role in solving many of these problems, and the techniques of modern biotechnology provide a means of increasing the pace of development of these species.

Oilseeds, Fats, and Oils

Another potential source of biofuel comes from converting vegetable oils into liquid fuels. Many different oilseed crops are grown in the United States, including soybeans, winter rapeseed, canola, crambe, flaxseed, mustard, peanuts, safflower, sunflower, and cottonseed, which is produced in conjunction with our largest fiber crop. In addition, the United States produces more than 6 billion pounds of inedible tallow that could be used as a biofuel feedstock.

Winter rapeseed, soybeans, and inedible tallow are the most likely sources of oil as feedstock for liquid biofuels. Soybeans are the largest oilseed crop, with nearly 60 million acres planted in a typical year. About 60 percent of annual production is crushed domestically, producing 13-14 billion pounds or 1.8 billion gallons of oil.

USDA and DOE jointly sponsored research on winter rapeseed oil as a diesel fuel substitute at the University of Idaho. Planting trials have also been conducted at the Universities of Georgia and Missouri. Genetic improvement of rapeseed species that will increase productivity has been a major focus of this research effort, along with the development of harvesting and handling systems to minimize harvest and post-harvest loss.

Economics of Biofuels Feedstock Production

A major question about our ability to produce liquid fuels from biomass concerns the economics of the biomass production process. Because there are many potential biomass feedstocks—including trees, herbaceous plants, and oilseeds—farmers will be faced with many options. Evaluating the economic potential of biomass feedstock production is made more difficult because markets for biomass feedstocks are currently limited.

Passage of the Clean Air Act amendments (CAA) of 1990 marked a major overhaul in the Nation's clean air laws. An important change in CAA has been the recognition that motor fuels themselves must be cleaner burning if air quality is to improve. Therefore, the law mandates reductions in fuel components that cause pollution and the addition of oxygen to improve fuel combustion. Given these changes in the Clean Air Act,

the future demand for biofuels, such as ethanol and biodiesel, is likely to increase, and the demand for feedstocks used to make these fuels also will increase.

While it is likely that some large tree farms that are now producing wood for lumber could begin producing wood for biomass, it is unlikely that such farms will be able to supply the quantities of biomass necessary to meet the demand for an expanding biofuels industry. Large quantities of herbaceous biomass will also be needed, and this will require a significant commitment of land and other agricultural resources on the part of farmers.[3]

Aside from the prices of biomass crops, which will be extremely important, several other important factors will play a role in farmers' decisions to grow biomass for energy production. For example: What kind of crops grow well in particular areas? What are the land and machinery requirements? How will growing biomass affect a farmer's participation in Government programs? What is the risk of growing biomass? What level of return is required before farmers will make the decision to grow biomass?

English and others have begun an extensive investigation of how growing biomass fits into the farm plan of typical farmers across the United

[3]B.C. English, R.R. Alexander, K.H. Loewen, S.A. Coady, G.V. Cole, and W.R. Goodman, *Development of a Farm-Firm Modelling System for Evaluation of Herbaceous Energy Crops*, U.S. DOE, ORNL, Jan. 1992.

States. Biomass production is an alternative that depends on the financial performance of the farm enterprise. It has potential impacts on biomass markets, the markets for other commodities, and the environment. A careful analysis of financial performance must consider factors such as input prices, taxes, insurance, land rental rates, equipment costs, labor costs, interest rates, output prices, inflation, oil prices, and Government programs.

Land availability is a major issue in determining the viability of a sustained biomass production program. In recent years, U.S farmers have placed in conserving use more than 60 million acres of cropland. This includes about 35 million acres in the Conservation Reserve Program, whose contracts will begin expiring in 1996. Some of this land may be suitable for producing perennial herbaceous energy crops, like switchgrass, or trees that would continue to provide erosion control while generating cash income for farmers. By incorporating energy crop production into farm plans, farm operators could bring set-aside acres into useful production using legumes or other herbaceous crops in rotation with traditional crops. The result could be an increase in farm income along with the economic benefits of increased use of productive resources.

In addressing questions of financial performance for individual farmers, English and others developed an analytical framework to evaluate representative farms in specific geographic locations. They considered factors such as farm size, soil types, susceptibility to erosion, current crop mix, and participation in Government programs. Their overall results indicated that farms producing biomass such as switchgrass offered farmers returns that are comparable or superior to enrolling highly erodible land in the Conservation Reserve Program. In addition, growing biomass in conjunction with other crops would maintain erosion control, diversify farm output, reduce farmers' risk to changes in output prices, and lower farm program costs.

Conclusions

There is great potential for producing liquid fuels from biomass feedstocks. USDA and DOE have been assessing the potential of a variety of biomass feedstocks. Land resources are available for growing biomass, but more work needs to be done to match the best crops with the best locations. Farmers will have to dedicate the necessary resources to biomass production if significant amounts are to be produced. However, biomass crops are complementary to corn, soybeans, and other traditional agricultural crops, and they should be considered as part of the whole farm plan.

Biomass production could improve the financial performance of farms in many areas of the country, and it has the potential to reduce farm program payments. Development of the domestic biofuels industry could provide significant opportunities for farmers and rural America through the increased employment of resources and people. ❑

Conversion of Biomass to Fuel and Energy

33

by W.L. Harris, National Program Leader for Engineering and Energy, Agricultural Research Service, USDA, Beltsville, MD, and Howard N. Rosen, Energy Coordinator, Forest Service, USDA, Washington, DC

In 1991, biomass provided over 3.5 quads (a quad is a measure of energy that equals 1 quadrillion British Thermal Units, or Btu's) of the energy used in the United States. This was equivalent to the energy contained in 604 million barrels of oil which equals about 22 percent of annual U.S. oil imports.

Of this biomass energy:
- Half was used for direct heating applications in the industrial sector. For example, the wood and paper products industry uses residues from its operations to supply almost all heating and about half of the electricity needed in making their products.
- One-quarter was used for residential heating using wood and wood residues.
- Wood and biomass from agricultural processing operations and municipal solid wastes were used to generate three-quarters of a quad of electrical energy for utility companies.
- One billion gallons of ethanol, approximately 0.1 quad made primarily from corn, was used in transportation fuels.

Some of the technologies for using biomass for energy are mature, for example, burning wood for heating and generating electricity, and making ethanol from sugar and starch. Other technologies are just emerging, for example, converting cellulosic material from agricultural and forestry crops and residues into ethanol, and making biodiesel from oilseed crops and animal fats.

The potential for increasing the production of liquid fuels and energy from biomass is very large. Some estimates of this energy potential are as high as 26 quads per year. A significant expansion will depend, at least partially, upon the continued improvements in mature technologies and the development of cost-effective technologies for converting cellulosic material into ethanol, and oil from oilseed crops into biodiesel. Demand for these specific fuels and the costs of competing fuels will also influence the rate of expansion.

Ethanol From Corn—New Technologies

Although interest in ethanol as an automotive fuel began in the early 1900's, the modern fuel ethanol industry began with the oil shortage in the early 1970's. It has grown from virtually zero production to a billion gallons a year. More than 95 percent of the fuel ethanol produced in the United States uses corn as the feedstock. The remainder is produced from molasses; other grains such as milo, wheat, and barley; and industrial and food processing waste products such as potato culls and cheese whey.

In 1991, more than 370 million bushels of corn were used to produce ethanol. Corn is used because of its availability and high starch content. The two main methods use proven wet- and dry-milling grain processing technologies. Dry milling is based on traditional technology for the manufacture of potable alcohol, while the wet-milling process is based on the refining of corn to starch and fructose. Except for the initial separation process, the technology for the conversion of the starches to fuel ethanol is generally the same for both types of milling methods.

Dry Milling. In the dry-milling process, corn is milled and mixed with steam and enzymes to liquefy the starch component. The next step in the process converts the liquefied starch to sugars by adding additional enzymes. The sugars are fermented to ethanol using yeast. The mixture leaving the fermenter is distilled into 190-proof ethanol (95 percent ethanol and 5 percent water) and residues, which are called whole stillage. The ethanol is dehydrated to produce the 200-proof fuel grade. A process developed at Purdue University with USDA support uses corn grits to adsorb the water in the dehydration phase and reduces the cost of production by approximately 3-4 cents per gallon. Water is removed from the whole stillage by mechanical

More than 95 percent of the fuel ethanol produced in the United States is produced from corn. The remainder is produced from molasses, milo, wheat, barley, and industrial and food processing waste products, such as potato culls and cheese whey.
USDA IA-2851-19A

and drying processes to produce the distillers dried grains with solubles (DDGS), which is used as an animal feed.

Using current technology, dry mills can produce 2.6 gallons of fuel-grade ethanol and approximately 16.5 pounds of DDGS per bushel of corn. The carbon dioxide (CO_2) that is produced may also be collected from the fermentation tanks for use in the beverage and food processing industry. The three products are produced in approximately equal amounts, or one-third each of the initial weight of the bushel of corn.

Wet Milling. In the wet-milling process, corn is separated into the germ, fiber, gluten, and starch components. The first step in the separation process involves soaking or steeping the corn in a mixture of water and sulfur dioxide. The soft kernels are then milled to separate the germ from the starch. The germ is dried and the oil removed. The remaining slurry is screened to remove the fibers and then centrifuged to separate the gluten. The gluten is dried to produce corn gluten meal, which is used as an animal feed. The starch is liquefied and converted to sugar, which is fermented, distilled, and dehydrated to produce fuel-grade ethanol. The thin stillage from distillation is combined with water used for steeping and the solids removed by evaporation and added to the recovered fiber to produce corn gluten feed. The corn gluten feed is exported, primarily for dairy cattle feed.

Ethanol yields from wet milling are slightly lower than yields from dry-milling plants. In addition to about 2.5 gallons of ethanol from a bushel of corn, there are about 1.7 pounds of corn oil, 3 pounds of corn gluten meal (60 percent protein), 13 pounds of corn gluten feed (21 percent protein), and 17 pounds of carbon dioxide.

Dry-milling plants generally require lower initial investment than comparably sized wet-milling plants. However, the higher cost of the wet-milling plant may be offset by the higher value of the coproducts produced.

Promising Newer Technologies. Improvements have been made during the past 10 years in reducing the energy consumption for processing the corn into ethanol and in increasing the efficiency in converting the starch to sugar and fermenting the sugar into ethanol. In 1981, the energy required for processing exceeded 120,000 Btu's per gallon of ethanol produced, approximately 40,000 Btu's per gallon more than the energy content of a gallon of ethanol. In 1991, the energy consumption for processing averaged only 43,000 Btu's per gallon. The reductions in energy use have resulted from efficiency improvements throughout the entire plant, ranging from the cogeneration of electric power and steam to the use of corn grits and molecular sieves to remove the last 5 percent of the water in the ethanol.

Improved enzymes for converting the starch to sugars permit more efficient conversion at lower enzyme costs. New yeasts for fermentation have resulted in shorter fermentation times, higher levels of ethanol in the fermenter, lower residual sugars, and more sugars being converted. Higher ethanol concentrations have resulted in lower processing costs, as less water needs to be removed.

One new approach developed at a land-grant university for preparing corn to improve the efficiency of ethanol production is to inject gas to reduce the steeping time; this treatment of the corn kernels facilitates the separation of starch and protein from the other components, reducing the time required from approximately 40 hours to 8 hours.

The current method for converting the grain starch to glucose sugar involves a series of processes using enzymes. Research using membrane technology has shown that the time can be reduced from approximately 48 hours to about 5 hours.

Using the new tools of biotechnology, researchers are developing new yeasts that are both more resistant to the concentration of ethanol in the fermenter and more heat-tolerant. As indicated earlier, the higher the concentration the less water will have to be removed. Less energy will also be required for distillation because the beer broth will enter at a higher temperature.

New technology is also under development that will improve the removal of both the water from the ethanol and the solids from the water that has been removed from the DDGS or corn gluten feed. An open heat pump is used to take vapor from the top of a distillation column and mix it with the incoming beer broth in order to reduce the size of the heating plant and the overall energy require-

ments. The use of molecular sieves and pervaporation technology, which involves membranes operating in a vacuum, is being tested by a number of universities and private companies. These technologies could reduce the energy currently required for both distillation and drying of the DDGS and corn gluten feed.

Additional uses for the carbon dioxide and the solids (DDGS and corn gluten feed) are under development. Technology from the work on converting the cellulose and hemicellulose in energy crops is being used in studies to convert corn hulls to ethanol. Technology to convert carbon dioxide into higher value products, such as acetic acid, would reduce the percentage of ethanol production costs that would go to buying the corn or other raw material. Work is focused on improving the structure and functional properties of corn proteins for use in food products such as spaghetti, cornmeal, soy flour, and nonfat dry milk. Efforts are also being made to use the solids as feedstocks for high-volume industrial products such as biopesticides, building materials, glues, and solvents.

Ethanol From Cellulosic Material

Although ethanol is produced from starch-rich materials such as corn and sugarcane, ethanol can also be made from cellulosic biomass materials such as wood, forage, and wastes. Cellulosic materials are composed primarily of cellulose, hemicellulose, and a binding material called lignin. The process for producing ethanol from cellulosic materials is somewhat more complex than that for starch-rich materials, but the supply potential for cellulosic materials is greater.

The three primary cellulosic waste categories that offer the potential for ethanol production are agricultural residues, forestry residues, and municipal solid waste.

> # Although ethanol is produced from starch-rich materials such as corn and sugarcane, ethanol can also be made from cellulosic biomass materials such as wood, forage, and wastes.

Agricultural residues include stalks and other fibrous materials from food materials. Forestry residues include that material remaining after the harvest of timber (branches, small trees, foliage, and roots) as well as materials not used at sawmills for producing wood products. The final category, municipal solid waste, includes waste paper, yard wastes, and waste wood materials. Surprisingly, municipal solid waste is composed of 40 percent by weight cellulosic material. The potential for ethanol production of all

this material could contribute about 4 quads to our energy needs.

Besides waste materials, the United States has enough existing and potential crop and forest land to produce 10-23 quads of cellulosic ethanol a year, depending on how the land is used. Land could be supplied from existing crop land which has excess agricultural capacity, potential crop land now in noncrop use, or forest land. These lands could be used specifically for growing cellulosic plants for conversion to ethanol. Additional research is needed to develop growing and harvesting strategies for wood or herbaceous high-productivity energy crops (HPEC) or short-rotation intensive culture (SRIC) tree plantations for the production of energy.

There are two general methods for producing ethanol from cellulosic material. The first is acid-catalyzed hydrolysis of biomass to sugars, followed by fermentation of the sugars to ethanol. The second method involves chemically or physically pretreating the biomass to yield a product from which the cellulose or hemicellulose can be hydrolyzed by enzymes to sugars. The sugar is then fermented to ethanol as in the acid hydrolysis method.

The production of ethanol from cellulosic residues is not new. Acid hydrolysis plants already existed in the United States during World War I for the production of ethanol. These plants closed after the war because of decreased supply and increased costs of material.

The chemistry for the production of cellulosic materials by hydrolysis has been known for over a century. The basic chemistry and processing are not very complex, but difficulties in practical application remain. The gathering of raw materials that are usually spread over large areas, the separation of contaminants (such as dirt, stones, and metals), prior to chemical processing, and the processing of a large variety of cellulosic material types are all problems that have slowed the development of ethanol production from cellulosic feedstocks.

Acid hydrolysis methods for producing ethanol from cellulosic materials can be divided into the dilute and concentrated acid methods. The dilute acid method of conversion involves subjecting cellulosic materials to a 0.5-1.0 percent sulfuric acid solution at temperatures from 150 to 180 °C. Concentrated acid hydrolysis using 40 percent hydrochloric or 72 percent sulfuric acid at 30 to 40 °C is also possible. The concentrated acids give higher yields because less sugar is decomposed at the lower temperatures, but the corrosive nature of the concentrated acids has resulted in high capital investment costs for this method.

Enzymatic hydrolysis requires pretreatment to render the material more accessible to the enzymes that enter into the hydrolysis reactions. Possible pretreatments include steam, milling, solvent, acids, and alkali. This process uses enzymes to break down the cellulose and hemicellulose into sugars at ambient or slightly above ambient temperatures. Although reaction rates are slower and the raw material must be pretreated, this process gives greater yields and fewer waste product disposal problems than acid hydrolysis. The enzymatic hydrolysis process is at a much earlier state of technological maturity, and major breakthroughs could make the process more economical than the acid hydrolysis process.

The use of ethanol from biomass has implications for global climate change. Carbon dioxide production comes from fermentation of the carbohydrate fraction of biomass to ethanol, combustion of unfermentable biomass fractions not converted to ethanol, and the combustion of ethanol itself. However, photosynthesis will remove carbon dioxide from the atmosphere during growth of energy crops, and the contribution of carbon dioxide to the atmosphere should be less than would result from using an equivalent amount of fossil fuel energy.

Although the cost of producing ethanol from cellulosic materials has been reduced, it is still higher than for gasoline. Significant innovations are needed to reduce the procuring and processing costs for cellulosic materials. Several promising areas of emphasis include:

- Harvesting methods for forest and herbaceous biomass materials
- Management of high-productivity energy crops and short-rotation intensive culture, including weed control, insect resistance, and genetically improved species
- Improvements in separation processes to remove contaminants from feedstock
- New and improved enzymes to increase the rate and conversion yield of cellulosic material to sugars

- Genetically engineered systems to improve breakdown to ethanol
- Pretreatments to increase hydrolysis efficiency
- Control over the quality and quantity of coproducts

The production of ethanol from cellulosic biomass is an emerging technology that ties directly into our country's National Energy Strategy. Successful innovations in procuring raw materials and processing cellulosic materials should make ethanol derived from cellulosic material an economic reality in the 21st century.

Biodiesel From Oilseed Crops

Biodiesel is a diesel-type fuel made from oils extracted from oilseeds and plants, or from animal fats, which can be used in unmodified diesel engines. The raw oils and fats must be modified by some chemical and/or thermal processes to reduce their viscosity and lower their high boiling point.

Many researchers have sought technologies to extract oil from seeds having high oil contents. Other researchers have evaluated the performance of the unprocessed oil in diesel engines. The interest is due, in a large degree, to the quantities of diesel fuel used in the critical sectors of the U.S. economy, such as production agriculture and the movement of food and other essential items by truck, rail, and boat. Currently, more than 25 billion gallons of diesel fuel are used annually in the United States. Production agriculture alone uses 2.5 billion gallons annually.

Evaluation of the unprocessed oil as a replacement and as a blend with diesel fuel revealed problems with engine deposits, ring sticking, injector coking, and increased viscosity of the lubricating oil. Results of research by USDA and several universities indicated that the problems were caused primarily by the high viscosity (thickness) and low volatility (high boiling point) of vegetable oils. The conclusion was that unprocessed oils may be used on a short-term basis both as a replacement and in blends; however, they are not dependable substitutes for long-term operations.

Researchers then began looking for ways to change the chemical and physical properties that would overcome the problems caused by the unprocessed oils. Three major technologies were developed and evaluated:

(1) Oils were blended with alcohols such as ethanol and methanol, plus a chemical additive (such as a detergent) to form stable microemulsions. An excellent blend was created, but too much carbon was formed on the interior parts of the engine.

(2) Techniques for cracking (heating) the unprocessed oil to reduce the boiling point were developed. The new chemical product contains acids that require a technology to neutralize them.

(3) The unprocessed oils were chemically converted (transesterified) to less complex chemicals known as fatty esters by combining the oils with alcohols, using a catalyst such as potassium hydroxide. Methyl and ethyl esters made from soybean and indus-

trial rapeseed oils using methanol or ethanol were found to have properties similar to diesel fuel and could be directly substituted in unmodified engines without significantly reducing performance or expected engine life.

A wide range of oilseed crops have been studied. We will discuss research conducted by scientists at the University of Idaho on industrial rapeseed oil to illustrate the process for making methyl ester.

A batch process using 40 gallons of rapeseed oil, 9 gallons of methanol, and 3.2 pounds of potassium hydroxide produces 40 gallons of methyl ester and almost 9 gallons of glycerine. The 40 gallons of oil were mechanically extracted from 860 pounds of seed. The 560 pounds of meal that remained contained 32 percent protein and over 10 percent residual oil.

In addition to the value of the meal as animal feed, the glycerine is valuable too, as it is used in various commercial products such as resins, cellophane, pharmaceuticals, and urethane foam. Natural glycerine is made from vegetable oils, and synthetic glycerine is made from propylene. Annually, over 10 million pounds are imported.

Several 200-hour engine tests, conducted in accordance with the Engine Manufacturer's Association specifications, indicated no significant adverse impacts on the engine; performance was similar to that of engines operating on diesel fuel. Limited emission testing in the United States and tests conducted in Europe with biodiesel and comparing biodiesel with diesel test results indicate: (a) little or no sulfur is emitted, (b) particulate and carbon monoxide are significantly reduced, (c) hydrocarbons are somewhat reduced, and (d) nitrogen oxides are similar.

Animal fat—and most any oilseed crop, including soybeans, rape, sunflowers, peanuts, and cotton—may be used to make biodiesel. Currently, biodiesel is not economically competitive with diesel fuels. Continued increases in the oilseed yield per acre and improved processing technology will help close the gap.

Direct Combustion of Biomass

The most common method of converting biomass to energy is direct burning or combustion. About 15 percent of the world's primary energy is derived from biomass, predominantly used in rural areas of developing countries. The use of biomass for energy has increased in the developing countries. In the United States today, more wood is used annually for energy production—from industrial waste to logs burning in the fireplace—than the amount used for the combined production of lumber and paper.

Although biomass from agricultural residues such as bagasse has been used to generate energy by direct combustion, most biomass energy is obtained from woody forest products. The surge in petroleum costs in the middle 1970's increased the use of biomass combustion to generate industrial energy, mainly in the forest products industry, which went from about 40 percent energy self-sufficiency to 70 percent in just a few years. The non-forest-based industries consume less than 5 percent of the wood energy used in the U.S. industrial sector.

The first step in the combustion of biomass is the evaporation of water that is present. Next, the volatile components, both combustible and noncombustible, are driven off at temperatures from 100 to 600 °C. Finally, the carbon in the biomass is oxidized.

The combustion process involves combining the carbon from the wood with oxygen to form carbon dioxide as well as combining the hydrogen from the wood with oxygen to form water. Heating values for biomass depend greatly on the initial amount of moisture in the material. Moisture reduces the heating value of biomass and thus biomass is usually dried or "seasoned" to improve its burning characteristics. For example, the heating value for dry wood is between 8,000 and 9,000 Btu per dry pound, which is about half that of gasoline. Wood with higher moisture content has a lower heating value.

Energy generated from biomass can be converted directly to heat, for example in a home fireplace; into process steam, such as for a steam-heated press for making plywood; or into electricity, such as in a processing plant. The basic equipment for using biomass energy for a variety of purposes has been available for many years, but as improved processing equipment comes on the market, new opportunities arise for more efficient use of biomass energy.

One application of biomass fuel is the generation of commercial electrical energy. Several commercial instal-

lations exist today, but these plants are small, 10-50 megawatts per year, and require considerable biomass for their power. For example, 500,000 wet tons of biomass per year are required to run one 50-megawatt plant. Continued availability of supply within a reasonable distance of the power plant is a major consideration for deciding whether to build a biomass-fired electrical power plant.

Biomass fuels have been mechanically converted to other fuel forms such as pellets, briquettes, and compressed logs. These forms of biomass fuel are expensive because of the extra steps required to form the fuel, and they are not used to any great extent in the United States.

The outlook for the use of forest biomass is good, but projections should be made with caution. The environmental effect of large-scale biomass operations must be determined and public concerns considered. Biomass can be effectively removed from many areas in this country with beneficial effects on the environment.

Besides the environmental considerations, many other areas of work in biomass combustion still need to be explored. The basic combustion process for converting biomass to energy still needs to be understood better, so that burning efficienciy can be improved and particulate emissions from burners can be reduced. Burning of waste materials containing contaminants needs to be explored so that direct combustion of municipal solid waste will be safe and the ash can be disposed of effectively. Better harvesting and transportation systems are

Part V. Focus on Renewable Fuels

needed to get the biomass to market as economically as possible.

Conclusions

We have made great progress in our development of technologies that convert biomass into energy. New technologies present the opportunity to expand our use of this resource more efficiently.

Making liquid transportation fuels from biomass economically and in large quantities could provide the Nation with a renewable source of fuel while reducing our dependence on imported oil. New technologies have made it possible to produce liquid fuels in large quantities, and in some cases the economics are becoming more favorable. However, the most important developments in technology and commercialization lie ahead. The greatest challenges are to learn how to utilize biomass material in a way that produces the maximum possible

amount of fuel at the minimum cost. For the material that cannot be converted into fuel, we need to develop new and higher value uses.

Biomass fuel technologies can also help mitigate the problems with waste disposal that threaten our land and water resources. By converting some of this waste into liquid fuels, a critical need in the transportation sector is filled. When combustion is the more economical alternative, valuable electricity and process steam are produced. At the same time, emissions are reduced when compared to burning coal.

Biomass energy offers many advantages to us as a renewable, domestically produced source of liquid fuel, electricity, and process steam. However, research dollars must continue to be invested in the development of new technologies that improve the economic efficiency of biomass fuel sources. ❑

The Ethanol 34 Market: Facing Challenges and Opportunities

by Hyunok Lee, Agricultural Economist, and Roger Conway, Director, Office of Energy, USDA, Washington, DC

President George Bush has issued a challenge to America. On November 15, 1990, President Bush signed the Clean Air Act (CAA) of 1990—the first clean air bill in 13 years. This act targeted automobile fuel emissions as a major source of air pollution. The

act mandates the use of cleaner burning fuels in problem areas to improve the Nation's mobile-source air pollution. Ethanol is one such fuel. Ethanol can help us reach our urban air-quality goals by reducing automobile emissions, the primary cause of air pollution in the United States.

Besides helping to achieve the Nation's goal of cleaner air, ethanol can also help create new value-added markets for our farmers, while it enhances our Nation's energy security with domestically produced, renewable fuels.

Ethanol's Evolving Role

Once considered a simple fuel extender, the role of fuel ethanol has evolved, first to an octane enhancer and then to an oxygen provider. As a gasoline extender, fuel ethanol had little market impact given ethanol's small market share in the U.S. fuel market. As ethanol's octane value was recognized, the resulting economic effects of ethanol were seen to be more positive. However, ethanol has played only a minor role in the octane market since other means—both economical and preferred by refiners—were available to boost the octane level. Such a market role for ethanol, however, changed with the passage of the Clean Air Act. The oxygen requirements mandated by the CAA spurred a market for oxygenates and ethanol's oxygenate value added a new dimension to the ethanol market. To fully appreciate the economics of ethanol, it is important to understand how ethanol's role has evolved over time in the U.S. transportation fuel economy.

Gasoline Extender/Octane Enhancer. From the turn of the century, both pure ethanol and ethanol blended gasolines were used on a limited basis for automobiles in the United States. The real impetus for commercialization came in the 1970's as a result of the oil embargoes of 1973 and 1979.

Fuel ethanol was then considered a means of extending the Nation's gasoline supply and aiding U.S. energy security. To provide economic incentives to ethanol producers, the Federal and State governments initiated support under tax incentives and loan programs. Those initial government programs played a positive role in the commercial development of ethanol as a gasoline extender.

Other types of government actions (mostly regulatory, environmental policies) also greatly influenced the ethanol industry. While the old concerns about energy security not only remained but also increased, new problems emerged in the arena of public health and the environment. In the late 1970's, the Environmental Protection Agency (EPA) initiated a public program to remove lead that was added to gasoline to boost the octane level. Ethanol, with its high-octane property, soon established its role as an octane enhancer. Blending ethanol at 10 percent (E10) raises the gasoline's octane level by an average of three octane points (table 1).

As an octane enhancer, ethanol had to compete with other octane enhancers. In the early 1980's, methanol blends gained a short popularity but soon disappeared from the market due to public health risks associated with methanol's toxicity as well as to its undesirable corrosive effects on engines and pipelines. While methanol blends did not experience a wide market success, a methanol-derived ether called methyl tertiary butyl ether (MTBE), also used to raise octane content, became popular as a blending

Part V. Focus on Renewable Fuels

Table 1. Oxygen and Octane Properties of Ethanol, E10, MTBE, ETBE*, and Gasoline

Property	Ethanol	E10	MTBE	ETBE	Gasoline
Octane number, approximate (R+M)/2**	113	90	112	111	87
Oxygen content (by weight)	34.7%	3.47%	18.2%	15.7%	0%

Source: Information Resources
* E10: 10 percent ethanol blended gasoline, MTBE: methyl tertiary butyl ether, ETBE: ethyl tertiary butyl ether.
** The two recognized laboratory engine test methods for determining the antiknock rating of gasolines are the Research method (R) and the Motor method (M). The antiknock index, which is the average of the octane numbers generated from the two methods, provides a single number as guidance to the consumer.

agent. MTBE, first produced in 1979 in the United States and Europe, was developed primarily as an octane enhancer by combining isobutylene and methanol. Unlike ethanol, MTBE can easily be blended with gasoline at the refinery and transported by pipeline.

Ethanol as an Oxygenate

In recent years, interest in ethanol has centered around its oxygenate use to attain urban air-quality goals through the reduction of automobile fuel emissions. The key chemical factor that differentiates ethanol from gasoline is the presence of oxygen in ethanol and its absence in typical hydrocarbon gasoline. The 1990 CAA calls for the use of oxygenated fuels in the oxygenated fuels program to control carbon monoxide problems and also as part of the reformulated gasoline program to control ozone problems. Refiners and blenders must use oxygenates, including ethanol, ethyl tertiary butyl ether (ETBE), MTBE, or tertiary amyl methyl ether (TAME), to meet the regulations.

Two titles of the Clean Air Act pertain to mobile-source air pollution. Title I defines standards for nonattainment areas where air-quality goals are not met and calls for specific actions to reduce air pollution in those areas. Title II mandates the sale of oxygenated gasoline in carbon monoxide nonattainment areas, and it also mandates the sale of reformulated gasoline in ozone nonattainment areas as defined in Title I. Ethanol has a role in both.

Carbon Monoxide Control. Carbon monoxide in an urban atmosphere comes primarily from the exhaust emissions of internal combustion engines. However, the presence of oxygen in the fuel raises the effective air-to-fuel ratio for combustion and reduces carbon monoxide (CO) emissions.

Thirty-nine of the Nation's urban areas are designated as either moderate or serious CO nonattainment areas. Approximately 21 percent of the U.S population is estimated to live in these CO nonattainment areas. The CAA mandates the oxygenated fuels program in these areas, and requires a minimum oxygen content in fuel of 2.7 percent by weight for a period of no less than 4 winter months, beginning no later than November 1, 1992. In some of the worst CO problem areas, such as Denver, Phoenix, and Tucson, oxygenated fuel use has already been required during the winter.

Most fuel oxygenates are derived from nonrenewable sources. The most widely used oxygenate in the market today is the methanol-derived ether, MTBE. Methanol is made mostly from natural gas and is converted into an ether by chemically combining it with a tertiary olefin, such as isobutylene or isoamylene, which respectively produce MTBE and TAME. TAME is not currently produced but it may have a future in the oxygenate market.

Ethanol contains a higher oxygen content than MTBE: ethanol has a 35-percent oxygen content by weight while MTBE has an 18-percent oxygen content by weight (table 1). In terms of the oxygen content, 1 gallon of ethanol is equivalent to 1.95 gallons of MTBE. To achieve a fuel with 2.7 percent oxygen would require a 15-percent blend for MTBE and a 7.7-percent blend for ethanol.

Ground-level Ozone Control. Almost half of the total U.S. population lives in ozone nonattainment areas. Ozone pollution not only causes a number of human health problems, but

The Clean Air Act mandates the use of cleaner burning fuels in problem areas to reduce the Nation's mobile-source air pollution. Ethanol is one such fuel. Ethanol can help us reach urban air-quality goals by reducing emissions, the primary cause of air pollution in the United States.
Ken Hammond/USDA 92BW0797-24A

Part V. Focus on Renewable Fuels

it may also contribute to global warming as a greenhouse gas. Urban ozone is generated from ultraviolet light acting on local concentrations of volatile organic compounds (VOC's), CO, and nitrogen oxides (NOx). VOC's result from the evaporation of gasoline and other solvents, and from vehicle exhaust. NOx results mainly from burning fossil fuels, including gasoline and coal.

Under the CAA Amendments, Title II requires the use of oxygenated fuels as part of the reformulated gasoline program for controlling ground-level ozone formation. Gasoline must be reformulated to meet the fuel formula and performance standards. The fuel formula required is: NOx no greater than baseline fuel, a minimum of 2 percent oxygen by weight, a benzene content not to exceed 1 percent by volume, no heavy metals, and a maximum of 25 percent of aromatics by volume. The performance standard sets the reduction limits on the emission of ozone-forming VOC's and air toxics, relative to baseline fuel.

Beginning in January 1995, reformulated gasolines are required to be sold in the nine highest ranking ozone nonattainment areas including the areas of Los Angeles, New York, Hartford, Baltimore, Philadelphia, Chicago, Milwaukee, Houston, and San Diego. In addition to those areas, 87 more areas are designated as ozone nonattainment areas. The CAA allows

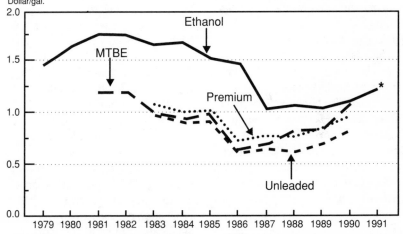

Figure 1

Historical prices of ethanol, unleaded, premium and MTBE

Dollar/gal.

Ethanol: Monthly avg. of Decatur prices. *Projected. Source: IRI
MTBE: Monthly avg. of New York spot prices. Prices prior to 1981 are not available.
    Source: Oxy-Fuel News, Alcohol Week
Unleaded gasoline, Premium gasoline: Monthly avg. of U.S. retail, before-tax prices.
    Source: Energy Information Administration, DOE.

ozone nonattainment areas to "opt in" voluntarily to the reformulated gasoline program.

The Role of Oxygen in Ozone Control. While there is general acceptance that oxygen in gasoline alleviates the CO problem, the role oxygen plays in ground-level ozone formation is not fully understood at this point. VOC's and NOx problems have been mentioned as issues regarding ethanol blends. According to EPA's guidelines for reformulated gasoline, ethanol is currently considered to be NOx-neutral only up to 2.1 percent oxygen unless emissions data show otherwise. Lower CO levels may reduce ground-level ozone through atmospheric chemical processes. If verified, this means that some of the predicted increase in ozone resulting from the use of E10 may be offset by the reduction in CO. This neutralizing effect of CO on ozone formation would vary from city to city because CO and ozone are seasonal problems.

There is still a great deal of uncertainty about ground-level ozone formation, particularly as to how a certain chemical compound reacts in different atmospheric combinations. This issue is called the "reactivity" factor. To enhance the effectiveness of ethanol blends as a measure to control ozone, more research is needed on the reactivity factor and also on strategies to reduce VOC emissions. Some suggested research approaches include: co-solvent and azeotrope research to mitigate ethanol's volatility, emissions testing on ethanol blends above 10 percent, research and emissions tests on mixed alcohol and ether blends,

and evaluation of the effect that enhanced inspection and maintenance problems have on the evaporative and exhaust VOC emissions of ethanol blends.

Market for Oxygenates. After a decade of development and growth, two oxygenates have found a solid place in motor fuel—ethanol, for blending downstream of the refinery, and MTBE, for manufacture and blending at the refinery. Since MTBE was first produced in 1979, world MTBE production capacity has grown very rapidly, from 0.3 billion gallons in 1979 to 3.9 billion gallons in 1991. The United States is the world's leading MTBE producer; it has 1.9 billion gallons of capacity, and that is expected to more than double by 1994. Currently, MTBE blends capture 14 percent of U.S. gasoline sales, while ethanol blends capture more than 7 percent of the market. MTBE is widely used because it can be transported in pipelines and because it is accepted by major gasoline suppliers. Current consumption of ethanol has reached over 0.9 billion gallons. MTBE consumption is over 1.3 billion gallons annually, which is equivalent to over 0.67 billion gallons of ethanol in terms of oxygen content.

With a new oxygenate market opportunity, MTBE production capacity is expanding. However, future MTBE production depends greatly on the availability of feedstocks. As domestic MTBE production increases, a substantial portion of methanol as the feedstock for MTBE production may have to rely on foreign imports—even now, about one-quarter of the methanol consumed in the United States comes from abroad. Today, the United States has the operating capacity to produce nearly 3 billion gallons of ethanol and MTBE per year.

Pricing of Ethanol

While the production cost of ethanol is only remotely related to oil markets, some industry analysts indicate that the price of ethanol is closely correlated to the price of gasoline. During early 1986, when oil prices abruptly plunged, the price of ethanol also fell, reaching $1.05 in 1987 from $1.54, its 1985 price (see fig. 1).

Ethanol has traditionally been sold at a discounted price, in part due to the conventional wisdom that ethanol may not be transported by pipeline because it is sensitive to water. As a result, ethanol has to be blended by local wholesalers. In addition to these extra blending costs, blenders have been given a margin in order to encourage them to use ethanol as a blending agent. As a consequence, the difference between gasoline prices and ethanol prices at the pump reflects Federal and State tax benefits, blending costs, transportation costs, and the blender margin, which ranges from 1 to 2 cents per gallon. The difference between the gasoline price and ethanol price began to narrow during the mid-1980's (see fig. 1). This trend coincides with a reduction in the State ethanol incentive programs which began in 1986.

The recent MTBE price continues to show an upward trend, having passed $1 per gallon in November 1991. In the past, the upward trend of MTBE price may have been due partly to its octane value, which can be priced at about 1.25 cents per octane number at the wholesale level. Unlike the case with MTBE, ethanol's octane value has not been fully realized in its price. The ethanol price has tended to stay rather stable compared to the MTBE price trend. For the past 5 years, the highest price was marked at $1.28 per gallon in August 1987 and the lowest price at $1.06 per gallon in January 1988. In general, the price per gallon remained around $1.15.

In the past, the value of ethanol has been derived mostly from its high octane and its role as a gasoline extender. Now, with oxygenated fuel use mandated by the 1990 CAA, an additional value for oxygenates is expected. Ethanol, for example, can be used as an oxygenate and octane enhancer, but the oxygen value of ethanol will likely be more important than its octane value.

Mandated Oxygen Requirements Boost Ethanol Demand

The net effect of the Clean Air Act Amendments will be a promising new market opportunity for ethanol. Future ethanol demand will come from the three major uses: as a blending component, as a feedstock for ETBE, and as a fuel for alternative fuel vehicles. The near-term ethanol demand will come as a blending component in gasoline, but ethanol's future potential exists as a feedstock for ether blends and as an alternative fuel.

The Renewable Fuels Association has estimated that the near-term effect of the CAA carbon monoxide program will be an additional 500-700 million gallons of ethanol demand annually. According to Fred Potter, Information Resources Incorporated, total ethanol demand could rise from 1,778 million gallons per year in 1995 to 2,402 million gallons per year in 2000.

Gasoline Additive. Prior to 1995, the demand for ethanol will be mainly in the 10-percent ethanol blend for the carbon monoxide nonattainment areas. The demand for oxygenates to control CO problems will depend on a number of factors: the possibility of oxygenates migrating from attainment areas to nonattainment areas, the extent of demand for 2.7-percent oxygenate gasoline from CO attainment areas, the length of the CO season, and the extent of the city boundaries specified as CO nonattainment areas.

Beginning in 1995, the CAA's reformulated gasoline program will further increase the oxygenate demand to meet the 2 percent oxygen requirement. About 20 percent of United States gasoline demand is in the nine worst ozone nonattainment areas. However, the real potential demand for reformulated gasoline depends largely on how many of the nonattainment areas "opt in" to the program. If all eligible areas opt in, 70 percent of gasoline consumption could be in reformulated markets.

Feedstock for ETBE. Just as ethanol has commercial potential for enhancing air quality, it also shows promise as a feedstock for an ethanol-based ether, ETBE. ETBE blends can easily meet the reformulated gasoline requirement of low-ozone-forming hydrocarbon emissions because ethers are low in volatility. With its lower volatility and superior blending characteristics, ETBE may ultimately be a more valuable oxygenate fuel additive than MTBE.

Even though ethanol can be easily transformed into an ether, the choice of alcohol in the ether process depends mainly on the relative cost of alcohol as the feedstock. As long as methanol costs less than ethanol, major ETBE production is not likely. However, this situation could change with a rising demand for methanol as a feedstock for MTBE. Any anticipated future shortage of methanol will likely be exacerbated by the new international demand for methanol, as more countries become concerned about automobile-source air pollution. If demand raises the price of methanol, and if the cost-reducing technological improvement of ethanol production continues, ETBE is likely to emerge as a major ether.

Alternative Fuel. Nearly neat ethanol (E85, or 85-percent blend) would be a promising alternative as a fuel for flexible-fuel vehicles or dedicated vehicles. The increase in ethanol demand due to the growing use of E85 is particularly important given the incentives in the 1990 CAA and the administration's National Energy Strategy, which directs public and private fleets to use alternative fuel vehicles.

E85 also could be a promising alternative in controlling ozone problems because of ethanol's low volatility. High fuel volatility tends to cause highly evaporative, ozone-forming, volatile organic compound emissions. Although the first few percent of ethanol added to gasoline will increase volatility, ethanol actually reduces volatility when the blending rate reaches about 20 percent. At 100 percent ethanol, volatility declines to a rate of 2.3 pounds per square inch (psi) compared to 9.9 psi for the 10 percent ethanol blend, 9 psi for gasoline, and 7.8 psi for MTBE, as measured in Reid vapor pressure (Rvp).

Ethanol Production Capacity Is Expanding

With the emergence of the oxygenate market, one major concern in the fuel market is how to secure a continuous supply of oxygenates. While U.S. ethanol production grew from 20 million gallons in 1979 to more than 900 million gallons in 1991, the market share of ethanol-blended gasoline also increased, from virtually nothing to more than 7 percent of all U.S. gasoline consumption.

In June 1990, 39 ethanol plants were in operation in the Nation. Seventeen of them accounted for almost 90 percent of U.S. production capacity. The five largest plants account for almost 60 percent of total capacity. While ethanol is sold in all 48 contiguous States, the Midwest is currently the strongest market.

The ethanol industry continues to grow. Some existing producers have announced expansion plans while other companies, such as Cargill (planning an annual 28-million-gallon-capacity plant in Eddyville, IA), are entering the market.

Furthermore, expanding the feedstock to broad classes of biomass will greatly complement corn-based ethanol production, (see chapter 32). Feedstocks other than corn that have been used include starch-based biomass and sugar crops. However, for the potential of ethanol from biomass to be realized, more plentiful and less expensive nonfood biomass must be developed as energy crops. Such energy sources include woody crops, such as fast-growing hardwood trees, and herbaceous crops. Cellulose a hemicellulose are the two principal components of wood and grasses, which can be converted to sugars and then fermented to ethanol. The U.S. Department of Energy (DOE) has been placing a high priority on cellulosic conversion research. Currently, DOE estimates the cost of producing ethanol from cellulosic materials at around $1.35 per gallon. Further efforts to bring down the production cost are under way.

The Future Ethanol Market

The ethanol market faces two major challenges. First, how do ethanol blends affect ozone formation and how will the implementation of the CAA affect ethanol? Second, can the future ethanol industry maintain and enhance its market strength in the increasingly competitive oxygenate market? To answer the first question, emissions research is needed to develop a better understanding of the basic physical and chemical changes in the volatility of gasoline to lessen the increase in VOC's associated with ethanol blends. To answer the second question, research and development can help drive down the cost of producing ethanol and thus enhance its market presence.

The environment of the motor fuels market is changing. Traditionally, the ethanol market extended only to the independent wholesale gasoline marketers rather than to refiners. However, refiners have begun to negotiate with ethanol producers on long-term contracts, as opposed to previous spot dealing, to ensure a continuous supply of oxygenates. Ethanol-blended gasoline is now marketed by major refiners. A new cooperative environment between ethanol producers and refiners might develop, which would benefit both parties. A joint venture between ethanol producers and refiners could emerge, as each provides necessary components for oxygenated fuel.

The general mood of the automobile industry toward ethanol is also changing. In the late 1970's and early 1980's, a lack of acceptance by the automotive industry was one of the major constraints preventing ethanol from penetrating the fuels market.

Now, all auto manufacturers approve of the use of ethanol-blended gasoline under their warranties. Some manufacturers, such as General Motors, actively encourage the use of ethanol blends by recommending oxygenated fuels in their owners' manual.

There are still many challenges ahead before the Nation achieves the clean air goal in the 1990 CAA and other opportunities of ethanol expansion—such as enhancing energy security and expanding value-added markets for U.S. farmers. In each case, ethanol will continue to play an important role. ❏

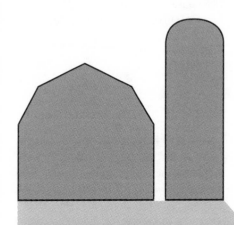

Part VI.
Innovative Products for Food Industries

For Consumer Convenience: New and Improved Quality Food Products

35

by Antoinette A. Betschart, Director, Western Regional Research Center, and Glenn Fuller, Research Leader, Crop Improvement and Utilization Research, Western Regional Research Center, ARS, USDA, Albany, CA

Americans deserve the best food that science and technology can provide. They like to eat, but they want to be certain that what they consume is nutritious, safe, and pleasing to the palate. For over 100 years, USDA researchers with the Agricultural Research Service (ARS) have played a leading role in introducing and improving foods in the United States.

In its early years, USDA research was directed toward the farmer by providing new crops and by increasing the yields of major crops. Recently, the consumer's needs have furnished important goals for ARS scientists, who work to improve the safety, taste, and nutritional quality of foods. New knowledge in biochemistry, plant and animal physiology, and especially genetics has led to more information from the laboratory that supplements breeding research in the field. The techniques and methods used to develop new and improved foods from plants are described here.

New and Hardier Crops Through Preservation of Plant Species

There is increased awareness that many species of plants and many strains within species are endangered because of the loss of habitat and because of cultivation of only the few varieties that produce the best yields. To avoid potential losses of species and strains, some ARS scientists spend significant parts of their careers searching the world for plant varieties. To preserve these species and lines, the National Plant Germplasm System (NPGS) was established for the collection, evaluation, preservation, and distribution of plant germplasm throughout the world. (Germplasm is the seeds or other parts of plants that can be grown into whole plants with inherited characteristics.)

Germplasm is difficult to preserve, since many kinds of plant seeds and propagative tissue do not store well and must be grown and recovered periodically. Promising research is in progress to store viable seeds and tissue at liquid nitrogen temperatures

(-320 °F) for many years, to reduce the labor and time required with present procedures. Many of the stored varieties of plants may be sources of important traits, such as disease and insect resistance or cold-hardiness.

In 1989, ARS scientists introduced a new variety of orange, called Ambersweet, in Florida. It had taken 26 years to bring out this new hybrid, which has the trait of cold-hardiness. Ambersweet trees were able to survive freezes of 18 °F without twig damage. Because the evaluation of each generation requires waiting several years for the young tree to bear fruit, it takes an especially long time to breed new varieties of trees.

Through systematic searching, unusual crops unfamiliar to most U.S. consumers have been found, especially tropical and subtropical fruits that may be grown in Hawaii, Florida, or southern California. Carambola, or star fruit, for instance, is now finding markets in Hawaii and on the mainland. Other interesting fruits under investigation include rambutan and lychee. Lychee, familiar to consumers of Chinese cuisine in the United States, is a soft and tasty fruit with milky-white flesh. It may be eaten fresh, canned, or preserved. Rambutan, a relative of the lychee, is a native of Malaysia. Its spiny-looking skin can be easily removed to reveal a sweet, crunchy, juicy fruit, which may

In 1989, ARS scientists introduced a new variety of orange, called Ambersweet, in Florida. Ambersweet trees can survive freezes of 18 degrees F without twig damage.

Randall Smith/USDA 92BW0838

be eaten fresh or cooked. Another candidate for the market is the pili nut from the Philippines. These nuts are high in oil and protein, and have a distinctive flavor when roasted.

Better Fresh Produce Through Biological Laboratory Techniques

The scientific breeding of plants has been immensely successful in creating and improving crops, but it is slow. New characteristics have to be found (if they exist) in the germplasm. Then the traits must be laboriously incorporated into the plant by crossing them repeatedly, for several generations, with a variety that has other good characteristics. Today, laboratory techniques based on plant physiology and biochemistry may accelerate the process of creating, identifying, and incorporating new and useful traits.

Grape breeding is one example. For a long time, the Thompson Seedless grape was the only significant seedless variety grown in the United States. It is a popular table grape and makes a good seedless raisin but does not have a strong grape flavor. In 1973 scientists with ARS in Fresno, CA, introduced the Flame, a seedless grape variety that has greatly increased the market for red table grapes. More recently, they used conventional breeding techniques to produce three more new grapes: Crimson Seedless, Autumn Seedless, and Fantasy Seedless.

Tomorrow's seedless grapes may be the result of a laboratory technique known as embryo rescue. Seedless grapes are not really seedless; their seeds just don't develop. Using em-

bryo rescue, ARS researchers capture immature seeds and, by proper culture of these seeds, produce new lines of seedless grapes from two seedless parents. Varieties resulting from embryo rescue may be available soon, giving the consumer more variety in table grape flavor and tasty seedless raisins.

Tomatoes grown for processing into paste, catsup, and sauces normally have a solids content of 5 to 5.5 percent, and the rest is water. A scientist at ARS' Western Regional Research Center (WRRC) in Albany, CA, has used a combination of laboratory procedures to develop tomato lines with 8 to 12 percent solids. Tomato plant parts are placed on a gel-like mix of nutrients, where they grow as a clump

Robert Knight, an ARS horticulturalist, displays the cross section of a carambola or star fruit to show the distinctive star shape. Markets for carambola are increasing in Hawaii and on the mainland.
Barry Fitzgerald/USDA 0786X886-22

of tissue. In this form, many of the plant's genes will vary. The growth medium is adjusted to select tomato cells that are capable of producing more solids. Cells that survive are nurtured into mature plants that produce tomatoes with higher-than-normal solids content. Second and third generations of many of these plants still carry the high-solids trait. Estimates are that each additional percent of solids in the U.S. tomato crop is worth $70 to $80 million annually in energy cost savings to industry. The new high-solids lines, now being incorporated into hybrids by a major seed company, will benefit the consumer by decreasing costs and improving quality.

ARS scientists at Salinas, CA, produced miniature iceberg lettuce heads that range in size from tennis balls to grapefruit, by treating ordinary lettuce seed with a chemical. The seed then produces lettuce plants that are deficient in a plant growth hormone, gibberellin. The mini-lettuce is a convenient size for small families or for singles.

Finally, scientists at Albany, CA, are using a technique called protoplast fusion to move needed traits from one type of plant into another species. By fusing protoplasts (cells with the cell wall removed) of tomato with those of tomatillo, researchers hope to bring the tomatillo's additional insect resistance to the tomato.

Lychee, a sweet tropical fruit, is a good source of vitamin C. The Florida lychee crop, shipped primarily to the east coast and Midwest, is worth almost $2 million a year.

Barry Fitzgerald/USDA 0786X886-6

Superior Wheat, Potatoes, and Tomatoes Through Genetic Engineering

Currently the most glamorous of the biological methods of plant modification is genetic engineering, the systematic alteration of DNA coding for the proteins of an organism. It is possible to create altered DNA or to incorporate a specific segment of DNA from another species, but this is not a simple process. Permanent change or transformation of a plant requires the incorporation of new DNA into the chromosomes along with pieces of DNA promoting "expression" of the gene (the actual process of converting the code into a protein). Several scientists at Albany, CA, are modifying plants this way.

One WRRC group is working to improve wheat through genetic modification of a group of proteins called glutens, which are responsible for the ability of wheat flour doughs to retain gas bubbles and "rise." The process of "transformation," or placing new DNA into wheat, cannot be done by the methods used to bring new DNA into some other crops, such as tomatoes or potatoes. When scientists find out how to perform wheat transformation consistently, they may be able to improve not only bread's quality but also its nutritional characteristics.

Another scientist at WRRC is directing experiments to correct an important problem of potatoes. Bruised potatoes develop black spots that are not visible through the skin. These

Graduate student Linda Lee and plant physiologist Richard Emershad transplant seedless grape varieties from growth chamber containers to soil plots in the greenhouse.
Jack Dykinga/USDA 89BW1906-28

Better, sweeter, juicier grapes are the goal. Four new varieties produced by the Agricultural Research Service are Crimson Seedless, Autumn Black, Fantasy Seedless, and Autumn Seedless.
Jack Dykinga/USDA 89BW1911-4

spots are the result of oxygen in the air reacting with an amino acid, tyrosine, in the presence of a potato enzyme. The strategy: give potato plants a new gene that will direct a protein to use up the tyrosine.

At the University of California/ ARS Plant Gene Expression Center, a group has controlled tomato ripening by incorporating "anti-sense" RNA that blocks the action of an enzyme. This enzyme is needed for the formation of ethylene, a hormone that promotes tomato ripening. Tomatoes having this gene will stay green on the vine for long periods. Then, when desired, ripening may be triggered by exposure of the fruit to ethylene gas. The technique will provide the optimum number of ripe tomatoes at a specified time.

Safer, More Nutritious, and Tastier Cereal Products, Fruits, and Vegetables Through Postharvest Research

Much of the abundance in the American diet is the result of what is done after crops are harvested. The system we have for storing, transporting, and processing food allows quality products to be sold year-round, although harvest may occur only once a year. An important goal of agricultural research is to bring food to the consumer with the best flavor and nutritional quality. This means that the texture and taste must be very close to those of the fresh product.

Many new and improved foods have resulted from postharvest research. The objective of one project at WRRC is to develop lightly processed fruits and vegetables in order to decrease the shipping cost and to improve consumer convenience. A method called dehydrofreezing is beginning to be used in the marketplace. In this method, fruits and vegetables are cut or peeled, some of the moisture is removed, and then the produce is frozen. The partial dehydration prevents cellular damage and results in fruits or vegetables with near-fresh texture and flavor. After the produce has been thawed and water has been added, it may be used in cooking or baking. Dehydrofreezing results in products, such as pies or baked goods, that have fresh texture and flavor.

Peeled or cut produce loses liquid and turns brown. Coatings that are tasteless and safe to eat would protect lightly processed products from water loss, air exposure, and spoilage from bacteria. WRRC scientists have devised coatings derived from carbohydrates, proteins, or fats, depending on the nature of the protection desired. These coatings can form an edible barrier between pizza and its topping, or bread and its jelly, so that pizzas and sandwiches don't become soggy.

Scientists at WRRC have been pioneers in the study of flavor. Recently a group analyzed the flavor of cooked tomatoes and found that although there are hundreds of components of tomato flavor, a mixture of only seven of these components can be used as a tomato-flavor enhancer or tomato seasoning. The tomato flavor discovery was patented and is being investigated by several large food companies.

Rice bran (the brown outer coating that is milled from rice grains) is 10 to

12 percent of the weight of polished rice. It has been used mainly for animal feed because it contains an oil that rapidly turns rancid, making it unsuitable for food products. A group of scientists at WRRC put the bran through a machine known as an extruder. By rapid uniform heating this stabilization process inactivates the enzyme responsible for the rancidity. Stabilized bran may be used in baked products, or oil may be extracted from the bran for salads or cooking. Nutritional experiments with humans and laboratory animals have shown that stabilized bran helps to decrease low density lipoprotein (the so-called "bad" cholesterol) in the blood. The same researchers have used a dry milling process to obtain high-fiber fractions from oats and barley that may find use in bran-containing breakfast products and baked goods. Many people are allergic to the wheat gluten proteins that are necessary to make a good loaf of leavened bread, but they are not allergic to the proteins of rice. Scientists at WRRC invented the technology to make a yeast-leavened bread from rice flour by using a gum ingredient that gives rice dough the strength to rise and form a loaf.

The Future

Many of the food products described in this chapter are already in the marketplace. Others may be introduced during the next few years. Research will continue to produce safer, more nutritious, innovative foods through the use of biotechnology and genetic engineering. Our goal is to maintain our country's place as one of the world's best-fed nations, and to enhance its position as a source of high-quality food for the rest of the world. ❑

For Consumer 36 Value: New Technologies Extend Shelf Life of Fresh Fruits and Vegetables

by John P. Cherry, Center Director, Gerald M. Sapers, Lead Scientist, Michael F. Kozempel, Lead Scientist, Ching-Hsing Liao, Research Plant Pathologist, John M. Wells, Lead Scientist, and Kevin B. Hicks, Research Leader, Eastern Regional Research Center, ARS, USDA, Philadelphia, PA; Charles L. Wilson, Research Leader, Appalachian Fruit Research Station, ARS, USDA, Kearneysville, WV; Kenneth C. Gross, Plant Pathologist, Beltsville Agricultural Research Center, ARS, USDA, Beltsville, MD; and Attila E. Pavlath, Research Leader, Western Regional Research Center, ARS, USDA, Albany, CA

Fruits and vegetables are enjoyed by many Americans for their flavors, colors, and textures. They are an important part of a healthy diet, as they provide a number of essential nutrients and dietary fiber. The Dietary Guidelines for Americans, developed by USDA and the U.S. Department of Health and Human Services, recommend that we eat plenty of fruits and vegetables.

With today's fast-paced lifestyles, many people do not have the time to pare, core, slice, or dice fruits and vegetables. Yet, many prefer not to use canned or frozen foods because they want the flavor and texture of fresh commodities. There is a similar trend in hospital, industrial, and school cafeterias. Generally, in such cafeterias, which typically serve 300-500 persons, manual fruit and vegetable preparation is too expensive, and machines for such a small volume are not cost-efficient. The best solution for this food preparation problem is to process produce at some centrally located area and ship the prepared fresh fruit and vegetable products to the consumer or cafeteria.

Considering the time required for packaging, shipping, distributing, and storing, one can estimate that 15-20 days will elapse between the start of processing and the time when the processed produce will reach the consumer. Unfortunately, the removal of the natural outer tissues from agricultural products immediately starts various physical, biochemical, and microbiological processes that will reduce flavor, taste, freshness, and consumer acceptance. If the processed fresh fruits and vegetables could be protected from desiccation, enzymatic and biochemical changes, and micro-organisms for 2-3 weeks, it would be possible to process produce on a large scale at a central location and get fresh, nutritious products to consumers, both domestic and foreign, in an aesthetically pleasing form. USDA research is making this possible, without threatening the nutritional quality of the product.

Edible Films

If the surface of the fresh fruit or vegetable could be uniformly covered by an edible material that acts as a barrier to water and oxygen, the stability problems could be diminished. Three major classes of materials are used in edible films: proteins, carbohydrates, and fats. It is not surprising that, individually, these materials do not provide the desirable protection for the preservation of freshness, but scientists at the Western Regional Research Center (WRRC), ARS, Albany, CA, found that their combination, in the right ratio, could be very effective. A composition of 1 percent alginic acid (a carbohydrate), 10 percent casein (a protein), and 15 percent "Myvacet" (a commercially produced fat-derived ingredient) decreased water losses from apple pieces by almost 80 percent. Coated apple, pear, and zucchini pieces retained their freshness for 4-5 days without any noticeable changes. The film does not alter the taste of the coated products, and it does not have to be removed before consumption.

Edible films can also be used on bread, pizza dough, cakes, etc., to prevent these freshly baked products from becoming soggy.

Preventing Discoloration

Many raw fruits and vegetables become brown or show other kinds of discoloration when they are peeled, sliced, or juiced. To prevent such discolorations in apples and potatoes, scientists at the Eastern Regional Research Center (ERRC), ARS, Philadelphia, PA, have developed treatments that apply "browning inhibitors" to peeled fruit and vegetable surfaces. These inhibitors (ascorbic acid-2-phosphates) are closely related to vitamin C, but will require Food and Drug Administration approval for food use. New approaches have also been developed to control browning in raw fruit and vegetable juices by addition of carbohydrate-like materials called cyclodextrins or vegetable

An edible coating compound developed at the ARS Western Regional Research Center in Albany, CA, promises to extend the shelf life of fruits and vegetables. The film does not alter the flavor of the coated products, and it does not have to be removed before consumption.
Keith Weller/USDA 90BW0146-10A

gums such as carrageenan. Other ARS work has eliminated whitening in pre-peeled carrots by means of citric acid dips.

Innovative Processes for Juices and Fruits

Research work by ERRC scientists has developed innovative new processing methods for extending the shelf life and improving the quality of fruit juices. Juices can be preserved without heat pasteurization (which detracts from the fresh flavor) by using gentler physical treatments such as membrane filtration and centrifugation, a combined approach called "cold blanching." Unblemished citrus sections can be prepared by treating the fruit with pectinase enzymes to dissolve the "glue" that holds fruit segments to-

gether. This approach, developed by the Quality Improvement in Citrus and Subtropical Products Station, ARS, Winter Haven, FL, was recently commercialized by a major citrus processor.

Research conducted at the Appalachian Fruit Research Station (AFRS), ARS, Kearneysville, WV, on the composition and suitability for processing of new berry varieties contributed to the introduction of a new thornless blackberry variety called Chester, which shows superior quality characteristics and is suitable for freezing.

Explosion Puffing— A Preservation Process for the 21st Century

Drying is an ancient yet still excellent method of preserving foods. Since

ARS researchers have developed a process for extending the shelf life and improving the quality of fruit juices. Juices can be preserved without heat pasteurization.

Keith Weller/USDA 90BW0688-16

fruits and vegetables consist of 80-97 percent water, removing most of the water not only preserves the food, but also greatly reduces the weight and therefore the cost of shipping. When beans or rice are dried, the product is excellent. Dried grapes are raisins and dried plums are prunes. But, drying also has disadvantages. Produce such as apples, blueberries, potatoes, and carrots, although well preserved when dried, unfortunately are difficult to rehydrate—frequently requiring 30 minutes or more.

Engineers at ERRC, ARS, Philadelphia, PA, have made improvements in dehydrated food products. They devel-

The three major classes of materials used in edible films are proteins, carbohydrates, and fats. The coating acts as a barrier to water and oxygen.
Keith Weller/USDA 90BW0150-22

oped a process that makes dehydrated fruit and vegetable pieces able to rehydrate rapidly so that they cook more quickly. The food returns virtually to its original size and shape with little loss in flavor, texture, and nutritional value.

First, the food is appropriately processed in preparation for drying. For example, blueberries are washed; potatoes are washed, peeled, sliced, sized, given the "Philadelphia cook" (a special blanching process that improves the textural quality of the potato pieces), and cooked; and apples get peeled, cored, and sliced. After the food is prepared, it is dried by a process that differs from traditional air-drying. The drying process is interrupted when the moisture drops to about 20-30 percent, depending on the commodity, and is then resumed in a continuous-explosion-puffing machine. The machine consists of two inlet valves, a steam-jacketed main heating chamber, an outlet valve, and an explosive discharge valve. A feed conveyor transfers partially dried fruits or vegetables into the feed chamber. The feed chamber is pressurized to the same level as the main chamber and the food pieces are then transferred to the main chamber and exposed to superheated steam for about 30 seconds. At the exit, the pieces are explosively discharged through a special valve.

Research in the ERRC kitchen shows explosion puffing improves the texture and appearance of food. Because explosion-puffed foods are porous, they can be rehydrated quickly. In 5 minutes, the food can be cooked and ready to eat. Generally, cooking time for fruits and vegetables can be cut by as much as 80 percent over conventionally air-dried products. Some of the puffed foods can even be eaten as a crunchy snack, without cooking.

The continuous-explosion-puffing process has been demonstrated on various foods, including potatoes, carrots, apples, blueberries, celery, strawberries, cranberries, and many more. Explosion puffing has been commercialized on carrots and blueberries in the United States and on potatoes in Canada.

Fending Off Rot in Apples, Peaches, Citrus, and Potatoes

Antagonistic Yeasts. It is estimated that 25 percent of our harvested fruit is lost to decay. Customarily, fungicides are applied to fruit after harvest to control these losses, but effective alternatives to these chemicals are needed. ARS Scientists at laboratories in Kearneysville, WV, Byron, GA, Wanatchee, WA, Fresno, CA, and Philadelphia, PA, have discovered that antagonistic micro-organisms, which normally inhabit the surfaces of fruits, can be isolated and applied as "living fungicides" to control postharvest rots. These organisms have been known to effectively control rots of peaches, apples, citrus, and grapes. Of particular interest is that, among the antagonistic micro-oganisms, yeasts have been discovered that block rot-causing fungi by occupying the wound sites on the fruit where infection has occurred. Here, these yeasts outcompete the rot patho-

gens for nutrients and space and thereby prevent decay.

Antagonistic Bacteria. Scientists at ERRC, ARS, Philadelphia, PA, are studying biological control strategies for soft rots that are caused by bacterial plant pathogens. They have succeeded in isolating and identifying 27 strains of bacteria that inhibit the growth of the most destructive soft-rotting pathogen, *Erwinia carotovora.* One antagonistic bacterium *(Pseudomonas putida* PP22) produces an antibiotic compound that is effective against a broad spectrum of bacterial plant pathogens, including 24 strains of soft-rotting bacteria. This antagonistic bacterium sup-

For after-harvest protection against rot, plant pathologists Charles Wilson (right) and Randy McLaughlin inoculate Red Haven peaches with a strain of yeast. The yeast outcompetes the rot pathogens for nutrients and space, thereby preventing decay.
Keith Weller/USDA 92BW0833

pressed the development of soft rot in potato tubers in three out of four trials and has potential as a biocontrol agent for reducing bacterial spoilage of vegetables.

Ultraviolet Light. Another pioneering study of approaches to control fruit rots by scientists at the AFRS, ARS, Kearneysville, WV, has shown that fruit has a hidden resistance to rot fungi. This resistance can be "turned on" with low-dose treatments of ultraviolet light. As fruit ripens, it becomes more susceptible to infection by rot organisms. The ultraviolet treatment appears to work in part by slowing fruit ripening, thereby delaying susceptibility to decay and extending shelflife, and by stimulating the production of natural fungicides within the fruit. These treatments have extended the shelf-life of peaches, apples, and citrus by weeks.

The new technologies being developed for the biological control of postharvest rots have a number of advantages over present technologies. By using natural organisms and preexisting defense systems in fruits and vegetables, ARS scientists hope to achieve postharvest rot resistance methods that are effective and safe alternatives to synthetic fungicides.

Moving Genes To Enhance Freshness

How often have you gone to your refrigerator for a fresh fruit or vegetable and come face to face with a small pile of mush, or had to cut out "bad" pieces before eating or cooking produce? ARS scientists are trying to understand what happens to fruits and vegetables during their natural ripen-

ing process and after they are harvested so that new genetic lines can be developed to maintain the quality of produce until it reaches consumers' tables. During storage, decreases in quality lead to losses of as much as 25-50 percent of all fresh produce harvested in the United States. This amounts to about $5 billion yearly. Thus, it is imperative to understand the underlying mechanisms that control the ripening process.

For a number of years scientists at the Beltsville Agricultural Research Center, ARS, Beltsville, MD, have studied ethylene, a gaseous ripening hormone in fruit. Recent experiments with gene transfer techniques at the ARS Plant Gene Expression Center in Albany, CA, have shown the importance of this hormone during the fruit ripening process. In these experiments, scientists removed and altered the gene for 1-aminocyclopropane-1-carboxylic acid (ACC-synthase), an enzyme that leads to production of ethylene. They then inserted this altered gene into tomato plants. The fruit from these genetically modified plants produced defective ACC-synthase, which consequently produced no ethylene, and the plants did not ripen.

In addition, the Beltsville scientists have discovered that sugars called N-glycans can control the *rate* of tomato fruit ripening. After N-glycans were put into green tomatoes, ripening was either enhanced or delayed, depending on the amount added.

These studies to control the ripening process will permit the produce industry to provide abundant supplies of tomatoes and other fresh fruits and vegetables year-round with no loss of nutritional value. Millions of dollars in refrigeration costs and spoilage losses will be saved as a result of these technologies. ❏

Protecting the Environment

37

by James Krysan, Leslie McDonough, Alan Knight, and K. Duane Biever, Research Scientists, Agricultural Research Service, Yakima, WA; Charles R. Brown, Research Geneticist, Agricultural Research Service, Prosser, WA; and James Kamm, Research Entomologist, Agricultural Research Service,Corvallis, OR

In the mid-20th century, agricultural science presented farmers with a class of "miracle" tools: synthetic, or manufactured, chemical pesticides. Pesticides helped farmers profitably produce an abundance of high-quality food and fiber. But there are concerns that those "miracle" products, as used, can have undesired side effects for the environment and human health. Future farmers must look for ways to produce the expected quality and quantity of food and also to eliminate, or drastically reduce, the causes of these environmental and health concerns.

The Problem

Most of today's synthetic chemical insecticides kill target pests by poisoning their life functions. Materials that are toxic to nearly all animals are called broad-spectrum insecticides. When they are applied, nontarget animals that happen to be in the environment are also affected. When misused, such pesticides can pose hazards to humans.

Aside from environmental and safety concerns, these pesticides have a doubtful long-term usefulness because of the speed with which many pests become resistant to them. Resistance is especially prone to develop when a pesticide is used as the single method of control on generation after generation of a pest. Often, after several generations of such exposure, the pesticide no longer works.

Science must devise ways to control pests while affecting little or nothing else in the environment and, for good measure, make it tough for the pest to adapt. This is not a pipedream.

Some solutions are here now, and others are on the way. These new, environmentally benign ways to control pests are the product of novel applications of advances in scientific knowledge.

Agricultural Science Responds

Some caveats exist in this search for environment-friendly products and approaches that farmers can use in farming profitably and in providing future consumers with ample supplies of attractive, tasty, and wholesome foods. First, it is critical that the control method be as specific as possible for the target pest. The goal is for nontarget life to be unaffected. Second, several different tactics should be integrated to solve the pest problem. An integrated approach reduces the possibility that the pest will quickly develop resistance. The development of the tactics will depend on a profound basic knowledge of the pest, its natural enemies, and the entire agroecosystem.

Third, all chemicals should not be ruled out just because many existing and past synthetic pesticides with problems are chemicals. Such a broad indictment is illogical: living things themselves are a complex mixture of dissolved and structural chemicals supported by a continual intake of nutrients and energy in chemical form. It follows that many schemes for affecting living systems will have a chemical component, and we should expect highly specific chemicals to be part of environmentally benign pest control.

The following case studies examine innovative methods of pest control. These techniques represent just a few of the many that are available for farmers to use.

Protecting Cabbage

Keeping pests out of cabbage is a tough job, and devising ways to protect cabbage in an environmentally benign way is a difficult challenge. Several pests attack the crop each year, and the final marketable product must be essentially free of insect damage. Therefore, many applications of broad-spectrum pesticides are routinely applied to achieve control.

Consequently, in an effort to cut back on the use of broad-spectrum insecticides, entomologists have worked for two decades to develop biological ways to control butterfly and moth (lepidopteran) pests of cabbage and related crops. These pests include the imported cabbage worm, the cabbage looper, and the diamondback moth.

The trick is to obtain compatible biological agents that together will control all the pests on the crop. Broad-spectrum pesticides are unlikely to be acceptable because they are generally toxic to many helpful biocontrol agents—that is, the pest's natural parasites and predators. Even one such application during a season can destroy the natural-enemy complex.

In a 1991 field test in the Lower Rio Grande Valley of Texas, an environmentally benign, biologically based method with no hazards to human health succeeded in controlling cabbage insect pests. The method has three major components: (1) methods to allow the grower to determine how many of each pest are present in the patch at any one time; (2) insecticidal materials that do not kill natural enemies (such as parasites) that attack the pests; and (3) a source of parasites of the pests to permit "inoculative" releases—that is, release of the parasites into the field to flourish and reproduce so subsequent generations will control the pests. To continue the medical analogy, the parasites *prevent*, and the insecticides *cure*.

Over two decades, entomologists gradually met these three requirements. However, the real advances

Cabbage worm.
Doug Wilson/USDA 90BW1468-2

Pests that attack cabbage crops each year include the cabbage worm (top), cabbage looper (bottom right), and diamondback moth (bottom left). The objective for protection is to obtain compatible agents that will control all pests on the crop. A benign, biologically based insecticide produced by a common soil bacterium, Bt-endotoxin has succeeded in controlling cabbage pests.

proved their usefulness when insects began to become resistant to the broad-spectrum insecticides. For example, in the late 1970's in Missouri, cabbage loopers had become resistant to existing broad-spectrum insecticides, and only those growers using Bt-endotoxin successfully controlled the loopers. Bt-endotoxin, produced by the common soil bacterium *Bacillus thuringiensis*, is an effective insecticide which does not kill natural enemies. Its use was improved and widely adapted until it was supplanted by a new class of easy-to-use broad-spectrum pesticides: the synthetic pyrethroids.

It was clear to researchers that while Bt-endotoxin was a key to noninsecticidal control, other strategies were needed to alleviate growers' sole dependence on it. In the 1980's, ARS scientists identified parasites that

Diamondback moth.
Doug Wilson/USDA 90BW1465-9

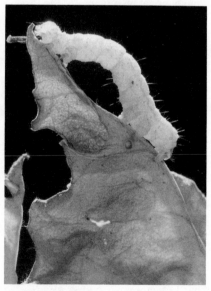

Cabbage looper.
USDA/ARS 1087X1150-9

attack the egg and larval stages of the loopers, and developed methods for growing the parasites in numbers sufficient to make inoculative releases of parasites possible.

In use, the parasites are released early in the crop season so that they can reproduce and keep pest-caterpillar populations at low levels. For the parasites to survive and establish themselves, some pests must be present in the cabbage early in the season; fortunately, early-season feeding by the cabbage pests does not result in significant damage to the harvested product. The level of "wellness" in the crop patch is determined through careful monitoring of pest numbers. If the pests begin to get out of control, Bt-endotoxin is then applied to reduce the number of pests.

In 1990, rapidly increasing resistance in the diamondback moth to conventional insecticides in the Rio Grande Valley of Texas provided the stage for a test of this two-pronged system of pest control. ARS scientists shared their parasite colonies and expertise with a private producer of beneficial insects. The producer contracted with five growers to supply parasites, and they were used to successfully inoculate 130 acres of cabbage. Protection of the crop equaled that expected from conventional methods.

An additional benefit of using the new system is the strengthening of an emerging industry: the production and sale of beneficial insects. Another benefit is the potential for reduced use of broad-spectrum pesticides. And finally, this success with cabbage is evidence that other difficult systems can be managed in purely biological ways to allay safety concerns for the environment and food.

Sex and the Cranberry Girdler

Another example of pest control and environmental protection is the case of the cranberry and the cranberry girdler.

Even though many serious insect pests attack crops only sporadically, growers must often routinely apply broad-spectrum insecticides. This practice usually kills beneficial insects, causes problems from the pests then released from natural control, and eventually leads to the need for even more insecticide treatments.

The case of the cranberry girdler represents a more subtle approach to environmental protection. The use of a sex attractant helps reduce the amount of insecticide applied to cranberries.

The adult girdler emerges from its cocoon in early summer. The male moth locates a mate by following a sex attractant, called a pheromone, emitted by the female. After mating, the female lays its eggs on the cranberry plant. Living up to its name, the immature (or larval) stage of the girdler feeds on the outer layer of underground roots and leaves a girdle (ring) of damaged tissue, which starves the plant.

The sex pheromone enters the pest manager's tool box as an attractant in traps used to gather information about cranberry girdlers—namely, where, when, and how many. In this technique, a sticky trap holds a small rubber plug loaded with a synthetic

version of the female's sex pheromone. As the attracted males are
caught, the farmer regularly checks the
trap to determine the number caught
and the time of catch. Based on that
information, the insecticide applications are tailored to the girdler population actually present at various times.
The result is more effective control
with reduced amounts of insecticides.

The attractant itself acts at very low
concentrations and is unlikely to affect
anything else in the environment. Several companies in the United States
manufacture and sell a cranberry
girdler pheromone trap, a novel product that contributes to the production
of food with reduced potential for
environmental contamination.

Pheromone To Control
the Codling Moth

Apples are a healthful food enjoyed by
children and adults worldwide. But the
enjoyment stops when your bite reveals a worm. That rarely happens
these days because of the great efforts
by orchardists to control the codling
moth, an insect whose larval stage is
the worm in the apple. Control currently depends on the frequent use of
broad-spectrum pesticides.

Research in the early 1970's revealed that the codling moth uses a
sex pheromone in a manner similar to
that of the cranberry girdler. As with
the cranberry girdler, the codling moth
pheromone has been used for many
years as a bait in traps to time the insecticide treatments.

But with the codling moth, the sex
pheromone can also be used to directly control the pest. The idea is to
release pheromones into the air in the
orchard so that the males will have
great difficulty in finding mates. Entomologists, chemists, pheromone producers, and now orchardists are
working together to develop and use a
method to control the codling moth by
preventing its ability to mate. Instead
of covering the apple trees with pesticides, farmers hang plastic dispensers
that release the pheromonal aroma into
the air. In this cloud of pheromone, the
male cannot locate the female. With
mating disruption, growers don't kill
codling moths: They simply prevent
reproduction.

This method for controlling the codling moth has been registered by the
Environmental Protection Agency and
is commercially available. Some problems remain to be solved: The pheromone fails to disrupt mating
sufficiently when a large number of
moths are present; or already mated
females from nearby orchards can fly
into the orchards protected by pheromone. But so far, the experience of
growers suggests the technique can be
effective. Furthermore, use of the

Great efforts have been made to control the
codling moth, an insect whose larval stage
is the worm in the apple.
Doug Wilson/USDA 90BW2007-14

Instead of covering apple trees with insecticides, farmers use plastic dispensers containing a sex pheromone. The pheromone disrupts the moths' mating habits, preventing reproduction.
Doug Wilson/USDA 90BW2007-3

pheromone will leave researchers and growers the option of turning to natural enemies and other more selective methods to control apple and pear pests and to supplement the pheromone against codling moth when necessary.

Plants That Kill the Pest

In the previous examples, environmentally benign solutions to pest problems have focused on devising new pest control methods. The next example involves changing the crop itself to protect it from the pest.

Bt-endotoxin was mentioned above as being specific for moth and butterfly larvae. Of the many different Bt-endotoxins, one is specific for beetles. Overall, these toxins are harmless to humans and other mammals, birds, fish, etc., and they break down very quickly when exposed to sunlight. They have been used for more than 30 years as spray-on insecticides.

Because Bt-endotoxins are proteins produced by living organisms, each type of toxin has a gene that codes for it. In the laboratory, those genes have been isolated from bacteria, modified as needed, and incorporated into plants, thereafter called "transgenic" plants. Once the bacterial genes are activated in the transgenic plants, the endotoxin will be present in the plant juices. When insects chew on the plant tissues, they are continuously exposed to the toxins.

In the United States, the main pest of the potato plant is the Colorado potato beetle. Bt-endotoxins that are available as sprays are relatively expensive, short-lived materials that are effective only when sprayed carefully and repeatedly with precise timing. Often, applications required in late season are especially difficult because the plants cover the entire field, making it almost impossible to take tractor-drawn spray equipment into the field. Aerial sprays cannot reach the real target on the undersides of leaves.

Transgenic potato plants that produce the Bt-endotoxins have been found to be extremely resistant to the Colorado potato beetle. Several advantages accrue when a plant produces a substance like Bt-endotoxin in its own tissues. Because the insecticide is already in the plant, there is no need to spray; this saves fuel, labor, chemical, and equipment costs. The insects killed are those that feed on the transgenic plant, so the specificity is perfect. As previously mentioned, the toxins themselves are environmentally benign proteins that are harmless to humans, break down quickly, and leave unharmed the native animals, including parasites and predators of the pest.

More research needs to be done to select the best transgenic plants, determine how they fit into the overall pest management scheme for potatoes, and obtain regulatory approval. Results so far are very encouraging.

Additional Approaches

The above case studies are only examples of a variety of new approaches. There are many other novel ways of attacking specific pests while avoiding effects on nontarget organisms. Basic studies of pest behavior have revealed that some materials are highly attractive to certain pests. These specific attractants can be put with an insecticide into a bait called an "attracticide." These formulations greatly reduce the amount of insecticide needed and focus the action on a particular pest.

Insect-growth regulators are chemicals that interfere with a target insect's growth and development. The regulators are selected or designed to affect insects and their close relatives and few other living things. The regulators also vary greatly in effectiveness among different insect groups and among the life stages of insects. These qualities permit the fine tuning of the use of insect-growth regulators so that they will affect only the target insect.

Another source of new chemistry for pest control is the neem, a tree native to India. This tree produces several chemicals that act as feeding deterrents and growth regulators of insects. One chemical from the neem is currently marketed in the United States as Margosan-O for insect control on ornamental plants. Further developments are expected in the near future.

Furthermore, insects have their own set of viruses, many of which are lethal to insects but have no effect on other organisms. Such viruses are being developed as pest-control agents.

This summary of pest-specific, environmentally safe options for pest management is not exhaustive. The options will continue to grow as scientists learn more about specific pests, their natural enemies, and new pest-specific materials. As knowledge increases, so does the ability to provide pest control in an environmentally benign way that is safe for humans and still allows growers to profit. ❑

Natural Products To Provide Flavor, Color, and Other Qualities

38

by Kevin B. Hicks, Research Leader, William F. Fett, Lead Scientist, Marshall Fishman, Lead Scientist, and Gerald M. Sapers, Research Food Technologist, Eastern Regional Research Center, ARS, USDA, Philadelphia, PA, and Arthur M. Spanier, Research Physiologist, Southern Regional Research Center, ARS, USDA, New Orleans, LA

Consumers and food processors alike are demonstrating a significant and growing interest in foods containing naturally derived flavors, colors, and properties. Around the United States, scientists from USDA's Agricultural Research Service (ARS) are making new and exciting discoveries in each of these important areas.

Enhancing Natural Flavor and Tenderness in Beef (Here's the Beef)

While people have enjoyed the delicious flavor of freshly cooked beef for centuries, only recently have the molecules responsible for the beefy taste been identified. Scientists at the ARS Southern Regional Research Center (SRRC) in New Orleans have recently developed a naturally occurring and nutritious flavor enhancer that could be used to make your steak taste even "beefier." This flavor enhancer, isolated from beef and called BMP for "Beefy Meaty Peptide," consists of eight linked amino acids. BMP appears to be produced during the aging of meat after slaughter. During aging, proteins in muscle tissue are naturally broken down by enzymes into smaller pieces called peptides.

Large-scale production of BMP is necessary if it is to be used as a flavor enhancer. But before such production is possible, scientists must find the protein from which BMP originates. Once that crucial protein has been identified, it may be possible to breed cattle for meat having a richer beef flavor. Information on the origin of BMP could also help the meat industry find slaughter methods or feeding regimens that stimulate BMP production. Alternatively, BMP could be synthesized by chemical or biochemical means.

Meanwhile, other researchers at SRRC have devised a way to halt meat-flavor deterioration. Much of the loss of fresh meat flavor is linked to oxidative reactions (reactions that occur in the presence of oxygen). In order to prevent loss in flavor quality, it is essential to prevent oxidation, particularly of fat in beef. A derivative of chitin—the fibrous portion of shells from crab, shrimp, lobster, and crawfish—has been found to retard fat oxidation and the resulting off-flavors in meat products. The chitin derivative does this by binding to iron, a mineral responsible for many oxidative reactions. However, studies have not yet determined if this process alters the bioavailability of iron. A recent ARS patent on the use of this derivative has drawn interest from industries that prepare institutional, airline, or other pre-prepared foods. The technique, however, must receive Food and Drug Administration approval before it is commercialized.

In related research from the Roman L. Hruska U.S. Meat Animal Research Center, ARS, at Clay Center, Nebraska, advances have been made in speeding up the natural tenderization process during the aging of beef. The scientists determined which natural enzyme system breaks down muscle fiber during aging. With the help of calcium chloride, this enzyme system can cut the time needed for tenderization from 2 weeks to just 24 hours. Calcium chloride is an approved food additive and is also a natural component of beef. Unfortunately, there is not enough calcium present naturally to produce the level of tenderness that consumers prefer, so it is necessary to inject cuts of beef with calcium to boost enzyme activity and accelerate the tenderization process.

Natural Colorants for Processed Foods and Beverages

When naturally occurring pigments cannot be used because of high cost, scarcity, or instability, many foods and beverages are colored with synthetic food dyes. This use of food colorants is subject to approval by the U.S. Food

Physiologist Arthur Spanier (left) and chemist John Bland compare the relationship of structure to flavor in peptides. Proteins in muscle tissue are broken down naturally by enzymes called peptides. Once the protein that is crucial in aging beef has been identified, it may be posssible to breed cattle for meat having a richer beef flavor. *Scott Bauer/USDA 91BW2208-15*

and Drug Administration. In recent years, the safety of certain synthetic dyes has been questioned, and several colorants have been banned.

Because of concerns about safety and the possibility that some synthetic dyes may be banned, the food industry is actively seeking safe, natural colorants to replace synthetic products. ARS and State agricultural experiment station scientists have been at the forefront of this search. Over the years, basic research on natural colorants by scientists at the University of Massachusetts, Michigan State University, the New York Agricultural Experiment Station, and the ARS Beltsville Agricultural Research Center (BARC) has established a foundation for the development of new colorants. More recently, the following significant developments have been announced:

- Research at the University of Florida and at the ARS Eastern Regional Research Center (ERRC) has led to the commercialization of red cabbage anthocyanins (the natural pigments in red cabbage) as food colorants.
- At the State agricultural experiment station at North Dakota State University, other anthocyanins are being extracted from sunflower hulls for their potential use as red food colorants.
- At the ERRC, a novel dyeing process for maraschino cherries uses natural carotenoids (colored compounds related to vitamin A) in place of red No. 3. This process has recently been patented and is under study by a major processor.

Plant and Bacterial Polysaccharides Impart Unique Properties to Foods

Polysaccharides (naturally occurring long chains of sugars) of plant and bacterial origin have many industrial applications for food and nonfood products—primarily to thicken solutions and to form gels (for instance, in commercial jams and jellies). Pectin, a well-known plant polysaccharide that is made up of a group of complex structural carbohydrates, helps to provide the natural structural "glue" that holds plant cells together. In addition, recent evidence has shown that this unique polymer, or fragments of it, is involved in human nutrition (consumption reduces sugar intolerance in diabetics and may lower serum cholesterol). This polymer is also involved in key natural biochemical reactions that help defend plants from disease.

In recent years, several food colorants, such as FD&C Red No. 3, have been banned. Because of consumer concerns, the food industry is actively seeking safe, natural colorants to replace synthetic products. One such product is a red dye manufactured from red sunflower hulls.
Ken Hammond/USDA 92BW 0806-30A

Scientists at the ERRC in Philadelphia have conducted research on the chemical and physical behavior of pectin in order to develop the baseline information necessary to understand its exceptional properties. In these studies, they have discovered how calcium in the diet combines with pectin to aid in the lowering of serum cholesterol. Cooked or raw carrots appear to be a good source of pectin for this purpose. Other ERRC research, in collaboration with scientists at the BARC, ARS, has shown that pectin has a unique compartmentalized (subunit) structure that interacts with minerals inside plant tissues to regulate the texture, softening, and ripening of produce.

Most consumers are familiar with plant polysaccharides such as starch and pectin; however, when reading food labels such as those for creamy salad dressings, few shoppers realize that a common ingredient known as xanthan gum comes from bacteria! Xanthan gum was discovered at the ARS National Center for Agricultural Utilization Research (formerly the Northern Regional Research Center), Peoria, IL, in the 1950's and was put into commercial production in 1964. In 1973, 4,000 metric tons of xanthan gum were used for food and nonfood applications in the United States.

Because of the great commercial success of this bacterial polysaccharide, researchers at the ERRC are now working closely with major U.S. companies in the search for additional "novel" bacterial polysaccharides with unique properties. The screening of over 200 bacterial strains has led to the discovery of 3 novel bacterial polysaccharides. Some of the bacteria were found to produce polysaccharides very similar to those called algin or alginate that are currently extracted from brown algae (kelp) in the Pacific Ocean. These latter polysaccharides are used in great quantities by the food industry. Having a bacterial source for these high-valued polymers could help prevent potential overharvesting of kelp beds and could result in a more stable supply of these thickening agents for food industry applications.

These are just a few of the efforts ARS has under way to develop natural materials that impart desired flavors, colors, and textures to foods. Scientific research in this area offers new choices that can enhance the appeal of foods for consumers, and offer opportunities for farmers, manufacturers, and marketers who strive to provide what these consumers will choose. ❏

The Lactaid Story

39

by Virginia H. Holsinger, Research Leader, Eastern Regional Research Center, Agricultural Research Service, USDA, Philadelphia, PA

Dairy products are an important part of a healthy diet. Millions of Americans have difficulty digesting milk and other dairy products. In fact, it is estimated that more than one-third of the U.S. population has some form of lactose intolerance—an inability to digest lactose, the principal sugar of almost all mammal milk. Cow's milk contains about 4.8 percent lactose. The degree of intolerance varies with a person's race or ethnic group (see table 1). Lactose intolerance arises because the human body has stopped producing an intestinal enzyme called lactase, which hydrolyzes lactose (breaks it down to the simple sugars glucose and galactose) during digestion. In the absence of the enzyme, sensitive people may suffer uncomfortable gastrointestinal symptoms such as bloating, cramps, diarrhea, gas, and nausea.

Dairy products are the best sources of calcium and are also rich in protein, magnesium, phosphorus, vitamins A and D, and the B vitamins. These nutrients are needed for development of strong bones and maintenance of good health, especially in children, teenagers, and the elderly. Lactose-intolerant people need to avoid milk as a beverage, although they may be able to tolerate small amounts of milk products such as yogurt or ice milk, especially if they are part of a meal.

In the 1950's, it was thought that it might be possible to modify lactose in milk by adding an enzyme. But this became possible only with the development of commercial processes that provide lactase from nonhuman sources. The enzymes most widely used to break down lactose are taken from yeasts such as *Kluyveromyces marxianus* var. *lactis* (formerly *K. lactis*) and *Kluyveromyces fragilis* and from fungi such as *Aspergillus niger* and *Aspergillus oryzae*.

Table 1. Estimated rate of lactose intolerance in various U.S. population groups

Population group	Intolerance (Percent)
African-American	45 - 81
Mexican-American	47 - 74
Asian-American	65 - 100
Native-American	50 - 75
North European	6 - 25

Source: Houts, S.S., 1988, "Lactose Intolerance," Food Technology, 42:110.

Research Developments

To evaluate the use of lactase in product manufacture, scientists at the Eastern Regional Research Center (ERRC), ARS, USDA, first evaluated the properties of the available enzymes, because the properties of lactase depend on its source. Lactase from fungal sources was shown to function most efficiently under acid conditions (such as in the digestive tract), whereas lactase preparations from the *Kluyveromyces* yeasts were best suited for the treatment of milk and sweet whey, a byproduct of cheesemaking.

In a series of test products made from lactase-treated milk, 87-95 percent of the lactose was broken down. The enzyme used was isolated from *K. marxianus* var. *lactis* in the form of a colorless, free-flowing powder. In this process, freshly pasteurized whole or skim milk was preheated to 32 °C, and then treated with 300 parts per million (ppm) lactase for about 3 hours with continuous stirring; another method was to treat refrigerated milk with 150 ppm lactase for 16-18 hours. Gener-

ally, about the only change in flavor noticed in the lactase-treated beverage was increased sweetness (glucose and galactose are sweeter than lactose). Taste-panel studies showed that the sweeter taste of the milk was acceptable and, in some cases, enhanced the milk's desirability.

Commercialization

The SugarLo Company (progenitor of Lactaid Inc.) of Pleasantville, NJ, contacted ARS after the first publication of ERRC, ARS research results in October 1974. The company first obtained an exclusive license for the *K. marxianus* var. *lactis* lactase enzyme, manufactured by Gist-Brocades, Inc., Delft, Netherlands. After the safety and effectiveness of this enzyme were thoroughly analyzed, a Generally Rec-

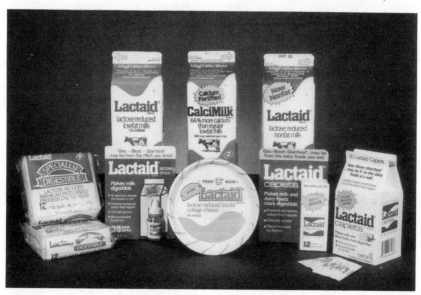

Lactose-free products are commercially available in supermarkets. Agricultural Research Service scientists at the Eastern Regional Research Center first evaluated the properties of the available enzymes to produce lactose-free products.
USDA 92BW1037

ognized as Safe (GRAS) Affirmation Petition was filed and subsequently granted.

SugarLo first marketed the enzyme in single-dose packets for the lactose-intolerant consumer to use to break down about 70 percent of the lactose in 1 quart of milk in 24 hours in the refrigerator. The powder was phased out in 1981 in favor of a sterile liquid form that is much easier to use. The liquid is sold in sizes to treat 75 quarts, 30 quarts, or 12 quarts of milk. Cost to the consumer is about 5 cents per glass of milk.

The availability of the liquid form of the enzyme made possible the commercial-scale production and marketing of a fluid milk already treated with lactase. In a milk processing plant, the sterile liquid (lactase) is added to previously pasteurized milk and held for 24 hours. After about 70 percent of the lactose has broken down, the milk is pasteurized again to stop further breakdown. Then the milk is packaged for retail sale. At present, the treated fluid milk is available as lactase-treated chocolate, nonfat, 1-percent-fat, 2-percent-fat, or calcium-fortified milk.

Further products developed by Lactaid Inc. include cottage cheese and pasteurized-process American cheese. Lactase-treated cottage cheese contains 50 percent less salt, with minimum effect on flavor.

Because treating milk with the liquid form of the enzyme may be inconvenient, Lactaid Inc. developed lactase capsules, which they began marketing to health professionals in 1985. Previous research had shown that if lactase is delivered to the small intestine, symptoms in lactose-intolerant persons are reduced. In addition, if the right dose is taken, milk lactose can be broken down in the body even in the presence of solid food. Tablets are now available for both consumers and health professionals. Each tablet contains lactase from the fungus *Aspergillus oryzae*; one to two tablets taken with a meal will usually handle the lactose in a glass of milk. In 1990, Sterling Drug Co. introduced a chewable tablet called Dairy-Ease.

This successful transfer of information between ARS scientists and Lactaid Inc. has resulted in assorted lactose-modified dairy foods and in lactase in liquid or tablet form for home use. Research and development activities are also continuing, for example in the development of new sources of lactase and in the development of new food products such as a low-lactose, low-fat, milk-based beverage powder. Because the total elimination of lactose-containing foods from the diet is nutritionally unwise, these new products have helped to make the nutrients of milk available to everyone. ❏

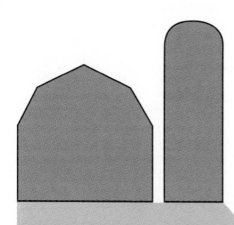

Part VII.
Environmental
Issues

Biofuels and the Carbon Balance

40

by Carol E. Whitman, Ecologist, and Gary R. Evans, Special Assistant for Global Change Issues, Office of the Assistant Secretary for Science and Education, USDA, Washington, DC

The burning of fossil fuels for energy has contributed to the buildup of carbon dioxide (CO_2) in the atmosphere. As the demand for energy continues to expand with population and economic growth, so will the need for alternative fuels that have no net effect on atmospheric carbon concentrations. One alternative is fuel made from crop biomass (biofuel).

This approach to balancing the carbon cycle has so far received scant attention, compared with proposals to plant more trees to sequester carbon from the atmosphere. But fuels made from plant biomass can reduce our dependence on imported, nonrenewable fossil fuels, slow the net increase of atmospheric CO_2, and help bring the Earth's carbon cycle back into balance.

The Carbon Cycle

Carbon is one of the basic elements of all living organisms. It exists in two principal forms: organic carbon derived from living things, and inorganic carbon, that is, gaseous and mineral compounds. Since carbon is central to life, its cycling between inorganic and organic phases is an important part of the Earth's ecology (see fig. 1).

CO_2, the predominant inorganic form of carbon, is found both in the air and dissolved in water. It is the principal source of carbon for living organisms. Aquatic and land plants convert CO_2, water (H_2O), and light energy into organic carbon during photosynthesis:

$$\text{light energy} + CO_2 + H_2O - (CH_2O) + O_2.$$

In this way, light energy is stored in organic compounds as chemical energy, and energy and inorganic carbon (CO_2) are made available to living organisms.

In order to meet their energy needs, plants break down some of these organic compounds through the process of respiration:

$$(CH_2O) + O_2 - CO_2 + H_2O + \text{energy}.$$

But much of the carbon remains in the plant's structure until it dies or is eaten by animals. On land, plant residues then become incorporated into the soil as soil organic matter. This constitutes a large pool of the Earth's organic carbon.

Animals also release CO_2 during respiration, eliminate carbon in waste material, and retain carbon in their bodies until they die. As the dead plants, dead animals, and animal waste material decay, CO_2 is returned to the air or water.

This cycle of carbon moving between an inorganic store and organic systems occurs on a relatively short time scale of several decades or less. Within this time frame, the carbon is balanced; that is, there is no net gain or loss in either carbon pool.

Other pathways occur over a much longer time scale. Sometimes the dead remains of plants and animals fail to decompose and under certain conditions are converted into fossil fuels (such as coal, oil, and natural gas), rock, or diamonds. This process takes place over millions of years, forming an almost permanent carbon reservoir.

Carbon Out of Balance

Over the past several hundred years, human beings have begun to alter many of the flows in the carbon cycle, and with them, the carbon balance of the Earth. The burning of coal, oil, and gas has released some of the permanent store of organic carbon to form CO_2. In addition, native forests and grasslands have been cleared for agriculture and development. Often forests are burned, prematurely returning carbon to the air. The reduction in number and size of forests has decreased the overall ability to assimilate CO_2 from the atmosphere. Without a steady

---

Figure 1

The Carbon Cycle

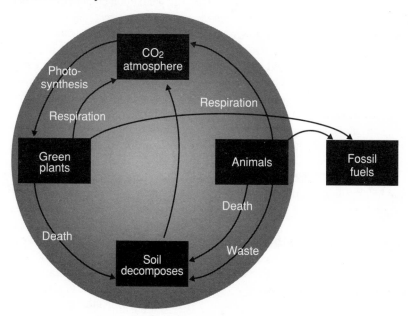

source of plant residues, the carbon tied up in soil organic matter also declines, resulting in a net release of CO_2 into the air.

Human activities have caused a net increase in atmospheric CO_2 from a preindustrial level of 280 parts per million volume (ppmv) to 350 ppmv today. At current levels of energy consumption, CO_2 is expected to double over the next century. This increase in atmospheric CO_2 is significant because of its role in regulating the Earth's temperature.

Like a blanket around the Earth, atmospheric CO_2 absorbs heat radiation emitted by the sun-warmed planet, and radiates it back to the surface. In effect, CO_2 helps to keep the Earth warm. This natural "greenhouse effect" provides human beings, animals, and plants with a comfortable living environment. But increases in atmospheric CO_2, like adding another blanket, may cause the Earth's temperature to rise.

The impact of increased atmospheric CO_2 is as yet uncertain. The global warming scenario does not take into account the effect of clouds or particles in the atmosphere on the Earth's radiation balance. Though we are in relatively uncharted territory, it may be prudent to take actions that can help bring the carbon cycle back into balance.

Biofuels and the Carbon Cycle

Biofuels are liquid and gaseous fuels produced from plant biomass (see chapter 32). The major types of biofuels are shown in table 1. These biomass-based fuels can be substituted for fossil fuels and thereby check the net increase in atmospheric CO_2.

As with fossil fuels, CO_2 is released into the air when plant biomass is burned for energy. But the carbon from biomass fuels is part of the shorter carbon pathway, cycling over a time scale of several decades. In contrast, the carbon in fossil fuels cycles over millions of years. The carbon released during combustion of biofuels is converted to biomass by plants within the same time frame that it is released. As a result, there is no net buildup of atmospheric carbon like that associated with the burning of fossil fuels. Thus, the biofuel cycle is part of the short-term carbon cycle.

In terms of displacing CO_2 emissions from fossil fuels, plant biomass yields, upon combustion, as much energy per carbon content as coal does, making it an effective substitute. In comparison with petroleum or natural gas, biofuels are currently less efficient on an energy output per carbon basis; but technological breakthroughs are making them more competitive all the time. Moreover, biofuels have the advantage of having less environmentally harmful exhaust emissions.

The Potential for Energy Crops

Over the last 20 years, research into alternative fuels has been driven by our need to reduce U.S. dependence on imported fossil fuels, improve our balance of payments, and reduce air pollutants such as sulfur, carbon monoxide, and ozone. The current concern over increases in atmospheric CO_2 is

Part VII. Environmental Issues

just an additional motivation. The major obstacle, to date, has been the conversion economics, that is, the ability to produce biofuels as cheaply as petroleum products. Recent technological advances could make biofuels cost-competitive within a decade.

Ethanol production in the United States through fermentation of corn now stands at 1.1 billion gallons per year. Ten-percent ethanol blends make up 7 percent of all gasoline sold in the United States. This capacity is expected to expand by 500 million gallons per year under the provisions of the Clean Air Act alone.

The greatest potential for this alcohol fuel, as well as for methanol, is in cellulosic feedstocks. Cellulosic materials (such as wood or crop residues) can be converted to ethanol by acid hydrolysis or enzymatic hydrolysis. The big promise lies with biotechnological advances in enzymatic conversion. This includes better enzyme preparation and process design, better pretreatments of cellulosic feedstock, and genetic engineering of bacteria for

Table 1. Types of biofuels, potential sources, and use

Type	Source	Use
Ethanol	Grains (corn feedstocks, grain sorghum), sugar crops (sugarcane, sweet sorghum), cellulosic feedstocks (wood, short rotation woody crops, kenaf), and food processing wastes	Can be blended with gasoline as ETBE*, or used as a substitute for gasoline
Methanol	Cellulosic feedstocks (wood, grass crops, crop residues)	Can be used as a feedstock in chemical manufacturing, or blended with gasoline as MTBE*
Biodiesel fuel	Oil seeds (rapeseed, soybean, sunflower, oil palm)	Seed oil can be converted to gasoline, diesel, or jet fuel
Methane (Biogas)	Cellulosic feedstocks (wood, crop residues)	Chemical feedstocks

* ETBE, ethyl tertiary butyl ether; MTBE, methyl tertiary butyl ether

faster and more efficient hydrolysis and fermentation.

There is considerable forest and crop land available in the United States for the production of energy crops. Marginal lands, although generally unsuitable for intensive annual cropping, could also be brought into production with less risk of erosion, because some energy crops have longer rotation times and need less intensive management (minimal or no tillage and less fertilizer and pesticide than annual crops). Initial expectations are that energy crops will have minimal environmental impacts.

Expansion in the use of energy crops to produce biofuels holds considerable promise for these non-traditional agricultural products. Technological breakthroughs are essential to reduce costs, increase production potential, and ensure environmental sustainability. USDA continues to support research into the production of energy crops, as well as biochemical conversion technologies for biofuels. ❏

Improvements 41 in Recycling Wood and Wood-Fiber Products

by Ted Laufenberg, Richard Horn, and Ted Wegner, Forest Products Laboratory, Forest Service, USDA, Madison, WI, and Stan Bean, Forest Products and Harvesting Research, Forest Service, USDA, Washington, DC (retired)

Since the turn of this century, the United States has been dubbed by some "the throw-away society," and it generates approximately 50 percent of the world's solid and industrial waste. Almost half the municipal solid waste (MSW) that goes into landfills consists of paper and wood fiber (table 1). Recovery and reuse of these materials would offer a significant opportunity for saving landfill space as well as for reducing our impact on the environment.

The pulp and paper industry has expanded recycling of some grades of paper, including corrugated containers and cartonboard, newspapers, and white office paper. In addition to this effort, alternative uses of recovered fibers and wood from MSW need to be developed. Wood fibers can be recovered from industrial operations or the MSW stream to produce useful, ecologically sound commodities.

This chapter highlights research on recycling that is being conducted by USDA's Forest Products Laboratory. These research activities represent a step toward achieving the technology needed to expand recycling opportunities in this country.

Table 1. Generation of municipal solid waste in 1988[1]

Source	Municipal solid waste (million tons)	Weight as proportion of total MSW (percent)
Paper and paperboard	71.8	40.0
Wood	6.5	3.6
Plastics	14.4	8.0
Yard waste	31.6	17.6
Metals	15.3	8.5
Food waste	13.2	7.3
Glass	12.5	7.0
Textiles	3.9	2.2
Rubber and leather	4.6	2.6
Miscellaneous inorganics	2.7	1.5
Other	3.1	1.7
Total	179.6	100.0

[1]Prerecovery values

Improved Technology for Recycling Paper

An intensive research and development effort by the USDA Forest Service promises to reduce disposal of wood fiber wastes by an additional 30 million tons per year by the year 2000. Research at the Forest Products Laboratory (FPL) in Madison, WI, is focused on (1) removing contaminants from and deinking recycled papers, (2) improving fiber bonding in recycled papers, (3) developing new bleaching technologies for recycled fibers, and (4) transforming the structure of recycled fibers.

Removing Contaminants.
Nonfiber components added to paper and paperboard products complicate the recycling of wastepaper. Before wastepaper can be reused as a fiber source, many of these components, such as adhesives, inks, dyes, metal foils, and plastics, have to be removed.

Many contaminants can be removed on the basis of size and density by cleaning and screening. However, some contaminants are similar in size and density to the fibers and are much more difficult to remove. Nonwettable synthetic adhesives, called stickies, fall into this category and are a major obstacle to wastepaper recycling. Current techniques for controlling stickies include furnish selection, improved pulping and deflaking, well-designed screening and cleaning systems, dispersion, and use of stabilizing additives.

Recent advances in stickie control have focused on pulper design. New pulpers are equipped with mechanical devices that remove stickies at the beginning of the stock preparation system. Drum pulpers and low-speed, high-torque agitators can gently fiberize the wastepaper without reducing the size of the stickies, resulting in highly consistent pulping. Low-density stickies are removed by through-flow cleaners, an energy-efficient process that reduces fiber loss. This type of cleaner design has been critical in removing contaminants from corrugated containers.

Deinking. Deinking poses a different set of problems. When ink is fused to paper, as in laser printing and the photocopy process, it cannot be dispersed by conventional methods for removing contaminants. Detaching nondispersible inks from fibers requires intensive mechanical, chemical, and thermal action. The detached ink is then removed by screens, cleaners, and the flotation process.

Recent deinking technology has resulted in brighter and cleaner paper through high-consistency dispersion, together with bleaching or use of agglomerating chemicals. Flotation units have been improved to generate a wider range of air bubbles, which permit removal of a wider range of ink particle sizes. Pressurized refiners have been adapted for dispersing noncontact inks. Dispersion has been especially useful in recycling high-quality office wastepaper into printing- and writing-grade papers. The process disperses both contaminant particles and stickies, facilitating their subsequent removal.

An important development in deinking technology is the multidisc refiner, which packs a large amount of refining surface in a single refiner housing. This technology reduces refining intensities drastically compared to conventional double-disc refiners and permits treatment of delicate pulps. Multidisc refiners are especially well suited for treating deinked newsprint. Increases in strength of 15 to 25 percent are possible without generating the short, unusable fibers (fines) that can clog papermaking systems.

Improved washing units have resulted in more efficient treatment of deinked stock and other recycled wastepaper pulp. Advanced diffusion washing technology, displacement wash presses, vacuum deckers, and other stock washing equipment are being used throughout the recycling industry. These new systems typically cost less than their older counterparts, an important feature for an industry with high capital costs.

Finally, researchers are using computer-aided visual analysis of paper samples to determine the number and size of ink specks.

Improved Fiber Bonding. In the final stage of papermaking, the sheet of paper is dried at a relatively high

Dave Bromett, a chemical engineer with the Forest Service Forest Products Laboratory in Madison, WI, begins the process of separating oversized particles, lumps, and other contaminants, called "stickies," by passing the liquid paper pulp over a vibrating flat screen to produce usable fiber.
Bob Nichols/USDA 92BW0734-15

temperature. The combination of dehydration and elevated temperatures hardens the surface of the wood fibers and stiffens their internal structure. These effects must be reversed if the fibers are to be recycled into paper. The surface hardening limits interfiber bonding and the internal stiffening reduces fiber conformability, which is needed to consolidate a paper web. Variations on traditional refining and stock preparation can reverse internal stiffening for some applications. However, the surface hardening effect is not as readily reversed.

Research at the FPL focuses on two new approaches for improving fiber-to-fiber bonding of hardened and difficult-to-bond recycled pulps. The first approach identifies processes that alter the physical structure of the pulp fiber surface by swelling—particularly those processes that alter the aggregation of cellulose and hemicellulose, two key chemical components of wood. Researchers are seeking swelling agents that act only on the outermost surface layers of the pulp fibers. Agents that promote internal swelling are undesirable because such swelling makes fibers less conformable.

The second approach is chemical modification of the fiber surface. Such modification can rehydrate the surface and contribute to interfiber bonding as a result of chemical changes on the surface. In these studies, the chemical action is confined to the fiber surface. Studies are focused primarily on oxidative treatments that form highly polar groups on the surface cellulosic microfibrils.

New Bleaching Technologies.

Paper products made from virgin fiber usually discolor during use. The degree of discoloration depends on fiber type and history. Researchers are seeking to develop pulp bleaching methods that are environmentally safe and appropriate for recycled fiber processing.

Most current bleaching technologies were developed through trial and error, rather than through understanding how discoloration occurs. Current systems also have technological or environmental disadvantages. However, the search for new bleaching technologies is handicapped by inadequate knowledge of the color-forming bodies, called chromophores, that need to be removed or modified.

The FPL research program focuses on state-of-the-art photochemistry and spectroscopy to discover how the chromophores are formed, where they occur, and how accessible they are to current bleaching processes. Most bleaching systems also attack the fiber constituents that are the key to the mechanical properties of the fiber. Therefore, another avenue of research focuses on the reactivity of pulp fiber constituents to different bleaching systems. This research will result in knowledge for developing new bleaching systems that target the chromophores while causing the least possible damage to the structure of the fibers.

Structural Transformation of Fibers.

One central challenge of recycling technology is finding ways to reverse the degradation of pulp fiber properties caused by structural changes during the original papermaking process. Research is focused on adapting materials science techniques that have been used extensively with synthetic polymers, synthetic fibers, and cellulosic fibers. These techniques include x-ray diffractometry, solid-state carbon-13 nuclear magnetic resonance, raman spectroscopy, and electron microscopy. Each technique is sensitive to a particular level of molecular structure and supplies information not available through the other methods. The knowledge gained through this program will supply fundamental information necessary for innovations in recycling technology.

Recycled Wood Fiber Technology

Expanding recycling will require expanded markets for recovered fiber, including solid wood (such as construction debris and discarded pallets) and fibers that can no longer be recycled into paper. Alternative uses for recovered materials provide options for balancing the performance properties of products with their production costs. Recycled wood fibers can be used for structural, composite, and panel products, for wood-plastic mats, and for fuel.

Molded Structural Products. The cleaning of recycled fibers before creating the final product adds expense to

Paul Kmiecik, a physical science technician with the Forest Products Laboratory, checks the quality of recycled paper produced at the lab. Research focuses on altering the physical surface structure of pulp

fiber by swelling and chemically modifying the fiber surface.
Steve Schmieding/FS M88-0014-17

the recycling process. Such costs can be avoided by using uncleaned pulp fibers to create wet-formed, molded-pulp structural products. The recycled fiber is press-dried against compressible rubber molds. Products can be made thin enough for strong, lightweight corrugated containers or thick enough for wall, floor, or furniture applications. The FPL has patented a concept for such a pulp-fiber-based structural product, called Spaceboard. Spaceboard components are produced in two symmetrical halves, which are bonded together to form a three-dimensional part. When joined, the molded ribs of each half create geometric-shaped cells in the part's core.

When used for applications such as shipping containers, Spaceboard can be made uniformly strong in every direction. Laboratory tests have shown that Spaceboard is between 30 and 200 percent stronger in both major directions than conventional corrugated fiberboard is in its strongest direction, using the same amount of wood fiber. This strength is imparted by the press-dry molding technology and the special core configuration.

Further refinements have demonstrated that Spaceboard can be produced with the wet strength and dimensional stability necessary for engineered structures. Spaceboard's unique characteristics as a building

John Hunt, a research general engineer at the Forest Products Laboratory and co-inventor of Spaceboard, reviews a product sample for defects and correct molding. Spaceboard is a new building material produced by press-drying recycled fiber against compressible rubber molds.
Bob Nichols/USDA 92BW0732-2

material are its high strength-per-unit-weight ratio, design versatility, and adaptability to a wide range of fiber feedstocks. The skin thickness, cell size and shape, sandwich thickness, and core density can be tailored for particular applications. Spaceboard is an excellent candidate for products that use ink-laden or unclean portions of the recycled fiber resource, and it offers a new and more efficient way to use recycled (or virgin) wood fiber for structural products.

A set of products related to Spaceboard are made without pressure application during the drying of the molded pulp mat. These products are popular in the egg and fruit packaging industries as a result of their low cost,

nestability, and cushioning ability. The products are also suitable for such packaging applications as corner guards, food trays, light tube separators, and horticultural trays or containers. Recycled newsprint has typically been used for these applications. As recycled newsprint becomes more valued in the paper industry, lower value fiber resources can be used for packaging.

Spaceboard components are produced in two symmetrical halves, which are bonded together to form a three-dimensional structure.
USDA/M860104

Uses for wood fiber panel products include insulating acoustical board; carpet board; wall, ceiling, and floor acoustical insulation panels; nail base board; and floor and roof insulation boards.
Bob Nichols/USDA 92BW0732-16

The Spaceboard construction technique yields products that can be made thin enough for strong, lightweight walls and floors.
Bob Nichols/USDA 92BW0732-29

Part VII. Environmental Issues

Fiber-Plastic Composites. Recycled wood-based fiber and plastics can be combined for a wide spectrum of products ranging from inexpensive, low-performance composites to expensive, high-performance materials. The plastics (such as polyethylene, polypropylene, and polyethylene terephthalate) as well as the wood fiber can be recovered from municipal solid waste. Composite products with complex shapes can be produced using extrusion, nonwoven web, and fiber melt matrix technologies.

Extrusion technology uses heat to form wood-plastic composites. In most current extrusion technologies that use wood or other lignocellulosic material, wood powder is used as a low-cost filler. The wood component contributes little to the performance of the product. However, if wood fiber were used as the wood component, it would contribute significantly to product performance, increasing the strength of the extruded part.

Nonwoven web technology is used to create flexible fiber mats that can be used to form wood-plastic composites. The mats can be pressed into any shape or size. The plastic acts as a binder, holding the mat together. A high-performance adhesive can either be sprayed on the wood fiber before mat formation, be added as a powder during mat formation, or be included in the binder fiber system. Using this technology, a complex part can be made directly from a wood-plastic fiber blend; current technology requires the formation of flat sheets prior to the shaping of complex parts.

Thermoplastic fiber melt matrix technology is used to make reinforced thermoplastic composites, using a melt-blending or air-laid process. These products are lightweight; have improved acoustical, impact, and heat reformability properties; and cost less than comparable products made from plastic alone. These features lend themselves to new processing techniques, new applications, and new markets for thermoplastic composites in such areas as packaging, furniture, housing, and automobiles. Thermoformed composites are currently used for interior door panels and trunk liners in automobiles.

Research priorities at FPL include improving or developing methods for (1) converting waste wood and waste plastics into forms suitable for subsequent melt-blending and nonwoven web processing and (2) processing the composites.

Wood Composites Made With Inorganic Binders. Recycled wood fiber can be used to make composites from particles or fibers of wood held

Recycled wood-based fiber and plastics can be used to produce a wide spectrum of products ranging from very inexpensive, low-performance composites to expensive, high-performance materials.
Steve Schmieding/FS M91-0138-3

together with an inorganic matrix, such as Portland cement or gypsum. Such composites can be used in a variety of structural and industrial applications and have unique advantages over conventional building materials. Some composites are water resistant and can withstand the rigors of outdoor applications; almost all are either fireproof or highly fire resistant and are very resistant to decay by fungi.

Inorganic-bonded wood composites are molded products or boards that contain between 10 and 70 percent (by weight) wood particles or fibers and, conversely, 30 to 90 percent inorganic binder. Many different types of material can be incorporated with the inorganic binder matrix, including recycled paper fiber, fiberized demolition waste or scrap pallets, industrial waste wood, wood residues, noncommercial wood species, and very low grade, nonmerchantable wood. The wood particles must be fully encased with the binder to make a coherent material. Thus, the amount of inorganic binder required per unit volume of composite material is much higher than that in resin-bonded wood composites. The properties of inorganic-bonded wood composites are significantly influenced by their density as well as the amount and nature of both the inorganic binder and the woody material.

Cement-bonded particle and fiber boards possess excellent machinability, thus allowing builders to construct a wall product for home construction that combines studs, sheathing, and siding into a single panel. Other uses include cladding, balcony parapets, flooring, industrial walls, sound barriers, garden and fence walls, interior partitions, and wall linings in areas of high humidity. Another application is an experimental mixture of cement, sand, and small wood chunks (less than 3 inches, or 76 mm, in size). The wood chunks can be used as a complete substitute or partial replacement for gravel or stone aggregate. This product, called chunkrete, is being developed by the Houghton, MI, Laboratory of the USDA Forest Service, North Central Experiment Station. Chunkrete is lighter but not as strong as standard concrete, not unlike other types of special lightweight concrete. Preliminary results of tests with chunkrete beams and cylinders have been encouraging.

Gypsum-bonded wood fiber panels are used as replacements for gypsum wallboard and are reported to have strong nail- and screw-holding properties, high moisture and fire resistance, and improved resistance to impact, mold, and mildew. Other reported advantages of gypsum-bonded wood fiber panels compared to conventional gypsum wallboard include improved anti-sag properties for ceilings, better sound insulation, and a system for finishing joints that doesn't require tape.

The combination of wood fibers with inorganic binders provides a unique opportunity to utilize recycled waste and low-grade wood fiber to make products that are environmentally safe, user friendly, and acceptable for many uses. Research to date has clearly indicated that inorganic-bonded wood composites can meet building and industrial needs.

Panel Products. Fiber-based panels of varying densities can be produced from recycled wood fibers. One family of products, called Homosote, was first produced in 1916. It is made from recycled newspapers and other groundwood paper publications. Other fiberboard-type products on the market also use all or partly recycled wood fiber as a raw material base stock. Uses for these types of products include insulating acoustical board, carpet board, and nail baseboard.

Research at FPL is determining the dimensional stability, moisture resistance, stiffness, and strength properties of dry-process hardboards made from varying blends of virgin wood fiber and newsprint fiber. Many other uses for fiber-based products of this type will be developed as collection, separation, and cleanup processes are further refined and developed.

Wood-Plastic Mats. Another potential use for recycled wood fiber is in low-density mats. Wood and plastic fibers are introduced into a turbulent air stream, transferred via the air stream to a moving support bed, and subsequently formed into a continuous, low-density mat. The fibers in the mat are further intertwined and strengthened through needling. The ratio of wood to plastic in this matrix can be in the range to 95 to 5 percent by weight. The plastic can also be replaced with a long lignocellulosic fiber such as jute or kenaf.

An interesting application for fiber mats is for mulch around newly planted seedlings. The mats provide the benefits of natural mulch. In addition, controlled-release fertilizers, re-

pellants, insecticides, and herbicides can be added to the mats. The combination of mulch and pesticides in producing agronomic crops has shown promise. Such applications in silviculture could ensure seedling survival and promote early development on planting sites where severe nutritional deficiencies, animal damage, or insect and weed problems are anticipated. Preliminary research conducted by the USDA Forest Service on loblolly pine seedlings in southern Louisiana, where the established vegetation is grasses, forbs, and blackberries, shows promising results.

Similarly, grass seed can be incorporated in a wood fiber or jute fiber mat. This product can replace sod for grass seeding around new home sites or along highway embankments. Advantages include better seed germination, good moisture retention, no need for soil, biodegradability, and quick installation.

A third application for low-density wood fiber mats is for air filters or other types of filters. These products must vary in density considering the material being filtered and the volume of the material moving through the mat per unit of time. A very low-density mat can be produced with enough structural integrity to be effective as a filter.

Fuel. When all other uses of a recycled wood fiber are exhausted, the fiber can be burned as fuel. Some types of recycled wood fiber, such as primary wood processing residue and refuse-derived fuel (paper and newsprint) from municipal solid waste, contain few contaminants and are easily mixed with other fuel and burned to recover energy. Other types of recycled fiber, such as demolition wood, pallets and containers, secondary wood processing residues, and preservative-treated wood from powerlines and railroads, are mixed with a variety of contaminants and are therefore more problematic.

Demolition Wood. Various methods can be used to sort demolition wood from other materials. Hand sorting, although labor-intensive, is inexpensive and the processing system is simple. Other methods use mechanical means to separate the wood. These methods are more complicated than hand sorting but can separate cement, bricks, metals, and dirt as well as the wood. Hand sorting can produce a cleaner fuel than mechanical sorting if the material does not include painted wood. Mechanical sorting can retrieve more wood than hand sorting, but the retrieved material may contain a greater amount of nonwood materials.

Pallets and Containers. The pallet, container, and reel manufacturing industry produces nearly 500 million new units per year and uses over 7 million board feet of lumber. This amounts to over 10 million tons of wood (dry basis) per year. About half the units are returnable and are reused. The other half are used only once. Eventually all pallets, containers, and reels must be disposed of. Some of these materials are ground for mulch and animal bedding and others are used for firewood, but most are disposed of in landfills. Some pallets and containers must be hauled hundreds of miles to landfill sites because their disposal at local landfills is either too costly or prohibited. In the near future, many more landfills will prohibit the dumping of such units. If the units were collected at central sites, they could be crushed and milled to produce wood fuel.

Uses for Pulp and Paper Mill Sludges

The disposal of sludges that result from the production of pulp and paper is an increasingly difficult problem. Effluent sludges at pulp and paper mills include primary, chemical, and secondary sludges. Primary sludge usually comes from a mechanical clarifier; it consists mostly of fibrous material and fillers. Chemical sludge comes from wastewater color-removal processes. Secondary sludge comes from the aerobic biological treatment of mill effluents. Most sludge is landfilled; some is mixed with hog fuel and burned or incinerated. Alternative uses for sludge include landspreading, compost, and animal feed.

Landspreading. Pulp, paper, and recycling mills produce nearly as much sludge as they do finished products. Pulp and paper mill sludges contain cellulosic and chemical compounds of nitrogen, phosphorus, potassium, and other elements. These compounds can increase the water-holding capacity of soils (especially sandy soils), improve soil structure, and supply nutrients for plant growth. The nitrogen content of the sludge is the most important component for landspreading.

An important factor in the suitability of a sludge for agricultural and silvicultural landspreading is its carbon to nitrogen ratio. This ratio indicates the tendency of the material to release or to immobilize nitrogen. Another measure of suitability is the ratio of calcium to magnesium.

Compost. Composted sludge is a humuslike soil amendment that enhances plant growth. Composted sludge is clean, has an agreeable smell, and is drier than sludge that has not been composted.

For composting, sludge should consist of at least 30 percent solids. The sludge is first thoroughly mixed with wood or bark chips and then composted in a pile, windrows, or a vessel. The sludge mixture must be aerated throughout the composting process because malodorous volatile fatty acids form under anaerobic conditions. The composting process can produce a useful material from pulp and paper mill sludges for agricultural and horticultural markets. Composting costs can be covered by income from sales, which will offset remaining landfill costs.

Animal Feed. Several years ago, FPL and University of Wisconsin-Madison scientists evaluated pulp and paper mill sludges, screener rejects, and fines for use in animal feed. Most materials contained too much ash, but pulp fines (mostly parenchyma cells) from two sulfite tissue mills were found acceptable if dye-containing paper-machine fines were eliminated. Unbleached southern pine kraft pulp fines were also found acceptable.

An experimental feed program was established. However, the program was discontinued because the tissue mill could not guarantee that no contaminated pulp fines would enter the feed. Adequate quantities of grain and forage make pulp and paper mill residues an unlikely source of animal feed in North America.

Responsibilities

In any approach to recycling, the Government and the private sector must cooperate as full partners. Government cannot logically mandate the increased use of recyclable materials without industry involvement—only the industrial sector has the technical knowledge and equipment to separate and process solid waste and to make useful, economically viable products from these materials. Industry is the market for recycled resources, and it must be a full partner in all aspects of the process.

As a society, we must take a broad look at both the opportunities for recycling and the accompanying responsibilities. We must be concerned with the reliable performance of products, their economic potential, and the health and safety of those making and using the products. We must also be concerned with the prudent use of renewable resources. Recycling is a critical element in the long-term management of these resources. ❏

Environmental Advantages of Agricultural Products

42

by Stephen R. Crutchfield, Agricultural Economist and Section Leader, Environmental Quality Valuation, ERS, USDA, Washington, DC

American farmers help feed and clothe the Nation and the world with the crops they raise and the raw materials they supply to create manufactured products. With the increasing emphasis on "green" farming, America's farmers are helping to protect the environment as well, by reducing the potentially harmful effects of farm chemicals and soil erosion on the quality of our natural resources and food supply.

Agriculture also plays a more innovative role in promoting environmental quality by supplying "environmentally friendly" products that can substitute for polluting products, such as petroleum products. Agricultural products can help the environment is several ways. Some agricultural products, like ethanol made from corn or biomass crops, can serve as substitutes for nonrenewable petroleum products and help reduce our dependence on fossil fuels. In addition, biofuels like corn-based ethanol can help improve air quality when they replace conventional gasoline.

The 1990 amendments to the Clean Air Act have focused public attention on ways to reduce the Nation's air pollution problem. Using ethanol-blended fuels rather than conventional gasoline can help reduce certain types of air pollution. This would create economic benefits by reducing the health-care costs associated with exposure to polluted air. However, some tradeoffs may be necessary; increasing acreage to corn to provide feedstock for ethanol production may increase soil erosion and water quality problems resulting from agricultural chemicals. Some of these negative effects could be reduced by using new "biomass" crops that would provide feedstock for ethanol production with smaller effects on water quality than those produced by growing additional corn.

Ethanol Blends Reduce Carbon Monoxide Emissions

Motor vehicles fueled by petroleum-based fuels such as gasoline or diesel oil emit gasses and toxic compounds that contribute to air pollution. When ethanol is blended with conventional gasoline, emissions of some of these pollutants can be cut down. For example, the most common formulation of ethanol fuel in use today is 10 percent ethanol and 90 percent gasoline. When this fuel, commonly called E-10, is used in place of conventional gasoline, auto emissions of carbon monoxide (CO) are reduced by 15 to 20 percent, depending on the age of the vehicle and the type of fuel system used. Chemical properties of ethanol also permit refiners to leave out some chemicals used to raise gasoline octane. Accordingly, switching from conventional gasoline to E-10 reduces emissions of potentially dangerous compounds such as benzene and butadiene.

On the other hand, switching from conventional gasoline to E-10 may increase evaporative emissions. Careful blending of ethanol with gasoline, or use of newer, less polluting forms of conventional gasoline as base stock may reduce or eliminate these evaporative emissions. Other fuel formulations, such as 85 percent (E-85), reduce both CO and ozone-related exhaust emissions, and may prove useful in the future if vehicles designed to burn them become available at competitive cost. Alternatively, ETBE (Ethyl tertiary butyl ether), which is 42 percent ethanol, can also be used to reduce CO without design modifications to existing automobiles.

Clean Air Act Amendments May Stimulate Demand for Ethanol-Blended Fuels

Recent changes in air quality laws establish new air quality guidelines and regulations to reformulate gasoline in order to reduce air pollution. In areas where CO pollution is a problem, motor vehicle fuels will be required to have a higher oxygen content to reduce CO emissions. Adding ethanol to gasoline increases its oxygen content, so this legislation is expected to increase the demand for ethanol-blended fuels in areas where CO is a problem. As of 1989, about 51 million people

lived in areas not meeting CO standards.

In areas not meeting ozone standards, gasoline will have to be reformulated beginning in 1995. Reformulated gasoline must contain higher levels of oxygen, reduce toxics, and reduce emissions of ozone-forming compounds by 15 percent. Nine cities with the worst ozone pollution will be required to allow only reformulated gasoline beginning January 1, 1995. However, there are provisions for other, less polluted areas to "opt in" to the program. Some analysts have estimated that 60 percent of the Nation's gasoline will be reformulated by the year 2000.

Other provisions of the amendments, such as the "clean fuels" fleet program, may stimulate research and development for fuels such as E-85, which have an even higher ethanol content. Over the long term, with advances in vehicle technology and fuel refining techniques, the market for ethanol-blended fuels is expected to grow. This year USDA will purchase 19 E-85 cars for the agency fleet.

Ethanol-Blended Fuels May Create Benefits by Improving Air Quality, but the Fuel Costs Must Be Considered as Well

To properly evaluate the tradeoffs of using ethanol-blended fuels versus conventional gasoline, we need to compare different fuel formulations on the basis of their cost-effectiveness. In weighing these environmental benefits and costs, it is important to keep in mind the relative production and other costs of the different fuel formulations. Table 1 shows how different fuel formulations change auto emissions, compared to conventional gasoline. We consider, in addition to E-10, reformulated gasoline (gasoline that meets EPA standards for ozone reduction), reformulated E-10 (ethanol blended with reformulated gasoline), and MTBE blends (MTBE is a petroleum product blended into gasoline to reduce emissions of CO and volatile organic compounds, or VOC's).

While reformulated gasoline and reformulated E-10 generate environmental benefits, they also cost more than either conventional gasoline, E-10, or 11 percent MTBE. Table 2 summarizes the cost differences among different fuels. Based on historical prices, E-10 costs 6.7 cents per gallon more than conventional gasoline, assuming 10 percent ethanol at a cost of $1.25 per gallon. MTBE costs less than ethanol, and so 11 percent MTBE fuels have a lower price premium (3.4 cents per gallon) when compared with conventional gas. However, E-10 contains more oxygen than 11 percent MTBE blends and this reduces carbon monoxide emissions by a greater amount. Reformulated gasoline and reformulated E-10 have a higher cost differential (16 cents per gallon and 21 cents per gallon, respectively, when compared with conventional gas), but they also have greater environmental benefits.

Other Ethanol Feedstocks: Impact on Water Quality

U.S. corn production will increase if ethanol output rises and if corn is the primary feedstock. Increased corn production may bring more cropland into production or shift acreage into corn from other crops, such as soybeans. Because continuous corn planting tends to be erosive and uses agricultural chemicals intensively, there may be an off-farm environmental impact in the form of impaired surface or ground water quality.

There are other ways of producing ethanol in addition to using corn as a feedstock. A variety of feedstocks can be used in the production process. New technologies for cellulosic conversion may mean that, in the future, more ethanol could be produced with-

Table 1: Differences in emissions among alternative fuels (percentage change compared to conventional gasoline)

Emission	E-10	MTBE	Reformulated E-10	Reformulated gasoline
VOC	0 to +15	-1	<0	-20
CO	-15 to -25	-5	-15 to -25	>-5
NOx	+5	+3	0	0

Note: E-10 is 10 percent ethanol and 90 percent conventional gasoline. MTBE is 11 percent Methyl tertiary butyl ether and 89 percent conventional gasoline. Reformulated E-10 is 10 percent ethanol and 90 percent reformulated gas. Estimates of emissions changes are derived from EPA studies and independent research reports.

out the adverse environmental impact that may result from increased acreage devoted to corn. For example, growing herbaceous energy crops (energy sorghum, switchgrass, sudan grass, sericea lespedeza, and weeping lovegrass) could provide feedstocks for ethanol production. These crops result in lower levels of cropland erosion and chemical use than corn, and may reduce the off-farm environmental impacts associated with producing more ethanol from corn.

Other, noncrop inputs can also be used to produce ethanol. Improvement in cellulosic conversion technology means that many other feedstocks may be used, such as yard clippings or wood and wood fiber products. Increased use of these feedstocks could have some additional environmental benefits by reducing the need for landfill and solid waste disposal sites.

Benefits and Costs of Air Quality Improvements and Increased Ethanol Use

Our understanding of all the expected benefits and costs of increased use of ethanol as a motor vehicle fuel is not yet complete. We need to consider the economic benefits (or costs) of the air quality changes associated with substituting ethanol blends for conventional

Table 2 - Cost differences between conventional gasoline and alternative fuels

Fuel component	Spot price ($/gallon)
Conventional gasoline	.58
MTBE	.89
Ethanol	1.25

	Difference from conventional gasoline		
Fuel	Fuel cost	Without excise tax exemption ($/gallon)	With excise tax exemption
E-10	$0.647	$0.067	$0.013
11 Percent MTBE	.614	.034	.034
Reformulated gas	.740	.160	.160
Reformulated E-10	.791	.211	.157

Note: E-10 is 10 percent ethanol and 90 percent conventional gasoline. MTBE is 11 percent Methyl tertiary butyl ether and 89 percent conventional gasoline. Reformulated E-10 is 10 percent ethanol and 90 percent reformulated gas. Prices are from EPA and the "New Fuels Report Price Watch," and they represent the period 1/6/89 to 3/26/91, excluding the Gulf War period. Prices for reformulated gas are for Arco EC-X. The Federal excise tax exemption is 5.4 cents per gallon for fuels with up to 10 percent ethanol.

gasoline. This would enable us to evaluate the tradeoffs between potential increases in evaporative emissions and reductions in CO emissions from increased consumption of E-10. The distribution of benefits and costs of producing and using ethanol-blended fuels will vary among different regions of the country. The primary areas of ozone impairment are concentrated in a few large, urban areas—notably southern California and the industrial areas of the Northeast. However, the environmental costs arising from soil erosion and impaired water quality associated with increased corn production will be primarily in the Midwest. This impact on the Midwest may be mitigated if we can control the off-farm environmental damage by preventing soil erosion on corn acreage or by using biomass crops as an ethanol feedstock.

Finally, we need to consider ethanol fuels in a larger, economywide context. We have considered here only the public environmental costs and benefits of switching to ethanol-blended fuels. However, other private and public costs could be factored in. For example, fuels with a minimum 10 percent ethanol are exempt from the Federal excise tax of 5.4 cents per gallon; this lowers the private costs of ethanol fuels to producers and shifts some of these costs to the general economy. Also, U.S. corn production is subject to a number of Federal agricultural programs. On the other hand, the petroleum industry is also granted tax allowances and other benefits that affect the private costs of production. A complete accounting of the full net economic benefits and costs of using ethanol-blended fuels would take into account all of these factors. ❏

New Farm Products, New Uses, and the Environment

43

by Claude Gifford, Office of Public Affairs, USDA, Washington, DC

New farm products and new uses for farm products offer promising opportunities to increase the demand for U.S. farm commodities, boost farmers' income, put new economic life in rural communities, and improve the environment.

These objectives are all interrelated. They tie together into an eco-nomically viable, sustainable method of farming and farm living.

Farmers are the only ones who can and do incorporate environmentally supportive practices on farmland. To do that, farmers need a level of economic return from farming that makes it possible to incorporate and maintain environmentally desirable practices.

That sense of economic security and well-being among farmers engenders a vision of the future that encourages the adoption of long-range, environmentally desirable farm practices.

That is one way new farm products and new uses for farm products contribute significantly to environmental farming.

New farm products and new uses for farm products also increase and broaden the demand for farm commodities. They enlarge farmers' opportunities for producing high-value products. They enable farmers to rely less on producing bulk farm commodities or enjoy better returns on traditional farm commodities. All this gives farmers more diversity in production selection, crop rotations, and use of land—and will make U.S. farm production more competitive, both at home and in farm export markets.

The interlocking relationships are evident: New farm products and new uses must be safe, environmentally acceptable, and profitable to produce. A more profitable agriculture supports a more environmentally responsive agriculture. And new uses for farm products can themselves be environmentally beneficial off the farm.

History of New Uses Effort

New uses is not a new idea, but the degree of action and the opportunities for success are new.

USDA's four Regional Research Laboratories—in Albany, California; New Orleans, Louisiana; Peoria, Illinois; and Wyndmoor, Pennsylvania— were built in 1938-41 to find new uses for farm products. A national Presidential Commission on Increased Industrial Uses of Farm Products studied new uses in 1956-57. Secretary of Agriculture Block in the early 1980's held a national conference "challenge forum" on new uses.

Predating all this was the formation of the Chemurgic Council under the leadership of Wheeler McMillen and with some financial aid from Henry Ford. The Chemurgic Council also had the support of such luminaries as inventor Thomas A. Edison, industrialist Irenee du Pont, MIT president Karl T. Compton, Nobel Prize winning physicist Robert A. Milliken of the California Institute of Technology, founder of the American Society of Farm Managers D. Howard Doane, Cornell University trustee H. E. Babcock, General Motors vice president Charles F. Kettering, and Sears, Roebuck & Company board chairman Robert E. Wood—all of whom served on the Chemurgic Council Board of Governors simultaneously.

Wheeler McMillen, long-time president of the National Chemurgic Council, was also executive director of the 1956-57 Presidential Commission on new uses, and was editor-in-chief of *Farm Journal*. He based his reasoning for the formation of the Chemurgic Council on the concept that the human stomach, as an outlet for food production, will stretch only so far—but the appetite for industrial uses of farm products can be almost without limit. The idea grew out of a comment made by Julius Barnes, a wheat exporter who was president of the U.S. Chamber of Commerce, in a speech at the American Farm Bureau

Convention in Chicago in 1924, where McMillen was present.

Subsequently, McMillen wrote about the concept in *Farm and Fireside*, of which he was then an editor. In 1926 McMillen wrote an editorial suggesting a national foundation to stimulate the creation of new uses for farm products. He discussed the concept with William M. Jardine, Secretary of Agriculture, and Herbert E. Hoover, then Secretary of Commerce. Both reacted favorably. In the next session of Congress, the Commerce Department requested a $50,000 appropriation to investigate industrial uses for agricultural raw materials.

In 1929 Jardine wrote a foreword to a McMillen book, *Too Many Farmers,* relating that when he was Secretary of Agriculture, McMillen came to him and "pointed out the inelasticity of the human stomach," and "proposed a campaign for the support of research to discover and extend nonfood uses for farm-grown materials, and to find more profitable uses for farm wastes."

The Chemurgic Council, formed in 1935, had three primary aims:

"1. Development of new, nonfood uses for established farm crops.

2. Establishment of new crops for new or old uses.

3. Discovery of profitable uses for agricultural wastes and residues."

This background is covered in McMillen's book *New Riches from the Soil.* Those former activities on behalf of new uses laid the foundation for the present emphasis on new uses for farm products. Secretary of Agriculture Edward Madigan has made the development of new farm products and new

uses for farm products one of his top priorities. There is even a greater opportunity now to be successful in producing new farm products and new uses for farm products.

Farm Capacity Is Available

The U.S. "farm plant" is running under capacity. From 60 million to 78 million acres of cropland have been idled in farm programs each of the last 5 years. New products and new uses can offer more opportunities for farmers to put this land to productive use. This would reduce Government farm program costs while increasing the per-unit efficiency of agricultural production.

About one-half of these idled acres—36 million of them—are in the Conservation Reserve Program (CRP), withdrawn from production under 10-year contracts that start expiring in 1996. Finding new uses for those acres—such as growing less soil-depleting biomass for alternative fuels—would offer part of the solution for what to do with this land as it comes out from under CRP contracts.

Rural Development Promise

New uses for farm products will make new rural jobs. New uses step up the economic activity of producing, processing, transporting, and retailing new, high-value products. Much of this economic activity takes place in rural areas. Increased economic activity in rural areas broadens the rural tax base and strengthens schools and other public institutions and services in rural areas. At the same time, it reduces the pressure for urban crowding by allowing people to find jobs in rural areas.

Farm families don't live just within the borders of their farms. They live in communities of schools, churches, libraries, health services, recreational activities, businesses, and off-the-farm jobs. Profitable farming helps make more profitable, more lively, more productive rural communities that benefit farm families and rural families alike. That elevates the sense of belonging, the vision of the future, and the environmental awareness of farms and farm communities.

USDA has a national program in rural development. It recognizes that a fundamental solution to the problems of rural areas is for the rural development programs to help find new rural-based sources of income for rural communities.

Nonfood Uses, Key to Increased Demand

There is a continued need for new nonfood, nonfeed uses for farm products, from the viewpoint of the finite number of human stomachs to be fed as a domestic market. U.S. population is not growing nearly as rapidly now as it was earlier—and it will likely grow even less rapidly in the future.

From 1990 to 2010 the U.S. population will increase by 30.6 million, population experts predict. The growth in the previous 20 years, 1970 to 1990, added 46.5 million people. This is a slowdown of 34 percent in actual numbers to be fed and clothed domestically in the next 20 years. This comes far short of keeping ahead of the expected increase in agricultural productivity.

In the 5 years 1966-70, we used the production from an average of 231.6 million acres to fill our domestic needs. In the 5 years 1986-90, we used an average of 212 million acres— nearly 20 million acres less—even with the increase in U.S. population. Increased agricultural productivity more than made up for the difference in population.

The slowdown in population numbers over the next 20 years will reduce our domestic market growth for agriculture and will put pressure on the farm economy. New crops and new industrial uses can help offset the market stagnation that will otherwise be created by a slowdown in the basic domestic food and fiber demand that is tied to the dynamics of population numbers. It leaves us looking for ways to create new market demand at home and abroad.

U.S. farm exports, another source of prospective increased demand for U.S. farm products, dropped drastically in the mid-1980's and are just beginning to climb back near levels of 10 years ago. When more favorable trade rules are achieved through the GATT, farmers will gain immediate benefits—but the full potential of enlarged export demand for U.S. farm products is expected to unfold gradually over a period of years.

In the expanded market that will accompany liberalized trade, U.S. agriculture can be more competitive through new farm products and new uses for farm products. The United States is the world's largest exporter of farm products and can fortify that position with farm products that have new uses.

Environmental Implications

There is now a growing urgency to adapt farm production to the need for a cleaner environment. This can be achieved partially through the beneficial effects of changes in farm production methods. It can also be achieved from expanding the role of renewable resource products as an alternative to fossil fuels and petroleum-derived products.

Alternative fuels can preserve our petroleum reserves, increase our favorable balance of trade, and make more jobs in rural areas.

Biomass fuels can release less net carbon dioxide into the atmosphere and can reduce fossil contaminants, such as from volatile petroleum distillate evaporations and exhaust fumes. Biomass fuels can also help the United States achieve greater fuel security and reduce our dependence on imported petroleum.

In the early 1930's young Iowa State University scientists published a bulletin on a fuel made from 10 percent anhydrous alcohol and 90 percent petroleum-based gasoline. Currently about 1 billion gallons of grain-based ethanol are used annually as a 10 percent mixture with gasoline.

Most of this time, ethanol has been regarded as an outlet for surplus grain competing with petroleum-based gasoline. The economics of production have required tax exemptions for ethanol for it to be competitive. But the Clean Air Act Amendments of 1991 require that more than 40 metropolitan areas meet minimum clean air requirements. The ability of ethanol to reduce carbon monoxide emissions and to reduce the net increase in the atmospheric load of carbon dioxide released from petroleum brings alternative fuels to the forefront for environmental reasons. Increased research is being directed at achieving more economical ethanol production.

The growing scarcity of landfills also increases the need for biodegradable products from renewable resource products. This introduces environmental considerations that will become more important in new uses for farm products.

Here, too, the need for new industrial uses of farm products that will increase farm income and broaden crop selection dovetails with the need for more recyclable, biodegradable industrial products made from renewable resources. We are seeing promising developments now in biodegradable packaging from corn, wheat, and potato starch. Soy inks are gaining ground because of their environmental advantages in producing and recycling printed materials.

The Promise of New Technologies

New developments in biotechnology are providing new tools for the development of new farm products and new uses of farm products that are environmentally supportive. These developments are unleashing a new power to create and control new farm products and new uses for farm products. The vast genetic instructions extant in plants and animals become potential building blocks for creating new and improved crops and livestock.

Genetic manipulation will speed up the development of new and improved crops and trees and improved livestock through genetically derived and driven special characteristics. Crops will be developed with higher content of essential amino acids, fiber, oils, and other qualities; and fruits will have less spoilage. Crops can be tailored with special characteristics to fit industrial demands, just as we produce certain wheats for better breads and pasta.

The environment will gain from biotechnology-derived crop resistance to diseases and pests and greater tolerance of heat, cold, drought, and saline soils. This will reduce the use of chemicals and the impact of their residues.

Through biotechnology, we will also speed up the propagation of hardier, faster growing trees and improve forest output. Other possibilities include pulp and paper from kenaf, and natural rubber, resins, and waxes from guayule.

We will also produce safer, more effective vaccines through biotechnology to prevent livestock diseases and reduce the need for antibiotics and other disease-treatment drugs. Other possibilities include natural pesticides from plants and new pharmaceuticals from plants and animals.

Biotechnology will also make possible improved processing—such as in fermentation—that will expand industrial-use opportunities and improve the quality and palatability of foods with longer and safer shelf life.

Human use of genetic selection in the production of crops and livestock is probably 10,000 years old. But only now are we discovering the tools to modify the genetic makeup of farm plants and animals, and transfer them, other than through sexual reproduction—which has been a very limiting constraint.

The biotechnology of the next 100 years may prove to have a greater beneficial influence on the environment—and on the development of new farm products and new uses for farm products—than all the science of agriculture of the last 10,000 years. ❏

Epilogue

Secretary Madigan has made research and development of alternative uses for our agricultural products a priority. Through his leadership and this initiative, we can boost farm income, create new jobs in America, and ensure a healthier environment.

Agriculture is our largest industry, providing jobs for more than 20 million Americans. That is why encouraging and investing in new ways to use our farm commodities are important not only to agriculture but also to the economy and the well-being of our society.

Americans today are more aware then ever of the interdependence of agriculture, energy, health, and the environment. This growing awareness has led to a demand for a generation of new products. Consumers want products that will help preserve resources for the future, promote healthier food choices, reduce our dependence on foreign energy, and ensure a productive agricultural industry.

In this Yearbook, we have emphasized the importance of new uses to America and to you and your family. We have reported on the progress achieved to date and highlighted the steps we are taking to reach even greater success. And, I hope, we have sparked interest in these exciting developments in American agriculture.

Looking ahead, our 1993 Yearbook of Agriculture will focus on the relationship between diet and health and offer practical information on nutrition.

Roger Runningen,
Director of Public Affairs
and Press Secretary

Credits

Executive Board

Catherine A. Bertini
formerly Assistant Secretary for Food and Consumer Services
Cameron Bruemmer
Deputy Director of Public Affairs
Ann Chadwick
Acting Assistant Secretary for Food and Consumer Services
Susan Fertig-Dyks
Director, Office of Publishing and Visual Communication
Bruce L. Gardner
formerly Assistant Secretary for Economics
James R. Moseley
formerly Assistant Secretary for Natural Resources and Environment
Harry C. Mussman
Deputy Assistant Secretary for Science and Education
Roger Runningen
Director of Public Affairs and Press Secretary
Jo Ann R. Smith
Assistant Secretary for Marketing and Inspection Services
Daniel A. Sumner
Assistant Secretary for Economics

Working Group

Diane Behrens, Mary E. Carter, Ruth Coy, William H. Tallent
Agricultural Research Service
Lillie Davis, Daniel Kugler, Paul O'Connell, Joseph Roetheli
Cooperative State Research Service
Andrew Jacobitz
Economics
Mitch Geasler
Extension Service
Chris Kirby
Food and Nutrition Service

Stan Bean (retired), Howard Rosen
Forest Service
Bruce Blanton
International Affairs and Commodity Programs
David Waggoner
Marketing and Inspection Services
Jeff Gabriel
Natural Resources and Environment
Roger Conway, John McClelland
Office of Energy
Susan Fertig-Dyks, Deborah Takiff Smith
Office of Publishing and Visual Communication
Patricia Barclay
Small Community and Rural Development

Production Team
(All with USDA's Office of Publishing and Visual Communication)

Susan Fertig-Dyks
Publisher
Deborah Takiff Smith
Editor
Dennis Carroll
Copy Editor
Bob Nichols
Photography Coordinator
James Boykin
Composition
Carolyn Cleveland
Proofreader
David Sutton
Design Coordinator
George Avalos, Sylvia Duerksen, Lisa Hempstead, and Julie Olson
Design Associates
Warren Bell
Printing Coordinator

Colophon

Printing

The 1992 Yearbook of Agriculture was printed
on a 38" Harris Web Press in Kingsport, TN.
The paper is recycled offset book with soy based
ink. The cover is Kivar-9 Cambric finish.

Design and Production

The text and tables were designed, formatted,
and assembled on a Macintosh IIx and IIfx
using the application Aldus Pagemaker 4.0. The
figures were drawn in Adobe Illustrator 3.2 and
placed. The cover design was created in Adobe
Illustrator 3.2 on a Macintosh IIfx.

Typography

Chapter heads, first degree titles, credits,
captions, and the like are set in Helvetica regular
and bold. The main text is Times Roman,
regular, 10 / 12 x 13 FLRR limiting hyphens to
two and the zone to one.

Camera-Ready Art

All elements except photographs were submitted
for film on a 44 MB Syquest cartridge.

Index